KINGDOM OF THE OCTOPUS

Laurence E. Perkins

THE BEST-KNOWN CEPHALOPOD IN THE WORLD—
THE COMMON OCTOPUS

KINGDOM
OF THE OCTOPUS

THE LIFE HISTORY OF THE CEPHALOPODA

by Frank W. Lane

SHERIDAN HOUSE · NEW YORK

Library of Congress Catalog Card Number 60–13164

Manufactured in the United States of America

To
BARBARA

CONTENTS

CONTENTS

ILLUSTRATIONS

Color

The best known cephalopod in the world—the common
octopus   *Frontispiece*

Black and White

ILLUSTRATIONS

following page 204

Diagrams

NOTE: *All indications of size in the captions refer to linear measurements, e.g. 10 × natural size means the illustration is 10 times longer than the animal itself.*

AUTHOR'S INTRODUCTION

Science's only hope of escaping a Tower of Babel calamity is the preparation from time to time of works which summarize and which popularize the endless series of disconnected technical contributions.

Carl L. Hubbs in *Copeia* (1935)

The first man to study cephalopods was Aristotle. In his *Historia Animalium*, written more than 300 years before the birth of Christ, he described the habits, appearance and anatomy of common Mediterranean octopuses, cuttlefish and squids. But the world had to wait over 2,000 years for the first extensive studies of cephalopods, and these were contained chiefly in French, Italian and German monographs which are seldom seen outside zoological institutes and technical libraries.

In 1866 Victor Hugo's *Les Travailleurs de la Mer* was published. One of the highlights of this book is the fight to the death in a Channel Island sea cave between the hero, Gilliatt, and an octopus. André Maurois, in his biography of Hugo, says that in France this episode "made the octopus the talk of the day." There was controversy in the newspapers about the alleged danger of the "devil fish," and a diver captured one alive which was exhibited in an aquarium in the Champs Élysées. Milliners created an "Octopus hat" to be worn by *Les Travailleuses de la Mer*, in other words a seaside hat for ladies. The restaurants featured *Octopus à la financière*—octopus meat served with a special sauce. No wonder Hugo's wife, writing from Paris, told her sister Julie: "Everything here has become octopusied. . . ."

Hugo's description of octopodan anatomy and behavior is stronger in dramatic effect than in zoological accuracy, but with twenty pages of a widely read novel he did more to arouse public interest in cephalopods, particularly octopuses, than any previous writer.

Then in 1875 there appeared a slim volume of 132 small pages which has become a landmark in cephalopodan literature. The book was called *The Octopus; or, The "Devil-Fish" of Fiction and of Fact,* and was written by Henry Lee. It was the first general popular book on cephalopods to be published in English, or, as far as I can discover, in any other language. Lee was the Naturalist at the Brighton Aquarium in England, and octopuses were the passion of his life. I doubt if anyone has known the common octopus more intimately than Lee, who has rightly been called "the Boswell of the Octopus."

The Octopus was published in 1875. But it has had no successor. Every other class of comparatively large animal has been the subject of popular books in several languages, yet since Henry Lee wrote over eighty years ago not one general, popular book on cephalopods has been published anywhere in the world.

Why? There are two possible answers. There are less than a dozen living teuthologists, as experts on cephalopods are called, and they have lacked the time—and perhaps the inclination—to translate their specialized knowledge into the language of the layman. And the popular science writers, who had the time and the ability, were unwilling to search the zoological literature of half a dozen countries to assemble the information necessary for such a book.

With some misgivings I have endeavored to fill this gap in the world's popular scientific literature. Scientists will criticize, as they have the right and the duty to do, whatever they consider the technical faults of the book, but they should remember that they are in some measure to blame for not writing such a book themselves. The world of Nature is not the sole preserve of the technician; the layman also has a right to be considered. As a master of my craft has said:

Scientists are justified if they do not forgive a writer who sets out knowingly to distort their meanings for effect. They have reason to be grateful to the expert journalists who faithfully translate their technicalities into the language of Everyman. . . . The purpose of science is knowledge, and everyone has the right to know. What science has discovered is common property, and should be made easily available to all. This is not always remembered by a great many scientific writers who have never spoken outside of classrooms where attendance and attention are compulsory, never written a book which they could not order their students to buy. If the scientists practicing inside the college close are not always and widely understood, they may not be always and widely supported. They take that support for granted, along with their intellectual liberties.

Donald Culross Peattie in *The Road of a Naturalist.*

I must at once add that I have been generously helped by scientists—I have shamelessly badgered scores, in every continent and on both sides of the Iron Curtain. To very few indeed did I appeal in vain. I have too much respect for the scientists' concern for accuracy—for truth—to regard their criticisms lightly, but the mass of comment and advice which I invited was not easy to deal with, especially as it was sometimes contradictory. Occasionally one scientist criticized me for including something which another said should be published.

I have attempted the difficult—some think the impossible—task of writing a book which will interest the layman, help the student and please the teuthologist. Some passages are in a more light-hearted vein than is usual in scientific works, and I have recounted a considerable number of anecdotes from popular sources. Generally, authors are identified when first mentioned. And I have given references which will enable readers to trace the source of every quotation. Incidentally, my quoting a source does not necessarily mean the author was the first person ever to record the fact, etc., mentioned.

The bibliography covers the whole of the Cephalopoda. As far as I know, no comparable bibliography is available elsewhere. The subject-matter of the book is drawn mainly from the sources listed, but it also contains hitherto unpublished information, especially in Chapter XI.

The technical reader may feel I have sometimes oversimplified. I have tried to give a *general* picture and I believe too many qualifications take all the life out of writing. To quote that great popularizer in another field, Sir Winston Churchill: "The reserve of modern assertions is sometimes pushed to extremes, in which the fear of being contradicted leads the writer to strip himself of almost all sense and meaning." (See *A History of the English-Speaking Peoples.*) Any reader desiring more information than I have provided should consult the bibliography.

Some lay readers may wish the text contained fewer "crack-jaw words" as one friendly critic put it. Wherever a cephalopod has a common English name I have used it, adding its scientific name in brackets at the first mention in each chapter. But most cephalopods have no common name, and can therefore be identified only by their scientific name. It should be remembered that whereas a common name may vary from country to country—even within the English-speaking world—the scientific name identifies an animal in any country in the world.

A few details about the writing of the book may be of interest. The whole undertaking, from research to proof-reading, took about five years. During that time I exchanged over 5,000 letters with people in more than 40 countries—over 12 letters for each page of the book. To ensure that the book should be as accurate and as readable as I could make it, I sent the manuscript, in whole or in part, to over 100 readers, most of them professional scientists.

In fairness to the host of helpers who have given so generously of their time and knowledge, I must stress that ultimate responsibility for everything in this book is mine. If I, with the greater knowledge that is now available, have done as well in my day as Henry Lee did in his, I shall be content.

FRANK W. LANE

Ruislip, Middlesex, England

ACKNOWLEDGMENTS

I believe I owe more than most writers of popular natural history books to the help of others. The 900-odd entries in the bibliography indicate the extent of my indebtedness to published sources. The labors of scientists, both professional and amateur, who have spent long years seeking and publishing information about cephalopods have provided the technical data on which this book is based. To these men and women I owe my greatest debt.

To list all the 120 or so people who have directly helped me would, I fear, prove tedious. But it would be churlish not to make public acknowledgment to any of those who have given so generously of their time and knowledge.

I believe I have corresponded with every living teuthologist, all of whom have helped. I am particularly indebted to Dr. Igor I. Akimushkin, Oceanographic Institute of the Academy of Sciences of the U.S.S.R.; Mr. Bernard C. Cotton, Curator of Molluscs, South Australian Museum; Dr. Grace E. Pickford, Bingham Oceanographic Laboratory, Yale University; Dr. W. J. Rees, British Museum of Natural History; and Professor Gilbert L. Voss, Marine Laboratory, University of Miami. They have read all the chapters and answered a multitude of questions. Other teuthologists who have read parts of the book and answered questions are Dr. Siegfried G. A. Jaeckel, Jr. (Chapters I, II, IX, X and XII), Dr. Adolphe Portmann (Chapter I) and Dr. Sven Thore (Chapters I and XI).

The following zoologists, and naturalists have read all the chapters: Mr. B. B. Boycott, Dr. John L. Cloudsley-Thompson, Mr. Ronald F. Le Sueur, Professor G. E. and Mrs. Nettie MacGinitie, and Mr. John S. Vinden.

I have consulted numerous specialists on various aspects of the book. The palaeontological and *Nautilus* sections of Chapter I have been read by 12 palaeontologists among whom I must mention Dr. Rousseau H. Flower, Dr. J. A. Jeletzky and Dr. H. B. Stenzel. Among others who have helped in various ways I desire to mention: Professor Z. M. Bacq (Chapters I, II, III, IV, VI, VIII and XI), Dr. Anton Fr. Bruun (Chapter I), Dr. Richard Bott (Chapter VIII), Dr. John Boyle (medical references), Mr. George W. F. Claxton (Bibliography), Mr. R. K. Dell (Chapters I, II, III, IV and VIII), Dr. N. B. Eales (Chapter VIII), Mr. Roy Fincken (Bibliography), Professor Alastair Graham (Chapters I, II, IV, VII, VIII and Glossary), Dr. Yata Haneda (Chapter VII), Professor E. Newton Harvey (Chapter VII), Miss Nora Jackson (geographical references), Mr. Norman V. Knight (physics references), Mr. Jørgen Knudsen (Chapter XII), Mr. J. Fyfe Robertson (captions), Mr. M. J. Wells (Chapters IV and V), Dr. Katharina Wirz (Chapters I, II, III and VIII) and Professor J. Z. Young (giant nerve-fiber references and Chapter V).

Among the half dozen translators who have helped I must mention Mr. John Dekin who has given generously of his time and skill for over three years. Miss Diana N. Noakes, of the staff of the International Commission on Zoological Nomenclature, has—in her spare time—done most of the work involved in compiling the cephalopodan family tree and systematic lists in Appendices II, III and IV. Cephalopodan systematics are far from straightforward and Miss Noakes has spent a great deal of time checking names with their original publication, including a search through the annual volumes of the *Zoological Record* since it began in 1865.

I wish to thank William Morrow & Co., Inc. for permission to include extracts from *We Chose the Islands* by Sir Arthur Grimble, and Dodd, Mead & Co. for permission to include extracts from *The Cruise of the "Cachalot"* by Frank T. Bullen.

I owe a special debt to those who have supplied illustrations. Miss Patience Forman has taken great care to ensure that the diagrams in the text are as accurate as we could make them. Miss Sabine Baur, under the direction of Dr. Adolphe Portmann, has drawn the anatomical diagrams in Appendix I. It would be difficult, if not impossible, to improve on some of the classic illustrations in the monographs of the German zoologists, Carl Chun and Georg Pfeffer, so I have had some of these photographed and reproduced as plates. Good photographs of cephalopods are very difficult to obtain, and those which illustrate this book have been assembled from various sources over a period of some three years. Tribute is due to the skill and patience of the photographers whose work has enabled me to illustrate this book with what is, I believe, the best collection of cephalopod photographs so far published. I am particularly indebted to Mr. Peter David, of the National Institute of Oceanography in England, for allowing me to use his unique collection of color photographs of live oceanic squids. Dr. Rees has helped in identifying some of these.

Such a book as this could not be written without the help of large special libraries. I desire particularly to mention the Library of the Zoological Society of London, of which I am a Fellow, with appreciation of the assistance given by Mr. G. B. Stratton, Librarian, and Mr. Charles R. Burman, Assistant Librarian. I am especially grateful to Mr. L. G. Ellis, of the Library staff, for all the help he has given me in the work of compiling and checking the bibliography. I have also made considerable use of the libraries of the British Museum of Natural History, and the British Museum Library.

It was not until I wrote this book that I fully appreciated the magnificent service which the British public library system places at the disposal of the serious student. It is not generally realized that the counter of the smallest public library is the Open Sesame to more than 65 million books which line the shelves of our public libraries—and to the books of many private libraries as well. During the five years I have been working on this book I have received volumes—often on extended loan—from dozens of public libraries, and from University and special libraries. On one occasion it proved impossible to obtain a book I wanted from any library in this country. In a comparatively short time the book was obtained for me from the Charlottenburg Library in Berlin.

To all who have helped me obtain the tools of my craft I offer my grateful thanks. In particular I desire to mention Miss A. M. Pollard, the knowledgeable and ever-helpful Head of the Reference Services of the Middlesex County Libraries and the staff of the Headquarters Students' Dept. of the Middlesex County Libraries, who have spent many hours on literary detection for my benefit.

An author is sometimes so immersed in his subject-matter that he is blind to literary faults which are obvious to readers. I think the best way to overcome this occupational hazard is to enlist the help of lay readers, asking them to criticize the manuscript as rigorously as they can. Among those who have helped to make this book more readable than it would otherwise have been I desire to thank my wife, Barbara; my secretary, Mrs. Cecily Morrison; Miss Valerie Jiles and Mr. Robert Newton. To Cecily Morrison's skill as secretary and critic I owe much. She has typed some 2,000 letters; helped to compile the Index; read the manuscript and proofs several times, making many valuable suggestions and criticisms; and generally helped to make this a better book than it would have been without her generous and enthusiastic co-operation.

Finally, I desire to thank my wife. In addition to helping in a thousand ways, she has cheerfully borne with the vagaries of an author in the throes of composition, and patiently suffered the partial disorganization of our household to accommodate the mountain of books, journals, papers, drawings, photographs and other impedimenta—including cephalopods canned, bottled and dried—inseparable from a work of this kind.

One CEPHALOPODS

Cephalopods are invertebrates—the backboneless animals to which over 95 per cent of all earth's species belong. The name comes from the Greek words *kephalē* = head, and (*pous*) *podos* = foot, meaning "head-footed"—the "foot" referring to the arms or tentacles which surround the mouth. Cephalopods are exclusively marine animals and die quickly if put in fresh water. They are found in all the oceans of the world, and range from inside the Arctic Circle to the edge of the Antarctic Continent.

Cephalopods are classified among the molluscs. All molluscs have a soft boneless body partly covered with a mantle of skin, most of them have a dental ribbon for rasping food, and they nearly all have a shell. The winkle, the snail and the oyster are also molluscs, but only a zoologist could recognize that these lowly creatures are kin to the highly organized cephalopods, some of which are among the most agile and ferocious animals in the sea.

These animals have an ancient lineage. Fossils of a small cephalopod (*Plectronoceras cambria*) have been found in Cambrian rocks believed to be at least 400 million years old, and are among the oldest fossils known.

Cephalopods swarmed in primeval seas and proliferated into thousands of species, and fantastic forms. Then, they were shell-armored animals, showing clearly their kinship with other molluscs. There were more than 3,000 species of nautiloids, ranging from the tiny *Plectronoceras* with a quarter-inch shell, to the giant *Endoceras* whose shell was shaped like a cone and was sometimes 15 or more feet long—the longest shells the world has ever known. Today, the sole representatives of this bygone host are six species of the pearly nautilus living in the Southwest Pacific.

In those far-off days whose history we can read only in the frag-

1

mentary story written in the rocks, another great order of cephalopods arose, an offshoot of the primitive nautiloid stock. These were
the ammonites, so named from the resemblance of their coiled and
chambered shell to the emblem of the ram-headed god Ammon of
ancient Egypt.

Ammonites are among the commonest of fossils. People who see
them for the first time sometimes think they are the petrified remains of coiled snakes, hence the name "serpent stones." Ammonites ranged from midgets such as *Cymbites* with the shell about
half an inch in diameter, to the molluscan juggernaut *Pachydiscus*
with a shell which sometimes reached about nine feet across. In
the British Museum of Natural History in London there is a plaster cast of an incomplete specimen which has a diameter of 6 ft.
8 in. It has been estimated that if the complete shell could have
been uncoiled it would have measured some 35 ft.

In shape, and in complexity of internal structure and external
sculpture, the ammonites ran riot. They reached their zenith some
200 million years ago. But eventually this great order became extinct—at the end of the Mesozoic era, some 80 million years ago.

Ammonites and nautiloids were not the only cephalopods to
flourish in primeval seas. Living during roughly the same immense
range of time there were the belemnites, and these are believed to
be the real ancestors of all modern cephalopods, except the pearly
nautiluses. The belemnites carried no external armor but bore instead an internal chambered shell. This was partly enclosed in a
cylinder with a solid cone-shaped point, called a guard. It is from
this that the animals have been named, the Greek word *belemnon*
meaning a dart or arrow. Fossil belemnite guards are often found,
and sometimes taken to museums by people who think they are
"thunderbolts." [1]

Belemnite shells ranged from about two inches in *Belemno-
camax* to seven feet in *Megateuthis*. With arms extended these animals would have measured about three inches and nine feet respectively.

Fossils represent organisms which died millions of years ago

[1] Nothing solid comes down with lightning, which is purely an electrical phenomenon. But sometimes when lightning discharges into sand, its heat fuses the
sand to form a solid tube called a fulgurite, which may have helped to foster the
idea of thunderbolts.

and may appear to have no practical relevance to the modern world. Yet the most important fuel in the world today—oil—comes from the decomposed remains of long-dead animal and vegetable life. And fossils, including those of cephalopods, help in the location and development of oil-fields.

The fossil record shows that there have been more than 10,000 species of cephalopods. The number was almost certainly much higher, as only a minute proportion of animals becomes fossilized, and a still smaller proportion of such fossils is ever found and scientifically examined and recorded. Today, the number of known species of living cephalopods throughout the world is about 650.

All known living cephalopods except the pearly nautilus have two gills, two kidneys and three hearts—two to pump the deoxygenated blood through the gills, and another to pump the oxygenated blood through the rest of the body.

Cephalopods are literally blue-blooded animals. The blue results from a copper-containing compound in their blood; in mammals the respiratory pigment is an iron-containing compound. Cephalopod blood is dark blue when oxygenated, but when deoxygenated it becomes a very pale clear blue.

Cephalopods have a mantle of thick skin and muscle which encloses the body or, more strictly, the "visceral mass," which contains the internal organs. At the "neck," or junction with the head, the mantle is either partially or wholly free according to the species.

When the mantle dilates, water is drawn into the mantle cavity at the "neck" opening and aerates the gills. The mantle then contracts and closes the opening, the water being expelled through a funnel, or siphon, which projects beneath the body through the same opening (see Appendix I). Anatomically, the funnel is part of the cephalopodan equivalent of the molluscan "foot," or underside of the body. On the mantle of those cephalopods, such as the common squids (*Loligo*), where the mantle is free at the "neck," there are cartilaginous studs which lock into corresponding sockets on the head and funnel.

In normal respiration the mantle dilates and contracts gently and rhythmically. In some species it can hardly be seen to move at all. But when the cephalopod wants to move quickly the mantle muscles work rapidly and powerfully, shooting water from the funnel and driving the animal by jet-propulsion.

Apart from the pearly nautilus, all living cephalopods are divided into three orders. These are the Vampyromorpha; the Octopoda, or eight-footed; and the Decapoda, or ten-footed. The "feet" are, of course, the arms and tentacles. The six species of pearly nautiluses are so different in structure from all other living cephalopods that they are placed in a separate group (see page 17).

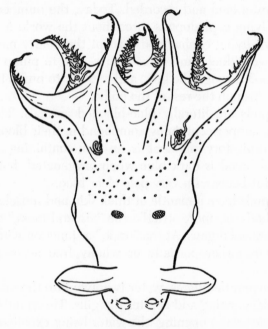

FIG. 1 *Vampyroteuthis infernalis*
View of dorsal, or upper, side. Redrawn from
Pickford (1950) with minor alterations suggested
by the author

The Vampyromorpha has been named by Grace E. Pickford from the deep-sea cephalopod *Vampyroteuthis infernalis* which, she believes, alone constitutes the order. She calls this cephalopod a "living fossil" the only surviving member of an order which otherwise became extinct millions of years ago—"less spectacular than the coelacanth (*Latimeria*), it is still one of the more exciting discoveries of the 20th century."

Vampyroteuthis has ten arms, but the second pair [1] is much more slender than the others, and can be completely withdrawn into pockets in the base of the web which unites all the arms for part of their length. These slender arms appear to be modified as sensory filaments, probably as "feelers." *Vampyroteuthis* has some characters which resemble those found in either the Octopoda or the Decapoda, and others which are more primitive. It has the consistency of a jellyfish and its color is an "inky purple." Females, which are larger than the males, grow to a length of about a foot. This cephalopod is widely distributed in tropical and subtropical seas, and appears to live between a third of a mile and two miles below the surface.

Although some 650 species of Octopoda and Decapoda have been described, it is impossible to give the exact number in the world today. Too many regions of the sea have yet to be explored. Moreover, the systematists whose work is to classify animals, are not agreed how to group the available material. Systematics, like every other branch of science, does not stand still, and new information causes constant revision of the smaller branches of the cephalopodan family tree (see Appendix II).

Many of the 650 or so species are known from only one specimen, and some from an incomplete specimen. It is probable that with fuller knowledge some cephalopods, now regarded as separate species, may prove to be the same species described by other teuthologists under a different name.

For the purposes of this book I have dealt with cephalopods under three main groups—Octopus (Octopoda), Squid (Teuthoidea), and Cuttlefish (Sepiidae). In this chapter there are also sections on *Spirula* (Spirulidae) and Pearly Nautilus (Nautilidae), and there are further references to them in later chapters. Cuttlefish and *Spirula* are included in the suborder Sepioidea which contains some 150 species, over half of which are cuttlefish. Apart from cuttlefish much less is known about sepioids than about octopuses and squids. All sepioids are decapods, and those species

---

[1] Cephalopod arms are numbered from the median dorsal (upper side) line, right and left of the mouth: Right 1, 2, 3, 4; Left 1, 2, 3, 4. The tentacles are generally omitted from the numbering and are designated R.T. (right tentacle) and L.T. (left tentacle). Their position is between arms 3 and 4 in the Decapoda, and 1 and 2 in the Vampyromorpha. Some authors include the tentacles in the numbering so that their scheme has 5 on each side.

which are not actually cuttlefish may roughly be regarded as coming between them and the squids in structure and appearance. The broad outlines of cephalopodan biology are, of course, generally applicable to the whole class.

OCTOPUS

FIG. 2 Common octopus

Octopuses[1] are the best known of all cephalopods. There are about 150 species, and they live in nearly all the seas of the world, from the tropics to the Arctic and Antarctic. Octopuses vary in size from midgets such as *Octopus arborescens*, spanning less than 2 in., to the Pacific octopus (*Octopus hongkongensis*), a large specimen of which from Alaskan waters spanned 32 ft. But the thimble-shaped body of this octopus was less than 18 in. long, and the arms were extremely tenuous towards their tips.

The typical octopus (*Octopus*) has a globular body, often with wart-like prominences. The body narrows slightly into a "neck" at the junction with the head. The only remnants of the great shells of distant ancestors are a pair of small internal rods. Some species have a thin plate and others have no shell remnant at all.

Eight arms spring from the octopus's head, being united at their base by a membranous web. In many species the arms are approximately the same length, but in other species some may be two or

[1] Other plural nouns which have been used for these animals are octopussies, octopi, octopods, octopoids, octopodes—and octopus.

three times as long as others. The arms are often wrongly referred
to as tentacles. In the Cephalopoda only decapods possess tentacles, which are the two long organs which shoot out to capture
prey. Incidentally, I understand in 1958 Japanese zoologists
trawled some specimens of an octopus in Antarctica which has
about 40 arms!

All the better known species of octopus are found in shallow
water. They live in lairs which they make themselves or in ready-
made holes. Many species, however, live in the deep seas, some
below 500 fathoms, or over half a mile down. Just how deep some
octopuses live is not yet known. They have been brought up in
trawls lowered from two to four miles, but as the trawls were open
the animals may have entered when the nets were being raised.
There is good evidence, however, that some species live at great
depths. The British worker on the Mollusca, G. C. Robson (1932),
says that in the Weddell Sea, Antarctica, an octopus (*Grimpoteuthis*) was brought up in a trawl from a depth of 2,425 fathoms. In
its stomach were the remains of bottom-dwelling crustaceans, so
there is little doubt that this octopus actually lives nearly three
miles below the surface. And Igor Akimushkin tells me that in the
Pacific a Russian marine expedition obtained an octopus egg from
the stomach of a bottom-dwelling fish trawled from a depth of
7,200 meters.

Pressure at a depth of three miles is about three tons per square
inch. In an experiment, sealed glass tubes were wrapped in cloth,
enclosed in a copper cylinder punctured to let in water, and lowered to this depth. When the cylinder was raised it was partly
crushed in the middle and the glass inside was smashed to snow-
like powder. (J. Y. Buchanan.)

It is exceptional for an octopus, or any other cephalopod, to live
at a depth of three miles. The Danish marine zoologist, Anton Fr.
Bruun, who has had much experience of trawling in the deep
oceans, tells me that he thinks a mile is probably the limit for the
great majority of cephalopods. The pressure at such a depth is
about a ton per square inch. The bodies of the octopuses which
live at such depths have a soft, jelly-like consistency. Carl Chun
says that the octopus *Cirrothauma murrayi*, which was brought up
from a great depth, was as fragile as a "jellyfish" (ctenophore) and
semi-transparent. It was also blind—the only blind octopus known.

How is it that the most fragile octopuses live where the pressure is greatest? The answer is simple. Their tissues are permeated with fluid, and as water is virtually non-compressible, their bodies are unharmed. As the depths of the ocean are calm, these jelly-like octopuses are not subject to any buffeting from waves.

Other deep-sea octopuses are sooty black, and the webs reach almost to the tips of the arms. Octopuses of the genus *Opisthoteuthis,* which live on the sea-bottom, are so shapeless that the American zoologist, S. Stillman Berry (1952), says when preserved, they "resemble in about equal degree a soggy pancake or a very dirty floor-mop." They have been called "flapjack devil fishes."

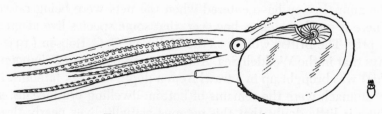

FIG. 3 Argonaut, or paper nautilus.
Male on right drawn to same scale

One of the most extraordinary genera of octopuses is *Argonauta,* which has six species. They are found in all the warm seas of the world, living mostly in the surface waters. The argonaut, or paper nautilus, (*Argonauta argo*) has been famed for over 2,000 years as the graceful little navigator which sails the seas in a boat of shell.

There is a remarkable difference in size between the male and female. A large female is sometimes over a foot long, including arms, whereas a male seldom measures more than half an inch. It is one of the smallest cephalopods known. It has a thimble-shaped body, there is hardly any "neck," and the arms are fairly short. A female argonaut may thus be over 20 times longer than the male, a size difference as great as that between a mouse and a lion!

It would be impossible to mistake a female argonaut for any other cephalopod. It has an octopodan body, it is true, but normally little of this is visible. The first arms on each side of the body have their tips expanded into broad oval membranes, which look like miniature sails, but their function has nothing to do with navigation as the ancients believed. The skin glands of these arms secrete calcium carbonate which forms a delicate, pearly-white, fluted "shell," or egg-nest, which is quite different from other cephalopod shells.

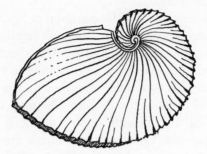

FIG. 4 Shell of argonaut with membrane removed

The shell is formed in the following manner. The two arms are held together and gradually a thin gelatinous material appears between them which is molded on the inner surfaces of the oval membranes. It slowly hardens through exposure to the water into a spiral papery substance, sculptured with parallel ridges. The two halves of the shell are joined on one margin to form a keel, decorated by a double row of brown knobs corresponding with the suckers of the arms, by which they are apparently formed.

The membranous arms sweep back along each side of the shell and hold it to the argonaut's body. The tip of the funnel, which is the argonaut's propulsion unit, projects beyond the shell like a speedboat's exhaust-pipe. The argonaut sometimes "takes a lift" on a jellyfish. P. L. Kramp records that when the Danish marine research ship *Galathea* was between Mombasa and the Seychelles "we saw the remarkable sight of a number of *Argonauta* ensconced on the top of jellyfish, *Crambionella orsini,* which drifted in large numbers round the ship. To the best of our knowledge this had never been seen before." (Quoted by Bruun *et al.*)

The argonaut occasionally leaves its shell, but if deprived of it permanently it does not form another and dies. Bernard C. Cotton, Curator of Molluscs in the South Australian Museum, tells me that they have a number of shells of *Argonauta nodosus* which have been badly damaged and subsequently repaired by the argonaut. "Some have patched big holes with fragments of their own shell replaced 'inside out.'"

Some 40 species of octopuses have been recorded in the waters of the Americas, more than 30 of which are found off the coasts of North America. They range from the half-inch male argonaut to the 30-foot Pacific octopus.

The best-known octopus is the common octopus (*Octopus vulgaris*). As its name suggests, it is the most familiar of all, having been studied, experimented on, and written about more than any other cephalopod in the world. It lives mainly in tropical and subtropical waters, and is especially abundant in the Mediterranean. It is seldom found north of the English Channel. The largest specimens span about 10 ft. with bodies about 9 in. across, and weigh 40 to 50 pounds. These outsize animals are generally found in deeper water than is usual for the species. Robson (1929) says that the maximum reliable depth record for a common octopus is about a quarter of a mile.

The common octopus is the species most frequently seen in aquaria. But only those who thoroughly understand them, and accordingly cater for their needs, can keep them for more than a few weeks. Nobody knows the maximum age to which octopuses live, but the British zoologist, Walter Garstang, thought the common octopus might live to eight years.

SQUID

FIG. 5 Common American squid

Squids are the most varied and colorful of all cephalopods. They are also the most numerous,[1] and among them are found the largest [2] and most ferocious of all invertebrates.

There are about 350 species, ranging from tiny squids such as *Sandalops pathopsis* measuring less than an inch, to the giant

[1] The American conchologist, George W. Tryon, says that on January 10, 1858, the Dutch ship *Vriendentrouw* sailed for two hours through a sea of dead squids. They were a small common species (*Loligo*), and they covered the surface of the ocean as far as the lookout could see.

[2] Some jellyfish (*Cyanea*) are *longer*. Alexander Agassiz measured one found off the coast of Massachusetts which had a bell 7½ ft. in diameter and tentacles over 120 ft. long.

Laurence E. Perkins

Plate 2   CHARACTERISTIC POSES OF THE COMMON OCTOPUS

Günter Senfft

A COMMON OCTOPUS AT REST

Specimens have been caught which spanned 10 ft. and weighed 40 pounds. Common octopuses live mainly in tropical and sub-tropical waters although they are found as far north as the English Channel

Plate 1

North American squid is the common American squid (*Loligo pealeii*), which ranges from Newfoundland to the north coast of Venezuela. A large specimen measures about three feet overall.

CUTTLEFISH

FIG. 7 Common cuttlefish

Under its scientific name of *Sepia* the cuttlefish has become a household word to many who are familiar with the artist's pigment, but do not realize that it comes from this cephalopod. And everybody who has kept a canary, or similar cage-bird, and has given it cuttlebone, has seen part of a cuttlefish.

There are about 80 species, and they live in most tropical and subtropical seas, generally in the shallow coastal waters. They are absent from American waters although they are found in the Atlantic. They are most abundant in the Mediterranean, the West Pacific and the Indian Ocean.

The different species do not vary in size as much as octopuses and squids. The smallest is *Hemisepius typicus* with a mantle length of about 1¼ in. When the tentacles are fully extended the overall length is about three inches. The largest cuttlefish is *Sepia latimanus* with a mantle length of some two feet, and an overall length of about five feet.

Cuttlefish have slightly oval, shield-shaped bodies. The margins of the mantle form two thin narrow fins. The comparatively small head bears eight arms, and two tentacles which shoot out like a pair of living tongs to capture prey. Normally, these tentacles are retracted into two pockets below the eyes, and the arms are held together to form a cone-shaped tip.

The body of a cuttlefish is strengthened by an internal shell—the canary's cuttlebone—which lies just beneath the upper surface. Glands in the mantle exude a liquid which hardens into the shell, which is shaped like an elongated shield and runs almost the whole squid (*Architeuthis*) whose overall length (tentacles extended) may be 60 ft. or more. Squids live in all the seas of the world. Some dwell in the surface waters, others live at varying depths down to a mile or more. The bodies of many deep-sea squids, like those of deep-sea octopuses, are soft and jelly-like, some looking like fragile crystal vases.

Most squids have a fusiform, or cigar-shaped, body, terminated either by one end or two side fins. All squids have eight arms and two tentacles. The arms are of unequal length in many species, and in others, such as *Histioteuthis*, some of them are united by a web (see Plate 24). The tentacles shoot out to seize the prey, and contract as soon as the arms have a secure hold.

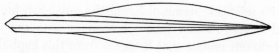

FIG. 6 Pen of the common American squid

Beneath the mantle is a delicate, chitinous, or horn-like, shell, which varies in shape from that of a broad blade to a narrow lance. This shell is called the pen, and varies from less than half an inch in the smallest species to four feet or more in the giant squid. In the larval form of *Chiroteuthis veranyi* the pen is extended into a "tail" as thin as a pencil-lead, and longer than the body mantle)—see Plate 5.

Some squids live in fairly deep water during the day and come to the surface at night. They probably follow the daily migration of plankton and small fish.

Very little is known about the longevity of squids. The American zoologist, A. E. Verrill (1881), thought that some of the smaller species might live for four years. It is almost certain that some of the large specimens of giant squids which have been taken were a good deal older than this. But how old nobody knows.

Some 80 species of squid have been recorded in the waters of the Americas, more than 70 of which are found off the coasts of North America. They range from species such as *Pickfordiateuthis pulchella*, measuring an inch, to the giant squid which grows to some 60 ft. These are overall measurements. The best known

Rotofilm, Hamburg

ARGONAUT, OR PAPER NAUTILUS
Very few photographs have been taken of these animals alive. This is a female, for a
male see Plate 27

Plate 3

LOOKING LIKE A FLEET OF JET AIRPLANES, FOUR COMMON SQUIDS
CRUISE IN A TANK AT THE ZOOLOGICAL STATION AT NAPLES

Franz Thorbecke

A SQUID TAKES ITS OWN PHOTOGRAPH A THIRD OF A MILE
BELOW THE SURFACE

This photograph of a two-foot ommastrephid was taken from the *Discovery II* in the North-East Atlantic at a depth of about 2,000 ft. with a camera designed by A. S. Laughton and R. Dobson. A jerk on the bait at the end of the white rod triggers an electronic flash which takes the photograph. Notice the four rows of suckers on the tentacle

Plate 4

Carl Chun (1910)

THE STALK-EYED SQUID
BATHOTHAUMA LYROMMA

Some teuthologists think this drawing
is of an immature specimen. Natural
size

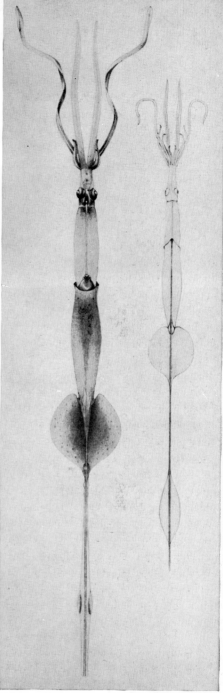

Georg Pfeffer (1912)

IMMATURE SPECIMENS
OF THE SQUID
CHIROTEUTHIS VERANYI

In this larval form (the so-called *Doratopsis* stage—see p. 127) the pen, or shell,
is longer than the mantle and 'neck' combined. For mature form see Plate 13.
Natural size

Plate **5**

Paul Trinkaus

CHARACTERISTIC POSES OF THE COMMON CUTTLEFISH

Plate 6

COMMON OCTOPUS IN FRONT OF ITS LAIR
Notice camouflage and rampart of stones

Rotofilm, Hamburg

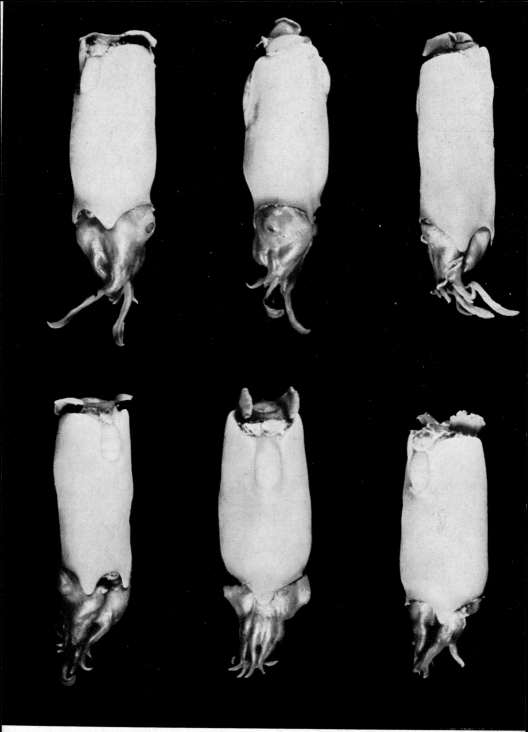

PRESERVED SPECIMENS OF THE RARE *SPIRULA*

This three-inch cephalopod lives well below the surface and very little is known about its life history. The middle specimen in the bottom row shows the small light-organ between the fins. The shell has broken free of the skin in some of the specimens but in life it is completely enclosed by the mantle

Plate **7**

TWO VIEWS OF THE MOST PRIMITIVE OF ALL CEPHALOPODS
—THE PEARLY NAUTILUS

Above: Section through the middle of the shell.   *Below:* X-ray view

length of the mantle, but does not reach quite to the sides. It is relatively the largest internal shell of any cephalopod, and gives rigidity to the cuttle's body. Because of its light structure the shell acts as an internal lifebuoy, aiding the animal in swimming and

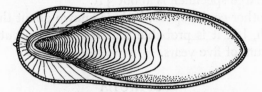

FIG. 8 Cuttlebone of the common cuttlefish. The layers in the center are the vestiges of the septa, or slender cross-walls, of the primitive nautiloid shells

floating. The actual structure of this, and other cephalopod shells, has been minutely studied and described by Adolf Appellöf in a technical treatise of over 100 pages and 12 plates of drawings.

Although the shell bears some analogy with the backbone of a vertebrate, especially in its position, there are several differences. In particular it is rigid, having no vertebrae, and is composed entirely of dead matter. It consists of three parts. The center is a large calcareous ("containing lime") shield, parts of which are honeycombed with minute gas-filled chambers. Completely surrounding this is a calcareous and horny margin ending, in most species, in a tiny projection, called the rostrum.

Such is the cuttlebone, seabiscuit or seafoam, specimens of which are washed up on the shores of the world in untold millions every year. The various uses man makes of this cephalopod flotsam are dealt with in Chapter X. In addition to the more mundane uses mentioned in that chapter, the shells of these and other cephalopods are of considerable use to systematists in classifying these animals. Some species are almost identical except in the structure of their shells.

The best-known species is the common cuttlefish (*Sepia officinalis*). It lives in the Atlantic along the eastern seaboard from the Cape of Good Hope to the English Channel. It is also found in the North Sea and is fairly abundant in the Mediterranean. Next to the common octopus, the common cuttlefish is the best-known cephalopod in the world. It was observed and described by Aristotle 22 centuries ago, and in modern times has been studied by many zoologists.

The maximum mantle length of the common cuttlefish is about 15 in. The tentacles can shoot out about 20 in. Thus the overall length of a large specimen is about 3 ft.

As with other cephalopods, little is known about the longevity of cuttlefish, but it is probable that the common cuttlefish lives to a maximum of five years.

SPIRULA

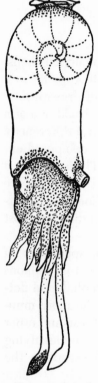

This rarely observed cephalopod has long been the problem child of the systematists. It is now generally agreed that it belongs to the sub-order Sepioidea, and is thus akin to the cuttle-fish.

There is only one species, *Spirula spirula*, and it is found in nearly all tropical and subtropical seas, except the Mediterranean, the Red Sea and the Sulu Sea. It lives at depths between 600 and 3,000 feet. Anton Fr. Bruun, an authority on the animal, tells me that he considers it is confined to water layers having temperatures between 10° and 20°C. (50°–68°F.).

Spirula is known to be widely distributed be-cause, although the animals themselves are very rarely caught,[1] their tiny shells are washed up on the shores of all five continents. Sometimes beaches are littered with thousands of them. Occasionally these shells are found on the south and west shores of England, and sometimes as far north as the Faröes, where shells have been carried by the Gulf Stream.

FIG. 9 *Spirula*   *Spirula* is one of the smaller cephalopods, rarely measuring more than 1½ in. excluding the tentacles. Its light brown body is shaped like a cylinder. *Spirula* has eight arms, and two tentacles which measure about 1½ in.

[1] Bruun (1955) thinks that this is mainly because too few attempts have been made to capture them in the right waters. He tells me that trawling in the right place and depth he once caught 26 in a single trawl.

when fully extended. When disturbed *Spirula* can withdraw its head, arms and tentacles into its mantle cavity, the edges of which then almost close the opening. Brunn says: "Animals too small to swallow a whole *Spirula* may experience some difficulty in attacking one protected in this way by the mantle wall, which is very tough and slippery, and hard to get hold of."

Spirula has two small end-fins, and when it is swimming these frequently aid the jets from the funnel by a constant fluttering movement. Between the fins is a circular disk, with a small bead-like organ in the center, which emits a steady yellowish-green light which "burns" for hours on end (see page 106). As the normal position of *Spirula* is vertical, with the arms hanging downwards, this disk acts as a top-light. Its function is probably to enable a school to keep together. Unlike the majority of animals, whose main movements are more or less horizontal, those of *Spirula* are mainly vertical, up and down through half a mile of sea-water.

Inside the top end is a small shell, coiled in a flat spiral. It is completely enclosed by the mantle, despite statements in numerous text-books to the contrary.[1] Bruun observed *Spirula* alive and dead, and had X-ray and ordinary photographs taken of them. And he says that the shell is enclosed. It is divided into 25 to 37 chambers which are filled with gas and air. A delicate hose-like extension of the body, called a siphuncle, runs through them.

The most comprehensive monographs on the biology of *Spirula* are by Bruun (1943 and 1955). He had at his disposal the 188 specimens brought to Denmark by the two *Dana* oceanographical expeditions.

Before 1920, when the first expedition set out under the leadership of the Danish zoologist, Johannes Schmidt, only 13 specimens had been captured by all previous expeditions throughout the world. Schmidt's main task was to try to solve what was then one of the major mysteries of world natural history: Where is the breeding-place of the American and European river-eels? Schmidt found the answer—about a quarter of a mile below the surface of the Sargasso Sea. In his search Schmidt trawled with special nets capable of catching tiny eel larvae. And these nets proved to be

---

[1] Probably because when preserved the mantle is often frayed and the shell protrudes (see Plate 7). But other zoologists before Bruun had pointed out that the shell is enclosed.

ideal for catching *Spirula*. As a result Schmidt not only solved the mystery of the eels' breeding-place; he also brought home by far the largest collection of *Spirula* seen up to that time.

In his study of these and other specimens which were available to him, Bruun paid special attention to *Spirula's* tiny shell, which rarely has a diameter of more than half an inch. How is it that this small shell can remain unbroken at depths where its surface has sometimes to sustain a pressure of nearly *half a ton?* Because the gas secreted by *Spirula* inside the shell presses outwards with the same force as the sea water presses inwards. Without such an equilibrium of pressure the tiny shell would be smashed to powder like the glass tubes mentioned on page 7.

But this raises another question: Why, as the animal rises and the sea pressure diminishes, is there no sudden outburst of compressed gas to shatter the shell? Exactly how this is avoided is not known. One theory is that the pressurized gas escapes by diffusion through very fine pores in the shell. Bruun, however, tells me: "I am not quite sure that the shell is porous when the animal is alive. It may only be when all the organic matter has rotted away that it is porous and the air can escape in that way. When the animal is alive the surplus air may be carried away by the blood of the animal." Whatever the mechanism, as the shell ascends, the gas slowly discharges, keeping an equilibrium of pressure with the weight of sea water outside. This is why shells of dead *Spirula* can make a journey through a vertical half-mile of sea water, with pressures varying between half a ton and a few pounds per square inch, and land unbroken on shore. Gilbert L. Voss tells me that he caught a very young *Spirula* in a high speed trawl at a depth of about a third of a mile. "It was intact after being hauled swiftly to the surface."

But this is not the end of the natural mechanics of *Spirula's* half-inch shell. It is built on a plan which makes the utmost of the few grains of material available. The shape is that of a slightly corrugated cone wound in a spiral. It is reinforced by the two to three dozen inner walls which separate the numerous chambers, and also by the corrugated pattern of the shell. Moreover, the whole shell is not made of one layer of a single substance, but of alternating layers of a horn-like material (conchiolin) and calcium carbonate. These layers are almost infinitesimally thin, each measuring about 1/25,000th of an inch, but the effect is to achieve on a Liliputian scale the characteristic strength of any multi-ply substance. Thus by its porosity the shell is enabled to resist the everyday pressures to which it is subject, and by its structure and material it is reinforced to withstand any sudden variations of pressure.

NAUTILUS

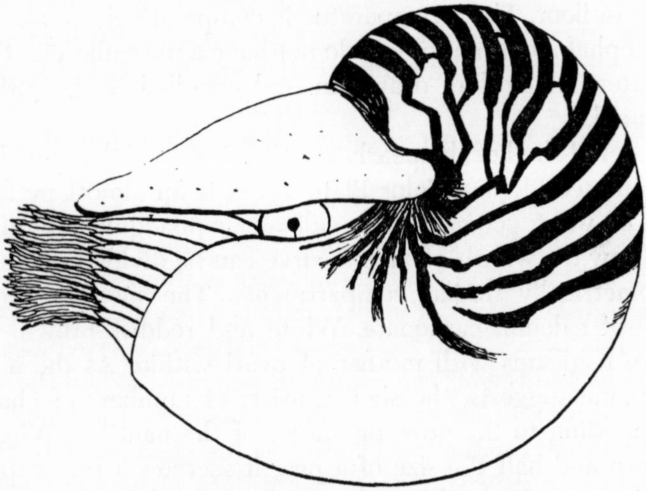

FIG. 10 Pearly, or chambered, nautilus

There is only one genus of pearly, or chambered, nautilus (*Nautilus*) living today of which there are six species (see Tom Iredale, 1944). The best-known species is *Nautilus pompilius*. These cephalopods are quite different from the paper nautiluses (*Argonauta*), with which they are sometimes confused.

The six living species of nautiluses are all that remain of the 3,000-odd species of the ancient order of nautiloids which left their record in the rocks millions of years ago. Then, myriads of nautiloids lived in all the seas of the world, as their widely scattered fossils bear witness. Some have been found in London clay. Today, nautiluses live only in the West Pacific. They are "living fossils," representatives of an order which goes back to the beginnings of animal life on this planet—an order which has witnessed the rise and final extinction of mighty animal dynasties which once flourished in primeval seas.

Like their distant ancestors, but unlike their modern relatives, nautiluses live in a shell. They have four gills and no ink sack. Whether this condition is ancestral or not it is impossible to tell, as the fossils are, of course, only shells. In contrast to the 15-ft. shell of some of their ancient forbears, no known modern nautilus has a shell more than 10 in. across.

Nautiluses live at various depths, probably down to about 2,000 ft. They swim about hunting for shrimps and other creatures of the ocean floor. The jet apparatus is comparatively weak. Unlike other cephalopods, nautiluses do not have a muscular mantle, and the water is therefore drawn in and expelled by pulsations of the funnel.

The spiral shell of the pearly nautilus is one of the most beautiful in the world (see Color Plate 1). It is an almost perfect example of what geometricians call an "equiangular spiral," and shows how the whorls of such a curve can be divided into a series of geometrically similar compartments. The shell is composed mainly of calcium carbonate. White and reddish-brown on the outside, it gleams with mother of pearl within. As the animal's other name suggests, the shell consists of numbers of chambers corresponding to the growing stages of the nautilus. When it is first born and half the size of a pea, it secretes a tiny cup. As it grows it moves forward into the enlarging shell, sealing off all but a small hole with slender cross walls called septa. A siphuncle runs back through the hole in each chamber to the original compartment. The animal's body lies in the last and largest chamber.

The total number of chambers varies. Arthur Willey, who made many observations on these animals, says that he has known a shell of *Nautilus pompilius* to have 36 chambers, but a specimen of *Nautilus macromphalus* had only 27. Very occasionally the nautilus secretes a pearl. One that Willey found was large but irregular, and the surface was impure.

The shell contains gas which makes it semi-buoyant. As the shell is large and heavy compared with the body of the animal, such buoyancy is essential for swimming. As the nautilus travels up and down the pressure at times—nearly half a ton per square inch at maximum depth—would probably crush it unless the pressure inside the shell were adjusted to that outside. How this adjustment is made is questionable. Rousseau H. Flower has suggested to me that it is by the amount of gas secreted in the chambers by the siphuncle, the amount varying automatically with the pressure on the shell.

The shell is made watertight by the body of the nautilus which fits into the last chamber. The animal can withdraw into this entirely and shut the entrance with a tough leather-like hood. When attacking, the nautilus darts the front part of its body forward.

The nautilus has numerous small arms which can be withdrawn into sheaths. The arms are in two groups: 42 in the outer series and a variable number in the inner. Some female nautiluses have 94 arms altogether, and the males about 60. There are no suckers on the arms, but ridged surfaces enable them to grip firmly.

The cluster of minute arms gives the nautilus a peculiar appearance when seen at the surface, and makes it look like a large sea anemone attached to a shell or "a shell with something like a cauliflower sticking out of it." A sailor, who saw one floating on the sea, never having seen one before and noticing the white and reddish-brown shell, called out: "There's a dead tortoiseshell cat in the sea!"

Although living nautiluses have rarely been seen at the surface by zoologists, they are believed to be numerous in the regions where they live. A correspondent who spent four years in Batavia (now Djakarta) tells me he was told that it is not uncommon to find them adrift in the Molucca Strait area. Cotton informs me that off the Philippines fishermen use nautiluses for bait, and their shells are often found.

Two FOOD

An octopus [1] catches its prey by seizing it with its sucker-clad arms, or by enveloping it in the web of membranes which connect the arms at their base. All octopuses have eight arms, which grow from the head—"eight radiating, supple, tapering thongs" as Henry Lee calls them. Victor Hugo's description is "supple as leather, tough as steel, cold as night"!

The arms vary in length with the species. Those of *Octopus arborescens* are about an inch long. Maximum length for the common octopus (*Octopus vulgaris*) is about 4½ ft. The arms of a Pacific octopus (*Octopus hongkongensis*) measured by the American zoologist, William H. Dall, were nearly 16 ft. long.

The tips of the arms can feather with extreme delicacy, and can

[1] Except where indicated, the information in this section refers mainly to the genus *Octopus*.

paper-thin openings (see page 77). A common
be seen gracefully curling and uncurling the
s into miniature Catherine wheels.

urface of each arm are circular suckers which
nds of muscular tissue. These suckers are called
g they are attached directly to the arm, com-
talked suckers of cuttlefish and squids. In some
the lesser octopus (*Eledone cirrhosa*), there is a
ch arm and in others, including the common octo-
vo rows. Suckers are small near the mouth and in-
num size at about the tenth sucker, or pair of
ng progressively smaller again towards the tip. In
opus they reach a maximum diameter of about
ge common octopus they range from about one-
o 1½ in. The number of suckers varies with the species and they are numerous in all. In the common octopus
there are normally 240 on each arm, making a total of 1,920.

Bruce S. Wright has sent me photographs of an octopus he obtained on the reef of Mafia Island, off the Tanganyika coast of
Africa, which has four irregular rows of suckers on the middle
section of the arms, the base and tip having two rows. It is possible, however, that this is an abnormal condition due to regeneration of the arm following amputation (see page 51). Sir Richard
Owen (1885) described an octopus which had three rows of
suckers on its arms.

Each sucker, even those at the tips of the arms of a young octopus of a small species, where they are pin-head size or less, is a
delicate piece of natural engineering. It consists of a muscular
membrane which is thickened and strengthened at the rim. The
center of the sucker acts like a piston and can be raised by muscular contraction, forming a partial vacuum. If a stronger grip is
required the octopus can retract a greater area of the central disk.

Should the octopus decide to move the position of its suckers it
can release the suction and clamp down somewhere else almost
instantaneously. Occasionally, however, the suckers will glide over
a surface, as Lee discovered when he used his own arm as a
testing-ground.

The efficient operation of the suckers is essential to the life of
the octopus. As it moves about its rocky lair, or over the sea-

bottom, the outer covering of the suckers becomes worn, but the frequent sloughing of their outer skins ensures that the vacuum effect is not impaired. In aquaria the cast-off skins can often be seen floating in the octopuses' tank. They are very thin filmy disks, with a hole in the center. When an octopus is shedding the skins it curls its arms close to its body and rubs them together, rapidly coiling and uncoiling them.

As the octopus grows the suckers increase in size, and frequent changes become necessary. Sometimes the whole sucker is renewed.

Although the whole surface of an octopus's body appears to be chemically sensitive, sensation—both chemical and mechanical— is particularly acute in the suckers, especially the rims. When an octopus encounters an object its suckers conduct the examination, the individual suckers being pressed against the surface (see Chapter V).

When the octopus's exploring arms touch something it wants to seize, it instantly raises the centers of the suckers, and the thickened rims immediately cling to whatever they are touching. The mechanism of the suckers is completely under the animal's control. Firmly clamped to its prey with a thousand vacuum cups one moment, the next it can be completely free. William Broderip once endeavored to capture with a hand-net an octopus which had its arms twined round a fish which it was tearing with its beak. The net crept nearer and nearer. The octopus waited until the last moment and then "in an instant it relaxed its thousand suckers, exploded its inky ammunition, and rapidly retreated under cover of the cloud which it had occasioned." (Quoted by Owen, 1855.)

The effect of the suckers on human flesh has been described by various writers. The American naturalist, Gilbert Klingel, found the sensation unusual but not unpleasant. The feel of a small octopus was like "hundreds of tiny wet, clammy hands pulling at the skin."

Guy Gilpatric, the pioneer goggler who had considerable experience of the common octopus while skin diving and goggling in the Mediterranean, says that if an octopus has a firm hold and the arm is then stripped off, "the sound as the suction breaks is that of tearing apart two sheets of flypaper. Also, flypaper-like, the arm which you peel from your leg will stick to your hand, so you'll have to begin all over again." Some people have been left with bleeding skin when the suckers have been ripped away.

For its size the octopus is a powerful animal. When Sir Arthur Grimble was gripped by one he felt its "Herculean power." The pearl-diver, Victor Berge, says that when he was held on the sea-bottom by a large octopus, three men pulling on the rope attached to his suit could not make the octopus budge (see p. 186).

The diver and traveller, Virgil Burford, who often encountered octopuses on the sea-bottom off Alaska, also had a healthy respect for their strength. When he found an octopus in its lair he occasionally prodded it with a pole. With several arms firmly gripping the rocks the octopus seized the pole with its other arms. "Unless I was braced the first yank of a four- or five-foot octopus took me off my feet or ripped the pike pole free. When he settled down to hanging on, his strength was a match for mine. On more than one occasion I had to kill him to rescue it. The best and quickest way to kill an octopus is to drive the pike pole through the soft, fleshy head just above and between the eyes."

The American zoologist, G. H. Parker, carried out tests with a spring-balance on the adhesive power of individual suckers. He found that a sucker with a diameter of one-tenth inch required a pull of two ounces to break its hold, and one with a diameter of a quarter-inch required six ounces. (If the increase were proportional this figure should be 12½ ounces.)

So many varying factors are involved in natural conditions that it is not possible to judge accurately the total adhesive power of an octopus from such experiments as these. Nevertheless, it is interesting to calculate that on Parker's figures the hold of the 2,000 suckers of a common octopus spanning no more than five feet could not be broken unless a total force of over a quarter of a ton were applied! Actually, of course, the hold would be broken long before anything like this force was applied, many of the suckers probably tearing out.

Lee recounts an incident which indicates the strength of a single arm. He tied a crab to a piece of twine, and asked an assistant to lower it into the octopuses' tank. As soon as the crab had been lowered about two feet an octopus darted out from a side of the tank, seized the crab and shot back to a ledge of rock.

Lee told his assistant to pull the crab away and start again as he wanted to see what another octopus would do with it. But the octopus in possession had other ideas. As soon as it felt the strain on the twine it anchored itself to the rock with seven arms and, stretching the eighth upwards, coiled it round the tautened line. Lee saw the suckers close on the string "as a caterpillar's foot grips a thin twig."

"Noticing several jerks on the string, I thought at first they were given by the man overhead, and told him not to use too much force; but he called out: 'It's not me, sir, it's the octopus: I can't move him; and he's pulling so hard that, if I don't let go, he'll break the line.' 'Hold on, then, and let him break it,' I replied. Tug! tug! dragged the tough, strong arm of the octopus; and at the third tug the line broke, and the crab was all his own." There is a legend in Sardinia that one night, in a small sea-robbers' village on a cliff edge, the church bell rang out again and again. The wild mysterious ringing terrified the villagers—until they found the cause. The end of the bell-rope had fallen over the cliff among the rocks below, and an octopus was tugging at it! (D. H. Lawrence.)

Gilbert L. Voss, comments: "Although undoubtedly some of the arms are strong in some species, I have always been rather struck by the ease with which they are broken off in *Octopus vulgaris*, *O. briareus* [the briar octopus], and *O. macropus*. In field collecting, it is often difficult to collect specimens that have not lost arms in the collecting process." Some of the damage is probably due to the octopodan power of autotomy, or self-mutilation (see page 52), but Voss assures me that neither this, nor cutting, will account for all the instances of arm breakage that he has seen.

If an octopus wants to "stick hold" it is almost impossible to wrench the suckers free. It has sometimes happened that the arms have been torn away but the suckers have remained firmly clamped to the object of their unyielding grip.

A marine zoologist made use of this characteristic of octopus suckers to hoax a fellow professor. The zoologist presented the professor with a piece of wood on which were some small disk-like bodies, making convulsive movements. The professor puzzled over these curiosities, racking his brains to identify them among the myriad marine animals with which he was acquainted. When at last he confessed he was completely stumped the zoologist sprung the hoax. The piece of wood had been wrenched from an octopus, and some of its suckers had clamped down so firmly that they had been pulled out of the living flesh. (William J. Dakin.)

The strength of an octopus's arms, and their ability to obtain a hold in the finest crevices, has sometimes been an embarrassment to aquarium officials. Octopuses can even pull out bungs lying flush with the bottom of the tank. Before the necessary precautions were taken at the Brighton Aquarium, one octopus drew up the waste valve of a tank one night and released all the water, leaving only a mess of dead octopuses for morning light.

The octopus catches its prey both by lying in wait and by hunting. Hiding in its lair, its chameleon-like ability to change color making it one with the rocks, it waits until likely prey comes within reach. Then, securely anchored by three or four arms, it grapples its quarry with the others.

Few men have made so many observations on the octopus and its prey as the British naturalist, Joseph Sinel, who for over half a century studied the common octopus in the Channel Islands. In addition to watching them in their natural state he also kept them in "rabbit hutches" with small-mesh wire-netting over the top. These hutches, firmly ballasted, he kept in the rock-pools which were once the octopuses' free homes. Writing from a wealth of experience Sinel thus describes the tactics of the common octopus with its favorite food, crabs:

"If the crab is in the open and the octopus is out on the hunt it rises above its victim, and with tentacles [arms] so outstretched that the web that joins them part of their length forms a parachute, it descends like a cloud on its victim.[1] Oftentimes the octopus lies in wait within a crevice, or a hollow under a boulder which it has excavated by blowing out the sand or gravel; there it watches, and if a crab passes by throws out a tentacle, which, neatly rolled into a vertical coil, *unwinds* itself gently towards the crab, flicks it with the sucker-clad tip of the tentacle, and draws it to its lair.

"It is remarkable that with little exception the crab does not attempt the least resistance to the octopus. If a crab, scuttling along,

[1] Crabs sometimes escape the first assault by self-mutilation, shedding a claw or another expendable part of their anatomy, but the octopus is usually victorious with a second attack.

espies the lair of an octopus it halts in its career, and raises its claws in a defensive attitude, but that is all. The tentacle 'flicks' it, and makes it fast to its suckers, and in its defiant attitude, as if petrified, it is drawn into the lethal chamber.[1]

"I have seen a moderate-sized octopus thus catch 17 crabs in succession, just storing them in the custody of its manifold suckers, to await their turn. The octopus does not break the shells of its victims, but simply disarticulates them, and with the slender tips of its tentacles removes every vestige of the edible parts. The horny beak does not seem to be employed, except in taking from the tentacle suckers the portions they have removed. The only active resisters I have seen to the attentions of the octopus are the lobster and the fiddler crab."

Other observers, however, have given different accounts on some aspects of the way octopuses eat crabs. Octopuses are much more abundant in Channel Island waters than they are off the Southeast coast of England. The English shore crabs have not, therefore, learned to fear the octopus in the same way as their fellows in mid-Channel. Lee says that the crabs fed to the octopuses in the Brighton Aquarium showed no sign of fear in their presence. When tossed into the tank they frequently ran towards an octopus and even scrambled on to and over its back.

The British naturalist and fisheries expert, James Hornell, says that he once saw a crab (*Carcinus*) that was thrown into a tank strike back when an octopus seized it. The crab's claws snapped at the grasping arm and the octopus, apparently surprised at such unwonted self-defense, cowered down and let go its hold. During the next few days several other octopuses tried to capture the valiant morsel, but each time the crab resisted and lived. But in the end it succumbed and was eaten. (See also P.–H. Fischer.)

Lee watched an octopus pounce on a crab held against the glass of a tank. The prey was pinioned in a moment, suckers gripping everywhere—legs, claws, carapace—in a complete stranglehold.

[1] Voss tells me that at the Shellfish Laboratory of the U.S. Fish and Wildlife Service at Woods Hole, Massachusetts, he noticed an interesting reaction of the common blue crab (*Callinectes sapidus*) to the common American squid (*Loligo pealeii*). In one of the tanks the crabs were hunting the squids and snapping at them as they shot past. When a squid was caught it "never struggled or showed the slightest fear, but quickly caressed lightly the carapace of the crab whereupon it immediately released its intended victim. Is this an inherited reaction to the touch of the octopus arm?"

"Not a movement, not a struggle was visible or possible. The crab's abdominal plates were drawn towards the octopus's mouth, there was a glimpse of the black tip of the hard horny beak, and then it had crunched through the shell and bitten deep into the flesh."

I have recounted on page 82 the story of a Homeric duel between an outsize lobster and an octopus in which the octopus was the victor.

Several observers have commented upon the patient hunting of octopuses. I have referred on page 79 to Klingel's description of watching his "tame" baby octopus hunt in its private tide-pool. He says "patience was its most evident virtue." It has been asserted that occasionally an octopus waits by a large bivalve, and when it opens its shell pops in a stone to prevent it closing again. The octopus, according to the story, then eats the mollusc. But other observers query the truth of this (see page 79).

Divers have claimed that occasionally they have seen octopuses patiently pulling on an abalone shell-fish (*Haliotis*) clamped to a rock until eventually its muscles tired and its hold was broken. And under water (say 50 ft.) the broad adherent foot of a 6-in. abalone is theoretically capable of holding with a "suction" of several hundred pounds!

While octopuses will sometimes hunt during the day, they are active mostly at night. Klingel saw a crab crawl safely over the relaxed arms of an octopus at high noon, yet in the evening the same animal would seize everything within reach.

The American marine zoologists, G. E. and Nettie MacGinitie, have often seen the mudflat octopuses (*Octopus bimaculoides*) hunting at dusk at low tide off Southern California. They slithered over the mud flats, then covered with about five inches of water, poking the tip of an arm into every hole they found. They were so intent on the hunt that they sometimes slid across the MacGinities' feet. When an octopus captured a clam (*Chione*) or scallop (*Pecten circularis aequisulcatus*) it pulled the shells apart and ate the mollusc.

When prey is secured the octopus has two weapons to administer the *coup de grâce*—beak and poison. The beak is in the center of the buccal mass, the rounded orifice at the base of the arms (see Plate 9). It is of black chitin, and is shaped like a parrot's beak except that the lower mandible is the longer and closes over the upper. Except when feeding, the beak is retracted and hidden. It is very hard and has sharp tips which can break the shells of lobsters, crabs and shell-fish—the chief items of octopodan fare. Iwao Taki says that he has known one of the very thick shells of a little-neck clam (*Protothaca jedoensis*) to be broken right across by an octopus.

With many octopuses, especially the common octopus, poison is often used for killing prey. But how it is injected is not known for certain. The Belgian zoologist, Z. M. Bacq, who has had considerable experience of captive octopuses for many years, tells me that when a crab is recovered from a common octopus a few minutes after it has been seized, the crab is paralyzed but there is never any mark of a bite. He wonders if the poison is absorbed by the gills of the crab. When an octopus seizes a crab its arms, web and mouth form, with the shell of the crab on the outside, a watertight compartment. It is probable that the poison is then discharged and absorbed by the crab.

The venom is secreted primarily from the posterior salivary glands. (The anterior glands are much smaller, and their secretions appear to be relatively unimportant compared with those from the posterior glands.) As far as is known it is poison and not digestive enzymes which are secreted. The glands, and their secretions, vary considerably between different cephalopods, the poison of the common octopus being particularly virulent. The relative glands in cuttlefish (*Sepia*) and the common squids (*Loligo*) are much smaller. The glandular secretions of octopuses have been dealt with in detail by Z. M. Bacq and Fr. Ghiretti.

Experiments have been conducted to determine the effects of the poison on various animals, especially the usual prey of octopuses. (For its effects on man see Chapter XI.) Poison has been removed and injected into crabs, lobsters and amphibians. The toxin principally affects the central nervous system. The Italian zoologist, Salvatore Lo Bianco, injected poison from the common octopus into shore crabs (*Carcinus maenas*). He found that the poison worked rapidly. First the crab lost control of its limbs, then it developed a series of rapid tremors and convulsive movements, and died within a few minutes.

G. E. MacGinitie (1938), saw the effects of the poison when he watched a common Pacific octopus (*Octopus apollyon*) attack a large crab in an aquarium. The octopus held the crab against the glass where it struggled violently for a few moments, one claw pinching the web. Then the octopus secreted poison which almost immediately took effect. The crab's claws opened wide, then slowly closed; it quivered and in 45 seconds appeared to be dead. But the beak of the octopus did not touch it until 20 minutes later.

"In order to eat the crab the octopus opened it at the dorsal juncture between carapace and abdomen, the place where the break comes when a crab moults. The octopus then pulled off the back of the crab, ate the viscera first, dropped the back, and then one by one pulled off the legs, cleaned out and ate the contents, and dropped the empty shell of each as it was finished."

Despite the fact that the poison is not considered to be a digestive enzyme, the octopus does appear to secrete a fluid which helps to break down the tissues of its prey. The British marine zoologist and photographer, Douglas P. Wilson (1947), says "it seems that a salivary secretion is poured into the body of the [crab] that not only kills it but partially digests and liquefies much of the soft tissues, which are then sucked up by the octopus." Bacq tells me: "I think that a good deal of the digestive process may occur *outside* the octopus. This may also explain how an octopus gets all the meat from crustacean limbs without breaking them."

But an octopus is by no means dependent on the secretions from its salivary glands for pulping its food; the tongue also plays a part in preparing the food before it is swallowed. It is strengthened by cartilage which helps to keep it rigid, and also provides a base for the attachment of the muscles which operate it.

The upper surface of the front part of the tongue of most octopuses is covered by the radula, meaning "a scraper"—a broad chitinous, or horn-like, ribbon of minute, recurved, sharp-pointed spines or teeth, arranged in rows about a relatively large central tooth. The radula can be thrust against the body of the prey and moved backwards, forwards and sideways, thus acting as a flexible rasp or file. It scrapes out small particles of flesh from the shells of crabs and other crustaceans, and also cards the scraps bitten off by the beak.

It has been suggested that the teeth of the radula are too small and fragile for rasping, and that its main function is to force food into the oesophagus. But Voss, who has had extensive field experience of cephalopods, tells me:

"The cephalopod radula is very strong when the animal is fresh, becoming brittle only after long periods of storing the animal in alcohol or formalin. The shape of the teeth are similar to those used for rasping in the gastropods and amphineura [marine molluscs], very unlike those used for scraping algae, or those that are browsers. From a functional standpoint, they should be for rasping flesh."

The front part of the radula wears away as the spines become blunted. But new spines are continually forming at the base of the radula, which gradually shifts forward to replace the worn part which falls away. In some species the radula is degenerate, and in the Cirromorpha, which live in the deep seas, it is absent altogether.

In addition to beak, salivary glands and radula, the alimentary system of octopuses and of other cephalopods, comprises oesophagus, stomach, caecum, pancreas, digestive gland, or liver, and intestine. In the pearly nautilus (*Nautilus*) the salivary glands are absent and the pancreas is very small.

In some species there are various structural modifications of some of these organs. In many octopuses the oesophagus is expanded to form a crop, which acts as a food reservoir when the stomach is full. In some deep-sea octopuses the intestine is so dilated that it forms a second stomach. Most octopus stomachs are small, but the grinding pads on the muscular hard-surfaced walls provide an efficient milling apparatus similar to the gizzard of a bird.

In the funnel is an interesting refinement of cephalopodan anatomy. On its upper wall there is a superficial patch of glandular tissue, called Müller's organ, which secretes a lubricant for promoting the expulsion of débris which might otherwise obstruct the bore of the funnel. Octopuses are essentially carnivorous, most of them being especially fond of crustaceans and shellfish, particularly crabs.

Very little is known of the feeding habits of the octopuses which live on the sea bed, but according to G. C. Robson (1932) they probably eat carrion, débris, and plankton. The fact that the suckers of some deep sea octopuses are comparatively weak may indicate that they live on food which requires no effort to capture. The absence of the radula in some of them (Cirromorpha) may again point to a soft diet, such as decomposed flesh and plankton.

During the British Antarctic Expedition of 1910 an octopus (*Graneledone setebos*) was found imprisoned in a rock pool. It was collected and brought back to England. When its gut was examined it was found to contain seaweed. A. L. Massy, who describes this, wonders whether the unusual fare was due to old age, or to the absence of animal food. In any event the change from a carnivorous to a herbivorous diet shows a remarkable adaptability.

Other strange fare sometimes figures in the octopodan menu. An animal collector, ferreting about the reefs on Pulau Pisang (Island) near Singapore, found a small octopus eating a spider. The octopus was identified as *Octopus filamentosus* and the spider as a semi-marine species, *Desis martensii,* which roams about the reefs at low tide, and when the sea comes in, holes up in small crevices. Why is it not drowned? Because it seals the entrance to its under-water den with a silken door. (W. S. Bristowe.)

Other unusual fare was discovered by Fred Vlès. He found that feeding a large number of captive octopuses with crabs and shellfish was too difficult, so he experimented with various substitutes. Butchers' meat, slices of potato and bread were unsatisfactory. Then he tried chickens' eggs—and the octopuses loved them. At first ordinary fresh eggs were used, but these had two drawbacks: much of the egg was lost when the octopus broke the shell, and the cost was prohibitive. These problems were solved by giving the octopuses hard-boiled rotten eggs. The ration was one egg per octopus every two days.

Strange feeding habits have also been reported from the South Seas. One of the most widely held beliefs is that octopuses come ashore at night and catch rats at the water's edge. One of the most popular lures employed by native octopus hunters is a rough model of a rat.

Another story is that on some of the islands octopuses leave the sea at night and go scrumping in fruit trees! The Rev. William Wyatt Gill, who spent over 20 years during the last century as a missionary in the South Seas, and was especially interested in natural history, recounts this native belief and seems to credit it. He says: "At dawn these curious fish [*sic*] may be seen in clusters on the outspread branches of the pandanus [trees] thus enjoying themselves; but as soon as their sharp eyes perceive the approach of their enemy, man, they instantly drop on the stones beneath, and hasten back to their proper element."

It is known, of course, that octopuses sometimes deliberately leave the water. B. B. Boycott tells me that he was told by a trustworthy Neapolitan fisherman that he has sometimes seen the common octopus crawl out of the water and seize a crab off the rocks. They, of course, are damp, and the fisherman said that the octopuses do not go far or stay out long. Octopuses are very sensitive to dryness. The German zoologist, Rudolf H. Fritsch, says that Reinhard Dohrn, of the Zoological Station at Naples, told him he also had seen octopuses pursuing crabs on to a rocky shore. Fritsch noticed that at dusk and in the night, when they normally seek their food, common octopuses in an aquarium shot water at the walls and at the covering of their tanks. He wondered if this habit was related to their occasional excursions on land. "It may be possible that the wetting of the land makes it easier for the octopus to travel. Perhaps it is an attempt to flood the fleeing crab back into the water."

Whether or not octopuses occasionally devour rats and go scrumping, there is no doubt that they sometimes eat one another. This is one of the rare occasions on which Aristotle was wrong about cephalopods, as he maintained that they did not eat their fellows. The extent of the cannibalism appears to vary with the species and conditions. Lee records only one instance of cannibalism in the Brighton Aquarium.

While out collecting one day Donald A. Simpson put five mudflat octopuses in a one-gallon jug, which was the only suitable receptacle he had at the time. At the end of five days two of the octopuses had eaten the other three, but then these two preserved an armed neutrality until Simpson got them home. Shortly afterwards one of them made a meal of the other.

Boycott (1954), who has had considerable experience in keeping the common octopus in aquaria for experimental purposes, says: "The disparity in size between individual animals must not be too great, however, since larger octopus easily capture, kill and eat smaller octopus; or at least prevent the smaller animals from obtaining food." Annie Isgrove, in her monograph on the lesser octopus, says: "They have been known to attack and eat one another, the arms only of the victim, which is not necessarily killed, being generally devoured." Gilpatric saw one octopus eating another on the sea bed.

It is by no means always hunger which prompts the cannibalism. The British artist and marine naturalist, L. R. Brightwell, tells me that when he was working at the Marine Biological Station at Plymouth in September 1951 he saw a common octopus attack a lesser. The common octopus was not hungry, having eaten its fill of crab-meat, but it deliberately reached down for its victim, which was apparently ill, and hauled it up to its perch. There it ate five of the lesser octopus's arms, taking about 15 minutes over each one. Eventually the victim was released, and died a day or two later.

Octopuses occasionally make a meal of part of themselves. Lo Bianco says that an octopus (*Eledone moschata*) in the Zoological Station at Naples ate five of its arms. Such autophagy is a frequent preliminary to death.

Octopuses can live for several weeks without food. When a female is brooding her eggs she often refuses to eat until they hatch, even removing food placed near. Such self-denial means that the female may fast for some two months. The MacGinities tell me that the mudflat octopus sometimes fasts for four and a half months!

Cuttlefish have eight arms, and two tentacles. These are about twice the length of the arms and are longer than the body (mantle). Normally the tentacles lie retracted in two large pockets within the head just below the eyes, with only the sucker-clad tips protruding. Cuttlefish have suckers on both arms and tentacles, but those on the tentacles are confined to the club-shaped end which grips the prey. The suckers are attached by a short muscular stalk, and around the rims there is a horny flange with tiny teeth.

Cuttlefish seek their prey in daylight, mainly in the surface waters. Their main food is small crabs, shrimps, prawns and fish, especially small whiting. Cuttles begin to hunt almost as soon as they are born, their prey then being tiny crustaceans, such as copepods.

J. Verwey, of the Den Helder Zoological Station in Holland, has described how adult common cuttlefish (*Sepia officinalis*) seek the common shrimp (*Crangon crangon*) which hides in the sand during the day. Even if the light covering of sand is removed the shrimp's protective coloration makes it almost invisible. But the cuttlefish has its own method of flushing these shrimps. It swims slowly over the bottom with its funnel pointed forward and downward, and puffs little jets on to the sand. Sooner or later a jet hits the sand covering a shrimp, which, feeling itself exposed, immediately throws more sand on its back. This is its undoing. The sudden movement in the otherwise still desert of sand reveals its presence, and the cuttlefish is on it in a moment. (Quoted by N. Tinbergen.)

J. Wickstead, a planktologist of the Singapore Regional Fisheries Research Station, witnessed another method of capturing prey which was particularly interesting, because cuttlefish are regarded as animals which hunt rather than lie in wait for their prey. Wickstead was on the Station's launch *Chermin*, six miles offshore in the Strait of Singapore. The engine was cut off and the launch was drifting in a dead calm sea in a large patch of *Sargassum* weed.

About a foot below the surface Wickstead saw a small cuttlefish lying horizontally and perfectly still except for its tentacles. These were extended forwards and upwards, and the suckered tips were hanging down, waving slowly to and fro. Except for the tips of the tentacles, the whole of the cuttlefish's body was colored a uniform dull brown, thus matching the *Sargassum* weed. Against this brown background the white tentacle tips stood out prominently.

"Several times during some ten minutes of observation, small fish, which were clustered under the *Sargassum* weed, left their place of shelter to investigate the white tentacle tips. When the fish approached close to the tentacular arms, the cuttlefish attempted to catch them by a sudden dart forwards and securing them with the arms. During the period of observation the attempts were, unfortunately, unsuccessful. The cuttlefish did not exhibit any color changes when approached by the fish, or when

attempting to catch them. Thus, although the actual capture of
the prey was not observed, it was an undoubted case of an animal,
accepted as being a hunter of its prey, deliberately and success-
fully luring its prey to it."

Wilson (1946) has studied the capture of prey by the common
cuttlefish in the tanks of the Marine Biological Station at Plymouth. When a prawn or crab is dropped into its tank the cuttle
immediately shows interest. Its eyes open a little, color changes
shimmer across its arms and back, and it turns to face the prey.
The cuttlefish swims slowly towards it, moving by undulations of
the side-fins and weak jets from its funnel. If the prey is a crab the
cuttle maneuvers to approach from behind—a nip from a claw can
make it abandon such uncooperative fare.

As the cuttlefish draws within striking range its eight arms
stretch out towards the prey, and color changes flicker over them
like summer lightning. The long pale tentacles partially protrude
from their sockets. The side-fins undulate gently as the cuttlefish
adjusts its body to the best position for attack. Then, in actions too
fast for the eye to follow, the head is craned forward, the tentacles shoot [1] out to their full extent and, like a pair of living tongs,
the sucker-bearing heads grasp the prey.

The arms are held in a half circle ready to embrace the struggling prey as the long tentacles spring back. The beak bites into
the flesh, the poisonous salivary fluids are poured in, and the cuttle settles down to another meal. It leaves very few scraps from its
meals; even crab shells are eaten except for a few fragments.

Wilson found that the cuttlefish he studied were frequently unsuccessful when they shot their tentacles at a prawn. One prawn
made five lightning dodges at the moment the tentacles leapt
forth, causing the cuttlefish to miss each time. But at the sixth attempt, when the prawn was caught in an awkward position in a
corner of the tank, the cuttle secured it. A crab circles to keep its
eyes and claws towards the foe.

"In a large tank crabs and prawns often get away, and this must
be a regular occurrence in the sea once the enemy has been
sighted; surprise must play a big part in aiding *Sepia* to catch its

---

[1] They can also move slowly. If the cuttlefish is offered dead prey the tentacles
may "sniff" at the food. If the prey is within reach of the arms these alone may be
used to secure it.

food. As it lies on the bottom, partially covered in sand, prey must often approach closely, unaware of its presence until too late. However, there is little doubt that *Sepia* does at times chase its prey, especially when really hungry, as can be seen in a large tank when crabs are dropped in many feet away and the *Sepia* rush towards them."

Sometimes a large cuttlefish will catch half a dozen crabs and prawns one after another during an hour or so and eat them all.

When the cuttlefish bites, the upper mandible closes within the lower one so that the sharp edges of each cut obliquely, like a pair of shears. Philip Henry Gosse, the Victorian naturalist, says: "The parrot-like beak presents a strong exception to the general softness of this animal; it is so hard, stout, and stony, and moved by such powerful muscles, that the strong shells of bivalves and univalves are not able to resist its force: even the hard and stony limpet is dragged from its attachment, and crushed to pieces in these powerful mandibles."

Sinel saw two cuttlefish feeding on a dead dogfish (*Scyliorhinus*). He claims that their beaks first cut openings in the flesh, and then the tentacles were inserted. They brought out morsels of flesh and conveyed them to the beak. "The long tentacles are thus used as spoons, with peculiar adaptations for taking up the portions of food."

Cuttlefish do not appear to use the radula as much as octopuses. The large fragments of shells which are found in the stomachs of cuttles show no sign of rasping. Yet the front of the radula is worn, showing that it is used for some purpose, probably to assist in swallowing.

When very hungry cuttles occasionally become cannibals, the larger ones eating the smaller. Wilson says that such cannibalism "is especially liable to happen in warm summer weather when their metabolism is at a high level and their feeding requirements correspondingly great." Even the tiny relative of the cuttlefish, the sepiola (*Sepiola*), is cannibalistic at times. Gosse, who kept some of these little cuttles in a home aquarium, says: "I saw one dart at an unoffending brother that was passing and, seizing him with murderous jaws, shed out his life in a few seconds."

The food of squids ranges from tiny plankton to fast powerful fish. Those squids, such as *Cranchia,* whose prey is easily caught, have comparatively weak arms and tentacles. But other squids, especially the many species which live on fish, have arms, tentacles and suckers which are among the most highly specialized grasping organs in Nature. Their mechanism exhibits an almost Machiavellian ingenuity for overcoming their prey—prey that has a slippery skin, and is probably turning and twisting when the sucker-armed tentacles lay hold.

While there are differences in detail with the various species, there are two general patterns: eight similar comparatively short arms, and two tentacles (as in *Loligo*); six arms of varying length, two medium, and two very long tentacles (as in *Chiroteuthis*). In some species, such as *Histioteuthis,* the six short arms are of the same length and are united by a web. The tentacles in *Chiroteuthis veranyi* are about ten times as long as the body (mantle). When not in use the tentacles in squids are partly retracted.

The arms of a giant squid (*Architeuthis*) may be as long—12 ft. —as a boa constrictor. Two tentacles of one of these squids (*A. longimanus*) each measured just under 50 ft.

The suckers are attached to the arms and tentacles by short muscular stalks. There is considerable variation in the structure of the two tentacles. In some genera, such as *Mastigoteuthis,* they are like a whip-lash, and bear on the distal end a great number of tiny suckers. *Cranchia scabra* and some other species have suckers along the entire length of the tentacles, but in the majority of known squids the suckers are confined to the club-shaped ends. The middle suckers on the clubs are the largest. In addition to the suckers on the arms and tentacles, some squids, such as some of the Loliginidae, have small suckers on the membrane surrounding the beak.

The suckers vary greatly in size. In the giant squid they may have a diameter of 2¼ in. or more. Yet Robson (1932) examined a cephalopod (*Inioteuthis bursa?*) caught off Singapore which had the smallest suckers of any adult cephalopod he had ever seen. The mantle was about an inch long, and the tentacles measured another three inches. The suckers could be seen only under a microscope and then they appeared as "a faint powdery dusting" over the club of the tentacle. Robson estimated that the diameter of the suckers was about one-tenth of a millimeter, or less than 1/250th in. Yet the suckers seemed to be perfectly formed.

The structure of the rims varies with the species. Some have arms and tentacles armed with both ordinary suckers and others having rims composed of sharp, tiny, chitinous teeth which sink into the slippery flesh of the prey. In the giant squid there may be 50 such teeth on the rim of a large sucker. Outside the toothed rims there is a membrane which closely surrounds it, and seals the ring so that a vacuum is created when the floor of the sucker is raised.

In some squids, such as *Onychoteuthis, Abralia* and *Galiteuthis,* some of the suckers are transformed into claws, similar to a cat's but, unlike that animal's, they cannot be sheathed or extended at will (see Plate 12). When the tentacles shoot out and grip wildly struggling prey, the hooks of the claw-armed suckers plunge into the flesh and the other suckers clamp on to the slippery skin.

Moreover, at the base, or "wrist," of the club-shaped ends of these tentacles there are wart-like growths, or tubercles, in addition to plain suckers. The tubercles on one tentacle are opposite the suckers on the other. When the two are brought together tubercles and suckers fit like press-studs, and lock the two tentacles. Thus their united strength can be used to drag in the prey.

An experience of the American big-game angler, Charles F. Holder (1908), illustrates the strength of a squid's suckers. A medium-sized squid had clamped its arms to the side of a tank. Holder tried to remove them, but although he used an oar in an endeavor to prize them off they remained stuck to the glass.

When the tentacles have caught the prey and the arms have brought it close to the mouth, the beak darts forward and bites it. The beaks of the medium and large squids are very powerful. Writing of squids weighing 10 to 15 pounds, the American angler, J. Charles Davis, 2nd, says that they can easily cut an ordinary wire leader, and even experienced fishermen, using a triple hook and heavy wire leader, meet with only fair success.

During the 1940 Michael Lerner American Museum of Natural History Expedition to Chile and Peru, the fishermen found that often the strongest steel wire they could obtain was bitten in two by the large Humboldt Current squids (*Ommastrephes gigas*)— they measure up to 12 ft. overall and weigh 300 pounds or so—

and that when gaffed a squid sometimes snapped big chunks out of the stout pole. (David D. Duncan.) These ferocious squids cause considerable damage to the coastal tuna fisheries, attacking 50- and 60-pound yellowfin tunas and eating all but the heads.

There are not many observations on record of squids feeding. In addition to the main diet of fish, the smaller species also eat shrimps and other small crustaceans. Being animals of the open seas squids seldom feed inshore. They are difficult to keep in aquaria for long,[1] but there are a few observations which give an idea of the undersea dramas which take place when squids go hunting.

Leonard W. Williams, in his monograph on the common American squid (*Loligo pealeii*), says that it zigzags slowly towards its prey. When within striking distance the squid turns towards the prey and shoots forward like an arrow. The arms spread out "like the rays of a chrysanthemum," the tentacles shoot out and clasp the prey, and it is drawn back and grasped by the waiting arms. But the squid is not always successful, and if a fish repeatedly escapes the squid gives up the chase.

In July 1872 many short-finned squids (*Illex illecebrosus*) swam among the wharves of Provincetown, Massachusetts, hunting schools of young mackerel (*Scomber*) four to five inches long. Two men, S. I. Smith and Oscar Harger, watched the hunt, and A. E. Verrill recorded their observations.

The squids, which measured 12 to 18 in. overall, attacked mostly about the time of high-water when the mackerel were abundant. Hunting was observed both during the day and in the evening. What happened at night is not recorded—most likely because the observers were in bed!

The squids attacked by darting backwards among the fish, their funnel-jets shooting them through the water like miniature torpedoes. With no perceptible change of speed a squid would turn obliquely to right or left and seize a fish. It was killed almost instantly by a bite from the sharp beak in the back of the neck. The bite always appeared to be made in the same place, the beak cutting out a triangular piece of flesh. Although the squids were relentless in attack, their agile prey frequently eluded them. Some-

[1] But F. G. Wood, Jr., tells me that the small squid, *Sepioteuthis sepioidea*, lives very well in captivity even in small aquaria.

times a squid would make a dozen attempts before a mackerel was caught.

Occasionally, after several unsuccessful attacks, a squid varied its tactics. Dropping to the sea-floor it would match its color to that of the surrounding sand so that it was almost invisible. Then, when a fish approached, it would shoot up and nearly always captured its prey. Normally, when swimming, the squids were thickly spotted with red and brown, but when hunting they appeared translucent and pale. (Williams noticed a common American squid in an aquarium capture a fish with exactly the same tactics.)

The mackerel kept as close to the shore as possible, as if they knew instinctively that the shallow water was safer for them. In pursuing them the squids frequently ran aground. And that almost invariably meant death, for as soon as a squid feels itself grounded it pumps jets of water from its seaward-pointing funnel with great vigor, and succeeds only in forcing itself farther ashore.

Such is an account of adult short-finned squids eating young mackerel. In the course of time, however, the wheel comes full circle, for adult mackerel eat young squid—including the short-finned.

The squid's method of attack varies with the prey. When a compartively large fish is attacked the squid will often approach from below and clamp on to its belly. It then cuts through the skin with its beak. The Channel Islands naturalist, H. J. Baal, tells me that the squid first reaches with its tentacles for the liver. "I have seen this done when a large dogfish and a squid were left by the ebbing tide in a lagoon among the rocks at La Rocque, on our south [Jersey] coast." I have referred on page 36 to Sinel's observation of a cuttlefish using its tentacles in a similar way.

Klingel thus recounts an experience he had one night while at sea in a fishing trawler off Chesapeake Bay, Virginia.

"I was sitting in the dark on deck watching the stars and swaying to the slight roll of the boat when suddenly I heard a rapidly reiterated splashing in the sea. The sound was slightly reminiscent of the pattering noise of flying fish. I knew that I was too far north for any quantity of these volant creatures. I went below and returned on deck with a flashlight. Its beam pierced the dark and glowed on the wave tops. The ship was passing through a school of small surface fish. They were being preyed upon by hundreds of *Loligo* [common] squid.

"The squid were shuttling back and forth through the water at incredible speed. Most wonderful was the organization with which they seemed to operate. Entire masses of these cephalopods, all swimming in the same direction, would dart at the fish, quickly seize and bite at them, then abruptly wheel as a unit and sweep through the panic-stricken victims which scurried everywhere."

Sometimes a school of squid seems to kill for the sheer joy of killing. The American naturalist, Paul Bartsch, watched such a school of small rapacious squids (*Uroteuthis bartschi*) attacking shoals of small fish attracted by a submarine electric light suspended from the deck of the *Albatross* in the Sulu Sea (see page 64).

The radula in squids is comparatively small. They appear to bite vigorously with their sharp beaks and swallow rapidly, leaving the internal secretions to prepare the food for digestion which in such squids as *Loligo* is very rapid—a useful adaptation for such a constantly active animal. The British zoologist, Anna M. Bidder (1950), who has made a detailed study of their complex digestive mechanism, found that the process lasts from four to six hours. This is some three to four times faster than in the comparatively sluggish common octopus, where the digestive process lasts some 18 hours. In the cuttlefish (*Sepia*) it lasts about 12 hours. (A. Falloise, and V. P. Gariaeff.)

Squids sometimes eat seaweed. Holder (1899), writing of some large squids which ran into shallow water off Catalina Island, California, says "their food was found to be seaweed, small pieces of *Ulva* ground up, nipped off by the beak." Williams says that the common American squid often bites off and swallows pieces of eelgrass (*Zostera marina*). But the grass is not digested as it is found unchanged in the rectum.

He also states that squids of every age "are greedy and persistent cannibals," and that larger squids often accompany schools of smaller ones and feed on them constantly. Adult squids prey upon the young of their own species. One squid's stomach contained the remains of at least seven other squids and also fourteen squid beaks—mementos of past cannibalistic feasts. And this was not an exceptional case. "The size of some of the suckers found in the stomach shows that squid devour others nearly or quite as large as themselves. It is certain that, in the aquaria, defensive power or abundant food is the only safeguard for a squid against the attacks of others of the same size."

Williams is writing primarily of the common American squid but his description is generally true of other species as well. During the Michael Lerner Expedition a hooked Humboldt Current squid at once became the target of attack for a horde of its fellows. Even when a squid was hooked, gaffed, and being drawn from the water, one of its brethren would sometimes shoot up and take a valedictory bite before it quit their element for ever.

Three ENEMIES

G. E. MacGinitie (1949) once kept a small mudflat octopus
(*Octopus bimaculoides*) in an aquarium tank without stones or
rocks among which it could hide. In another tank was a moray eel
(*Gymnothorax mordax*)—traditional enemy of small cephalopods.

One day MacGinitie tried an experiment. He prodded the eel
with a long pipette, sucked up some of the water from alongside
its body, then squirted this water, redolent of moray eel, into the
octopus's tank. Immediately it reacted with the typical signs of
cephalopodan alarm. Color changes flowed over it, its eyes wid-
ened, and protuberances appeared and disappeared over its body.
But its alarm, though great, did not reach panic proportions. It remained stationary, and did not expel a cloud of ink.

MacGinitie then went a stage further. He pulled a black sateen
microscope cover over his hand, and undulating it to simulate the
action of an eel, moved it along the side of the tank. Immediately
the octopus shot across the tank and expelled a cloud of ink. Mac-
Ginitie says:

"We often demonstrated this performance for visitors, but the
combination of the stimulus of both smell and sight was required

to induce the full response. From this we know that the octopus and the eel have been prey and predator for many millions of years—such an instinctive reaction could be built up only after millions of years of evolutionary association."

A trace of octopus ink in water is sufficient to excite an eel. If a few drops are introduced into a moray's tank the eel dashes wildly about, seeking its ancient prey. The American biochemist, Denis L. Fox, tells me that he once offered to a moray eel a mussel (*Mytilus californianus*) which had been removed from its shell. The eel refused it. Fox then dipped the morsel in some octopus ink and offered it to the eel again. This time it was devoured avidly.

The ink, or sepia, is possessed by nearly all cephalopods and is their chief means of defense. It is absent only in the nautilus (*Nautilus*) and some deep-sea octopuses. The ink is contained in a small, pear-shaped organ called the ink sack, situated between the gills. The ink sack ends in a long neck which leads into the funnel from which the ink is discharged. The sack is divided into the gland which produces the ink, and a larger cavity which acts as a reservoir. The cephalopod ink sack is the subject of a detailed study by Paul Girod which was published in France in 1882.

The ink is a thick darkish fluid, and is so durable that the ink from cephalopods fossilized over a hundred million years ago can be diluted and used for writing today (see page 173). The ink belongs to the melanin group, and is thus related to the pigments in the hair and skin of man, exemplified especially in the dark-skinned races. An analysis of the ink is given by Girod, and Maurice Piettre.

The color of the ink varies with different species. According to the British worker on the Mollusca, Ronald Winckworth, generally it is sepia-brown in squids, blue-black in cuttlefish, and black in octopuses.

Although there is no doubt that the ink confuses the enemy, exactly how or why is still debatable. The theory that the ink cloud is merely an aquatic smoke-screen is now known to be an oversimplification. It has been noticed that sometimes, when the ink is first expelled, it remains as a definite shape in the water. Jacques-Yves Cousteau, who often had experience of cephalopod discharges while on his under-water excursions, says: "We found

VICTIM'S-EYE VIEW OF A SQUID (*OMMASTREPHES PTEROPUS*)
The 'buccal mass', with the black parrot-like beak in the center, shows as a circle in the middle of the arms. About half natural size

SUCKERS OF THE COMMON OCTOPUS

Several arms are held together. Unlike the stalked suckers of squids, those of octopuses grow on low mounds of flesh.

A COMMON CUTTLEFISH LOOKS THE CAMERA IN THE EYE

The two long tentacles, which flash out to seize the prey, are completely withdrawn
when the cuttlefish is at rest

Plate 10

A COMMON CUTTLEFISH'S TENTACLES SHOOT OUT AND
SEIZE A SMALL HERRING (*CLUPEA HARENGUS*)
The exposure for this remarkable photograph was 1/250th sec. but this was not sufficient
to stop all movement

Plate 11

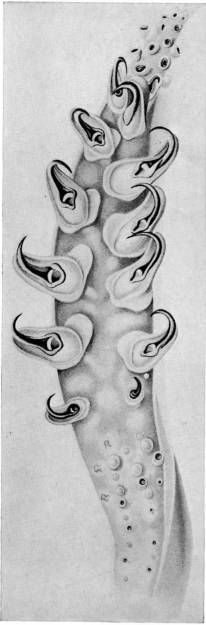

Carl Chun (1910)

THE CLAW-ARMED SUCKERS
OF THE SQUID *GALITEUTHIS*

These squids have cat-like claws on the tips of their tentacles. Below the group of claws, which are non-retract-ile, can be seen the 'press-studs and holes' which lock the two tentacles together (see p. 38). About 16× natural size

Ronald F. Le Sueur

THE TOOTH-RIMMED SUCKERS
ON A TENTACLE OF THE
COMMON SQUID

The tiny teeth can be seen on some of the large suckers. About 1½ × natural size

Plate 12

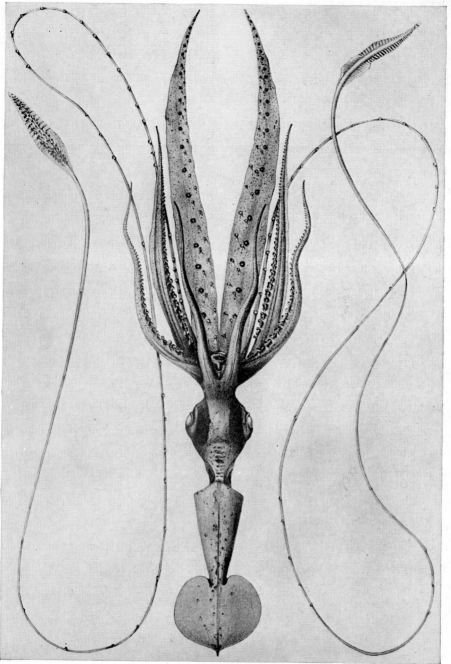

CHIROTEUTHIS VERANYI
This squid has the longest tentacles in proportion to its size of any known cephalopod. It is shown here a little smaller than natural size

Plate 13

Jacques Yves-Cousteau

WITH STREAMLINED BODY, AN OCTOPUS LAYS DOWN A LIQUID SMOKE-SCREEN AND JETS AWAY FROM A SKINDIVER

The ink, seldom ejected except when the octopus is in danger of its life, appears to have three functions: it produces a dummy shaped roughly like an octopus; it acts as a smoke-screen; and it paralyzes the sense of smell of its chief enemy, the eel

Plate 14

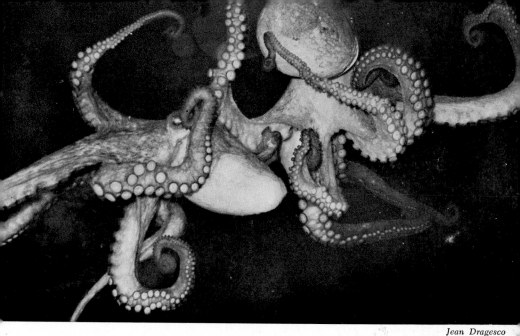

Jean Dragesco

COMMON OCTOPUSES FIGHTING

Plate 15

MORAY EELS, ONE OF THE CHIEF ENEMIES OF OCTOPUSES
Notice the attitude of the eel at bottom right (see p. 50)

Franz Thorbecke

Laurence E. Perkins

A COMMON OCTOPUS STREAMLINES ITS BODY AS IT TAKES OFF FROM A ROCK

Most cephalopods travel backwards when swimming by jet propulsion although by moving the funnel they can swim forwards as well

Plate 16

that the emission was not a smoke-screen to hide the creature from pursuers. The pigment did not dissipate; it hung in the water as a fairly firm blob with a tail, too small to conceal the octopus. . . . The size and shape of the puff roughly correspond to that of the swimming octopus which discharged it." (See also David H. Tompsett.)

The ink thus probably acts as a dummy to confuse the attacker while the octopus, rapidly changing color, darts off in another direction. It must indeed be confusing to pursue a variously colored body and then see a uniformly dark one suddenly appear out of the blue—or sepia!—between chaser and chased. In the momentary confusion the octopus, sometimes changed to near-transparency, darts off on another tack to safety (see page 55). If necessary ink can be ejected several times in quick succession. The common octopus (*Octopus vulgaris*) has been observed to make six ejections, the second replacing the first as it faded, and so on. (Lee Boone.)

From an experience of Gilbert Klingel's, it is apparent that not all octopus discharges are the same as those Cousteau witnessed. While skin-diving off Great Inagua in the Bahamas, Klingel disturbed an octopus under water. He thus describes what happened:

"The octopus flashed out of the fissure and ejected an immense cloud of purplish ink. For a brief moment I saw it swimming away, long and sleek in shape, and then I was surrounded by the haze. The fog was not opaque but imparted much the same quality of non-vision as thick smoke in dry air, except that I did not notice much in the way of wreaths. In fact I was so confused and startled that my only thought was to get away.

"From underneath the helmet there arose a faint odor quite unlike anything else. Fishy musk is the nearest description I can think of. The color was most interesting, as I had always been under the impression that cephalopod ink was black. Rather it appeared dark purple which later faded to a somber shade of azure. I can also remember, when it thinned considerably, seeing vague shafts of reddish when the rays of sunlight far above caught the substance at oblique angles. The ink spread out in a cloud extending over several yards; and in the still depths of the ravine took quite a time to dissipate. Actually it floated away as a hazy smudge before it evaporated."

Cephalopod ink confuses the enemy in another way. The Mac-Ginities occasionally put a moray eel into a tank containing a mudflat octopus. Whenever they did so the under-water duel generally followed the same pattern. The moray, whose sight is poor, immediately searched for the octopus. When it came within a foot or two, the octopus discharged its ink. The moray continued to hunt long after the ink had dispersed, but something was obviously wrong. It would go right up to the octopus, touch it with its nose, and yet show no more excitement than if it had touched a stone.

This strangely inhibited behavior lasted for one to two hours after the octopus had discharged its ink, the period depending upon the "dose" the moray received. This prolonged reaction was probably due to the strong concentration of the ink—in the sea it would have dissipated quickly.

What had the ink done to the eel? In some way it had paralyzed its olfactory sense so that, while the effect lasted, it was incapable of smelling the octopus, even when its nose touched it. And without such olfactory stimulation the moray would not attack. (As mentioned on page 44, a very weak concentration of ink actually excites the eel.)

Whether the ink has a similar paralyzing effect on the senses of other enemies is not known. But as the large carnivorous eels—rock-dwellers like the octopus—are one of the chief predators, the defensive discharge undoubtedly saves countless numbers of octopuses from attack.

Incidentally, the ink may help cephalopods to locate one another. It has been suggested that minute quantities of ink are ejected and affect the olfactory organs of other cephalopods.

Judging from experiments carried out by Guy Gilpatric the ink in strong concentration is fatal to its owner. Gilpatric caught five small octopuses before they ejected their ink, and put them quickly into separate buckets of sea water. He was careful not to injure them. He then annoyed them so that they ejected their ink in the buckets—and every time the octopus died in three to five minutes. The Channel Islands naturalist, Ronald F. Le Sueur, tells me that he has had a similar experience. He put two small octopuses in a gallon jar and ten minutes later they were dead, both having discharged their ink.

Octopuses sometimes deliberately squirt water, and are able to "fire" like archer-fishes. (*They* can shoot down insects on the wing!) Lee experienced the marksmanship of an octopus when he carried out experiments on its swimming powers in a tank at the Brighton Aquarium. At first the octopus was comparatively co-operative but at last it became irritated. "Instead of sinking to the bottom as he had previously tried to do, he swam along the surface away from me till he reached the back of the tank, where he sustained himself motionless for an instant, and then shot forth a jet of water which struck me on the breast, and drenched my shirt-front, though I was five feet distant from him."

Z. M. Bacq informs me:

"I can confirm this observation of Lee. I was accustomed, when in Naples, to have a small octopus as a pet in an aquarium in my office. When this animal was not fed properly it would often eject water (only water without a trace of ink) when it saw me passing along the aquarium. The quantity of water was generally quite large."

Charles Darwin also experienced this octopodan water barrage. While on St. Jago, in the Cape Verde Islands, he was looking for marine animals along the rocky shore, holding his head about two feet above the ground. Several times a jet of water was shot at his face, "accompanied by a slight grating noise." It came from an octopus, and Darwin says "it appeared to me that it could certainly take good aim by directing the tube [funnel] on the underside of its body."

The blast of water from the funnel of a large squid is shot with great force. The Humboldt Current squid (*Ommastrephes gigas*), which measures up to some 12 ft. and weighs 300 pounds or so, has been described as shooting water "like a blast from a fire hose." But it remains for Pierre Denys de Montfort, the Baron Munchausen of cephalopodan lore, to have the last word. He had his *Poulpe colossal* deluge a whole ship with a discharge from its funnel!

Like nearly all sea creatures, octopuses are attacked by various enemies from their first moment of existence—even as eggs they are eaten by crabs and probably other animals. I have dealt with cannibalism among cephalopods in Chapter II. Fish prey upon both young and adults, the size of the predators varying with the size of the octopus. Gilbert L. Voss found 24 argonaut (*Argonauta argo*) beaks in the stomach of a sailfish. Large octopuses are attacked by sharks, seals [1] and whales. The old fish-reptile *Ichthyosaurus* preyed upon the distant ancestors of modern cephalopods. This is known because traces of their suckers have been found in the coprolites, or fossilized dung, of ichthyosaurians.

Occasionally shell-fish are a danger to octopuses. The traveler, George Herbert Sunter, says that when he was crossing Popham Bay on the Coburg Peninsula, North Australia, he saw an octopus spanning about six feet with one of its arms held fast between the shells of a clam (*Tridacna?*). As Sunter watched the octopus ejected a cloud of ink. When this dispersed he saw the octopus going away with only seven arms.

Sometimes a shell-fish kills an octopus. When the naturalist, Bruce Cummings, was collecting at Green Island, off the coast of Queensland, Australia, he put a cone shell (*Conus textile*) into a pail of sea-water containing an octopus. These cone shells are poisonous, the venom being injected by a radular tooth which is modified to form a hypodermic needle. Men have been killed by these shells. (L. C. D. Hermitte.)

The octopus, which spanned about 20 in., put the end of one of its arms into the cone shell. After some 20 seconds the arm was withdrawn. The octopus appeared to be violently agitated. Cummings at once examined the cone shell and saw that its spike-like radula was being withdrawn. It had almost certainly attacked the intruding arm. A few minutes later the octopus shed one of its arms, the break occurring near its body. The octopus was transferred to a tank with an abundant supply of fresh sea-water, but it was found dead the next morning. The cone shell showed no sign of injury. Cummings suggests that in the natural state there are frequent encounters between the two molluscs.

Waldo L. Schmitt, of the Department of Zoology of the Smithsonian Institution, has told me of an interesting experience he had which indicates that starfish (Asteroidea) may be dangerous to octopuses. While Schmitt was on an expedition to Alaska, he and his companions were trying to put a small octopus into a tank on

---

[1] Lorenz Hagenbeck records that a young sea elephant, kept behind a palisade off Sarasota, Florida, lost an eye through an encounter with an octopus spanning about seven feet.

board a ship, but the animal repeatedly slipped from their hands. A halibut fisherman who was watching the proceedings said to Schmitt: "Don't you know how to handle them?" On Schmitt admitting that he didn't, the fisherman seized one of the many starfish that had come up in the same trawl net as the octopus, and threw the starfish on to the octopus which was then slithering across the deck. After several more starfish had been thrown on it the octopus "froze" and Schmitt picked it up and dropped it into the tank as easily as if it had been dead. The fisherman said that any starfish would have the same effect on an octopus.

It is obvious from the remark that the fisherman made to Schmitt that he knew in advance what effect the starfish would have on the octopus. This seems to rule out coincidence. Does the starfish secrete a substance which temporarily paralyzes the octopus? I know of only one other encounter between an octopus and an echinoderm. Voss informs me that he once put a small common octopus (*Octopus vulgaris*) into a jar containing a brittle-star (*Ophiocoma echinata*). "Its reaction upon touching the brittle-star immediately brought to mind Schmitt's story. At first it tried to crawl out of the jar as is usual but finally, when dumped into the center, it dropped down on to the brittle-star, upside down. Upon touching the star it suddenly gave a violent shudder, extended all its arms straight out, shivered a couple of times and died."

The chief enemies of many of the best-known species of octopuses are large eels. Both moray and conger eels average some six feet in length, have bodies as thick as a man's forearm, and have numerous stiletto-like teeth. Although normally harmless to man, if attacked they sometimes react with dangerous ferocity. Leonard P. Schultz tells how off Johnston Island in the Pacific, a giant moray eel (*Enchelynassa?*), ten feet long, with a body a foot wide and a mouth a foot long armed with inch-long teeth, attacked Vernon Brock, the Director of the Division of Fish and Game in Hawaii, after he had put a spear through its head. To protect himself Brock raised his elbow. With one bite the moray crushed it—and it took a surgeon two and a half hours to repair the damage.[1]

[1] In the Bermuda Government Aquarium two morays rushed for the same piece of fish. One of them missed—and crushed the other's brain. (Beverley M. Bowie.)

Brock tells me that the eel was half dead from the effects of fish poison, and he thought there was little danger in spearing it. "Eels weighing upwards of 75 pounds have been taken at Johnston Island, so it is not surprising that I ran into a large one there."

It may be imagined that the soft-bodied octopus is easy prey for such sea-tigers as the moray and conger eels. Their muscular serpentine bodies are well adapted for exploring the holes and crannies in the under-water rocks where the octopus lives. When an eel finds a small octopus it swallows it whole. Often the octopus fastens its arms round the eel's head. The eel then forms a loop with its tail, slides its head—wrapped in octopus arms—backwards through the loop, thus forcing the arms to slide along its slippery body and release their hold. At the same time the eel gulps the octopus still further down its throat. This performance may be repeated several times before the octopus is completely swallowed.

If the octopus is large the eel applies a different technique—as gruesome an example of animal mayhem as can be found in all Nature. Grasping an arm in its vice-like jaws, the eel stretches its body full length and then spins itself round and round until the arm is twisted off. It is then swallowed, and unless the octopus has managed to escape during this slight pause, the eel continues to eat it an arm at a time. The spinning technique requires only enough space for the eel's straightened body, and an octopus caught in its lair can, therefore, be eaten piecemeal with little possibility of escape.

Such an attack is rarely observed under natural conditions, although the MacGinities tell me that they have often witnessed it in a large concrete tank in which conditions were very similar to those on the sea-floor. They say: "We have observed this performance many times with the moray eel as the predator, and both the mudflat octopus (*Octopus bimaculoides*) and the two-spotted octopus (*Octopus bimaculatus*) as the prey."

One of the curators of the Havre Aquarium witnessed a conger eel (*Conger*) kill an octopus (*Octopus vulgaris?*) in a similar way to that described by the MacGinities. The octopus, which had been thrown into a tank of congers, at first escaped detection by stretching along a rock and changing color. But an eel found it, and the octopus then shot away and discharged its ink. It then fixed itself to a rock and awaited an attack.

"A conger approached, searched with its snout for a vulnerable place and, having found one, seized with its teeth a mouthful of the living flesh. Then, straightening itself out in the water, it turned round and round with giddy rapidity, until the arm was, with a violent wrench, torn away from the body of the victim. Each bite of a conger cost the unfortunate creature a limb, and, at length, nothing remained but its dismembered body, which was finally devoured." (Quoted by Lee.)

If an eel attacks a large octopus it may not always win. The travel writer, Wilmon Menard, saw a fight between an octopus and a giant conger at Macassar on Celebes in the Pacific, which, he states, the octopus won. Fox tells me that at the Scripps Institution of Oceanography at La Jolla, California, a medium sized moray eel was put in a tank containing a hungry two-spotted octopus. The octopus attacked the eel repeatedly. For a time the eel's agility enabled it to escape but eventually it tired and the octopus killed it and ate part of its head.

One of the outstanding characteristics of octopuses is their vitality. They can suffer severe injuries and mutilation and yet survive. The under-water fisherman, Bernard Gorsky, had to harpoon an eight pound octopus "at least ten times before it surrendered, completely chopped up." Gilpatric once speared an octopus spanning about 18 in. twenty times and it was still prepared to fight back. But a spear thrust between the eyes, severing the central nervous system, will kill an octopus instantly.

Octopuses often lose the whole or part of an arm, especially from attacks by eels. Like many other molluscs they then re-grow the lost part. The Danish zoologist, Japetus Steenstrup, says that every octopus he examined which had suffered damage to its arms showed partial or complete regeneration. Some octopuses had lost, and subsequently re-grown, all eight arms at one time or another. The octopus shown in the frontispiece to this book has an arm in process of regeneration.

Mathilde M. Lange made a detailed study of octopodan (*Octopus vulgaris*) regeneration and its related mechanisms. Some octopuses can cast off part of an arm at will. If, for example, the octopus is held by an arm it sometimes frees itself by automatically breaking it off—as some lizards shed their tail when hard pressed. Lange found that when this happened with the common octopus it generally freed about four-fifths of the arm. But there was considerable variation, and she found no place which was modified to facilitate the autotomy, as such self-mutilation is called. In those species of lizards which possess the power of autotomy there is a natural breaking area, a weak line passing right through the tissues.

Although there is no such area in the arms of common octopuses, there is a mechanism for regenerating the lost part. Lange found that if an arm was cut there was no bleeding, probably because the moment the arm is cut or cast off the blood-vessels contract at the site of the wound. At the same time the skin round the rim curls inward and covers the circumference of the wound. Some six hours later the muscles of the blood-vessels relax, and blood flows slowly into the wound, forming a protective clot over the central area.

Some wounds healed completely in less than 24 hours, but others took from 36 to 48 hours. Six weeks after a third of an arm had been cut off it had regrown, complete with suckers and chromatophores, or pigment spots. Although thinner than the corresponding part of the undamaged arms, it was fully functional. Squids and cuttlefish can also replace lost arms, although the mechanism is different.

A remarkable example of defense involving autotomy is found in the blanket, or handkerchief, octopus (*Tremoctopus violaceus*). It has thin gauze-like membranes attached to two of its dorsal, or upper, arms which are considerably longer than the others. There are several dark spots on the membranes, somewhat like the eye-spots on the wings of some insects. Observations on living blanket octopuses are rare but apparently, when threatened, part of a membrane breaks off along a weak line and, fluttering in the water in the wake of the fleeing octopus, distracts the pursuer. (Adolphe Portmann, and Gustav Kramer.)

Lange found some evidence that if part of the eye of an octopus is damaged it can regenerate it. Even total loss of both eyes does not seem to handicap octopuses unduly. E. V. Cowdry observed two such maimed common octopuses in an aquarium and found that their behavior was very little altered. "They remained alive and active, and fed whenever the opportunity offered." The British zoologists, M. J. and J. Wells, have described the behavior of blind common octopuses in aquaria. They say they are "hypersensitive and hyperactive."

Octopuses are frequently infested with parasites, but G. C. Robson (1929) says "signs of disease are singularly rare." Although he dissected some 400 specimens he found signs of disease in only two.

Of all cephalopods, cuttlefish (*Sepia*) have the largest supply of ink for their size and are the most ready to use it. Lee removed a half-developed cuttlefish from the egg when it was about the size of a grape pip, and it sprayed ink over his fingers. Francis Bather says that a cuttlefish only one minute out of its egg sprayed ink twice when irritated. But all such records of precocious self-defense are surpassed by the experience of L. Kuentz. He forced a baby cuttlefish from its egg, and when he continued to irritate it the tiny creature shot ink at him five times!

Like other cephalopods, cuttlefish frequently eject a single puff of ink when first disturbed. If, however, this does not stop the pursuer clouds of ink pour from the cuttle's funnel. Their abundant ink supply makes them unpopular with aquarium-keepers, and is one of the reasons why they are displayed less frequently than octopuses. Lee says:

"The fluid is secreted with amazing rapidity, and the black ejection frequently occurs several times in succession. I have often seen a cuttle completely spoil in a few seconds all the water in a tank containing a thousand gallons.

"When first taken, the *Sepia* is most sensitively timid. Its keen, unwinking eye watches for, and perceives the slightest movement of its captor; and if even most cautiously looked at from above, its ink is belched forth in eddying volumes, rolling over and over like the smoke which follows the discharge of a great gun from a ship's port, and mixes with marvelous rapidity with the water, whilst the animal simultaneously recedes to the best shelter it can find.

"But, like all of its class, the *Sepia* is very intelligent. It soon learns to discriminate between friend and foe, and ultimately becomes very tame, and ceases to shoot its ink, unless it be teased and excited."

Le Sueur tells me that he has known a small cuttle, trapped in a tide-pool 30 ft. long by 15 ft. wide and with a maximum depth of about 1½ ft., turn it into a "sea of ink" in which the cuttle became invisible.

Cuttlefish, in addition to their more abundant ink-supply, also have a greater power of changing color than other cephalopods (see Chapter VI). Their chief enemies appear to be sharks and cetaceans—whales, dolphins and porpoises.

More marine animals prey upon squids than upon all other cephalopods combined. Their predators range from Antarctic penguins to the 50-ton sperm whale (*Physeter catodon*).[1] Millions of squids are caught each year by man; they provide food for innumerable fish; large sea-mammals such as seals prey upon them; small ones are eaten by jellyfish; and they eat each other with relish.

To defend themselves squids possess the standard weapons of ink and color change, and the fastest turn of speed of all cephalopods. When the British marine zoologist, D.N.F. Hall, tried to catch a small squid he was given an object-lesson in how these protective devices combine to outwit an attacker. Hall had a three-inch squid in a large, light-colored, wooden tub on board the Singapore Regional Fisheries Research Vessel *Manihine*. One evening he tried to catch the squid by hand. When his fingers were about nine inches away the squid turned dark and seemed to stay still. Hall made a grab—and seized a small blob of ink. The squid was at the other end of the tub.

Hall tried again, and this time he watched exactly what happened. After turning dark the squid ejected ink which roughly simulated the shape of its own body. Simultaneously it turned

---

[1] About 10,000 squid beaks have been found in the stomach of a bottle-nosed whale (*Hyperoodon*). (George W. Tryon.) Most of the toothed whales feed on squids.

pale and shot away round the perimeter of the tub. Hall had the
advantage of watching the squid and its ink discharge from
above, but a natural predator would most probably have had the
ink discharged at eye-level between itself and the squid.

Bernard C. Cotton informs me that he witnessed a similar performance in an aquarium by the common South Australian squid
(*Sepioteuthis australis*). He accidentally touched the squid with a
hand net, and in a flash the squid "turned dark-gray-brown, discharged ink discoloring a volume about equal to the entire squid
and shot away like a silver streak."

Voss tells me that Stewart Springer, who observed *Ommastre-*
phes pteropus in action on numerous occasions, noted that they
emitted a cigar-shaped cloud of ink of the same length and diameter as themselves. The ink coagulated upon exposure to water
and did not dissipate. As this "phantom squid" slowly sank, the
real squid turned sharply away.

The German zoologist, Wilhelm Schäfer, made a number of observations on the ink-discharge of the squid *Alloteuthis subulata*
in the Wilhelmshaven Aquarium. He found that it remained as a
distinct shape in the water for about ten minutes, but if disturbed,
as by a fish attacking it in mistake for a squid, the ink was scattered over a wide area. Schäfer points out that as a number of
squids under attack all eject ink-dummies the enemy must become thoroughly confused. Sepiolas (*Sepiola atlantica*) also discharge dummy-forming ink. Schäfer suggests that cephalopods
possessing ink sacks may be divided into two groups: those discharging ink which forms a shape, and others whose ink diffuses
over a wide area (see Plate 21). But some cephalopods, at least,
can discharge their ink in both forms at will.

Some squids certainly appear to discharge their ink in a form-
less stream. The larger species in particular squirt theirs with considerable vigor often, at least, with none of the finesse of dummy-
shaping. The American photographer, David D. Duncan, writing
of the Humboldt Current squids (*Ommastrephes gigas*) that were
caught with rod and line during the Michael Lerner Expedition,
says: "We found that the squid, when hooked and lying on the
surface, could eject this sepia, together with water, under tre-
mendous pressure, sufficiently far, in fact, to carry it over the side,
past fisherman and photographer alike, to drench and stain the

cabin of the boat." To protect themselves against this ink-and-water barrage, the fishermen wore pillow-cases over their heads and the upper part of their bodies.

Some small squids (*Cranchia*) are able to withdraw their head, arms and tentacles into the mantle cavity, and this may protect them from some enemies. As mentioned on page 15, *Spirula* is also able to do this and Anton Fr. Bruun believes that it is a defensive action. Voss informs me that he has retrieved specimens of *Cranchia scabra* "from plankton tows with the eyes staring at me from within the mantle. It is quite eery."

The smaller species of squid can travel faster than other cephalopods—and many fishes—and such speed often saves them. The so-called flying squids (*Onychoteuthis*) can emulate flying fish and, when their under-water attackers get dangerously close, they can shoot out of the water and sail through the air.

Schools of flying squids and other species are often followed by predators. Off the Californian coast immense schools of the Pacific coast squid (*Loligo opalescens*) are invariably followed by seals, sea lions, salmon and other fish. Three large squids were once chased into the shallows of Catalina Island by tunas, and on another occasion about a score were chased into the harbor by a large school of jewfish.

The Michael Lerner Expedition discovered that the broadbill swordfish ate squids voraciously. The stomach of a broadbill that was dissected was found to be so full of squids that it was a wonder it could swim. The dolphin fish (*Coryphaena hippurus*) is another eager predator of squids—and argonauts—in the open seas.

The lancet fish (*Alepisaurus ferox*), so named from its lancet-like teeth, feeds voraciously on deep-sea species, and Voss informs me "stripping the stomachs of this fish is one of the approved methods of collecting deep-sea squid and octopods."

Sea mammals eat vast quantities of squids, from the smaller species up to the one-ton giant squid (see Chapter XII). The Falkland Island sea lion eats so many squids that its digestive tract is stained by their ink. They are also the almost exclusive diet of the sea elephant.

H. J. Squires, a zoologist of the Fisheries Research Board of Canada stationed in Newfoundland, says that the pilot whale (*Globicephala melaena*) appears to feed almost exclusively on the short-finned squid (*Illex illecebrosus*) in the Newfoundland area. The whale "is considered to follow these squid in their migrations, and when seen south of the Grand Bank may be feeding on pelagic schools of squid."

Surface-swimming squids, both the smaller species and the young of larger ones, are preyed upon by sea birds, especially albatrosses and giant petrels (*Macronectes gigantea*). Robert Cushman Murphy found that the stomach contents of a number of Pacific boobies (Sulidae) contained flying fish and squids in equal amounts. Squids are the main food of the king penguin (*Aptenodytes patagonicus*), and they also form a large part of the diet of the emperor penguin (*Aptenodytes forsteri*). Paul Bartsch says that 96 cephalopod beaks were recovered from an emperor penguin collected in the Bay of Whales, Antarctica. Sometimes the ground of a penguin rookery is littered with the ejected beaks of cephalopods.

Four LOCOMOTION

Ages before man discovered jet-propulsion cephalopods were jetting through primeval seas. Some of the smaller species of squid are the best examples of these natural jets, their swift movements earning them such names as sea arrow and flying squid (*Onychoteuthis*, etc.). The propulsive force is sea-water, shot in fast-repeated pulses from a single nozzle, called the funnel, or siphon, on the ventral, or under, side of the body.

Water enters round the free edge, or collar, of the mantle at the "neck." It is drawn by expansion of the mantle walls into the mantle cavity which acts as a compression chamber. During the intake of water the funnel is partially collapsed and closed. Then the inlet is sealed in three ways. Cartilaginous ridges on the inside of the mantle lock into corresponding depressions on the sides of the funnel; the head is retracted towards the body (visceral mass); and valve-like extensions of the sides of the funnel seal the rest of the opening. The heavily muscled walls of the mantle cavity contract violently, and the water is driven at high speed through the muscular funnel which protrudes through the inlet. It is the pressure of this escaping water which distends the side valves of the funnel. A muscular valve inside the external opening of the funnel controls the flow, and stops water entering from outside. The squid can point the funnel forwards or backwards, and as the jet of water shoots one way the squid, by the law of action and reaction, is driven in the opposite direction.

Although the principle of jet-propulsion is the same throughout the Cephalopoda, there are differences in the mechanism. The above description is generally true of all fast and medium-fast species of squid, but some of the slower swimmers, such as the

Cranchiidae, have parts of the mantle permanently fused to the head. Octopuses have only the ventral edge free and the locking mechanism at the "neck" is weaker than the cartilaginous mechanism of the decapods. Octopuses have no internal funnel valve and some, such as the Cirromorpha, have only a very narrow opening. In other octopuses (*Chunioteuthis*) the only opening is the funnel, so that water enters and leaves the mantle cavity by the same aperture. In the nautiluses (*Nautilus*), the most primitive cephalopods, the water is drawn in and expelled by pulsations of the funnel.

A peculiarity of the common squid's (*Loligo*) nervous system enables it to react almost instantaneously to stimuli, and to drive its body to attack or escape at high speed in a second. The speed of conduction of a nerve impulse depends largely on the diameter of the nerve-fiber, the velocity of the impulse increasing with the increase in diameter of the fiber. In the mantle of the common squid the longer the fiber, the greater is its diameter. Fibers with small diameters carry impulses comparatively slowly to the nearer parts of the mantle; fibers of largest diameter carry impulses swiftly to the mantle extremities—as fast as 50 miles per hour. The result is that impulses arrive at approximately the same instant at all parts of the mantle, enabling it to contract as a whole. It thus acts as a unit in supplying the power to drive the squid through the water. The giant nerve-fibers enable the squid to react in half the time it would take without them. (J. Z. Young, and R. J. Pumphrey and J. Z. Young.)

The largest fibers in the common squid measure about one-twentieth inch in diameter, which means they are about 50 times thicker than those in most other animals.[1] They have proved of great value to physiologists for experimental work on nerve conduction (see page 176). Giant nerve-fibers are found in other fast-swimming squids, such as the large Humboldt Current squid (*Ommastrephes gigas*). The cuttlefish (*Sepia*) also has them, but they are smaller than the giant fibers of the fast squids.

[1] Which is why this squid has been described as "a little squirt with a big nerve"!

The squid's torpedo-shaped body, strengthened by the internal shell, is streamlined for swift movement through water. Some observers, impressed by the darting motion of small squids, have thought that they are the fastest of all aquatic animals. I do not think, however, that any squid could equal the speeds of the fastest game-fish. A wahoo (*Acanthocybium solandri*) traveled 200 yds. in 11 sec., or 37.2 miles per hour, and even faster speeds have been claimed for other game-fish. (See my *Nature Parade*.)

How fast can squids swim? Very little authentic information is available. The American marine zoologist, Conrad Limbaugh, who has spent many hours skin-diving among cephalopods, tells me the common Pacific squid (*Loligo opalescens*) "travels approximately 5 to 8 m.p.h. judging from those being chased by sea lions. Common heavy-bodied squid in the Bahamas travel approximately 4 to 6 m.p.h." A large squid shoots water with considerable force. According to A. E. Verrill (1879) a giant squid (*Architeuthis*), measuring about 45 ft. overall, was stranded at Trinity Bay, Newfoundland, and in its desperate struggles to regain the water it ploughed a deep trench in the beach about 30 ft. long. The jet from a Humboldt Current squid has been likened to a blast from a fire-hose. According to the incidents recounted on page 223 a ship traveling at 12 knots was rapidly overhauled on three occasions by large squids, which indicates a speed in the region of 20 miles per hour. Such a speed seems reasonable for a large ommastrephid.

When traveling at full speed the squid shuts down its fins against the body. Writing of the short-finned squid (*Illex illecebrosus*) Verrill (1881) says:

"When darting rapidly the lobes of the caudal [end] fin are closely wrapped around the body and the arms are held tight together, forming an acute bundle in front, so that the animal, in this condition, is sharp at both ends, and passes through the water with the least possible resistance. Its caudal fin is used as an accessory organ of locomotion when it slowly swims about, or balances itself for some time nearly in one position in the water."

This description is largely true of the other species of swift-traveling squids. All squids have two fins, but in some species they are fused together. The fins may be on either side of the body; at the end, forming a single tail-fin; or they may encircle the mantle

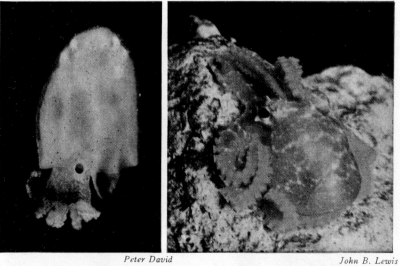

SPIRULA, IMMATURE FORM   BRIAR OCTOPUS

SHELL OF PEARLY NAUTILUS

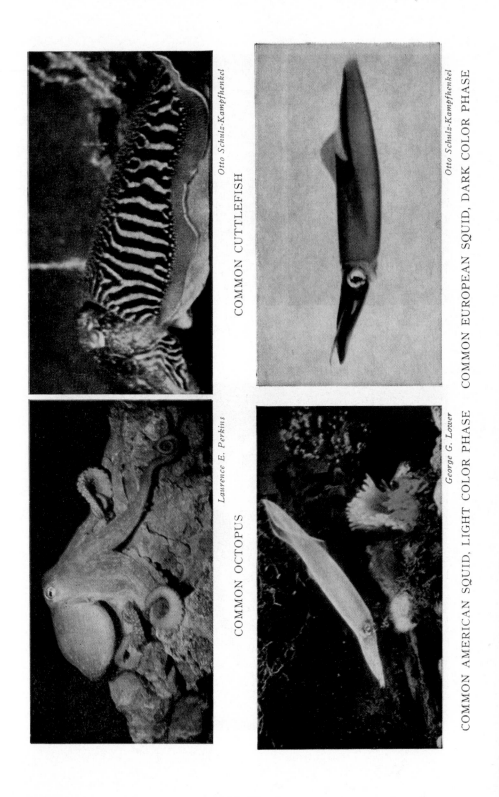

Otto Schulz-Kampfhenkel

COMMON CUTTLEFISH

Otto Schulz-Kampfhenkel

COMMON EUROPEAN SQUID, DARK COLOR PHASE

Laurence E. Perkins

COMMON OCTOPUS

George G. Lower

COMMON AMERICAN SQUID, LIGHT COLOR PHASE

AN ENOPLOTEUTHID SQUID

THE SQUID *ONYCHOTEUTHIS BANKSII*

The 'splashed-ink' effect is due to expansion of the dark chromatophores overlaying the eye. Magnification about 2 × natural size

All photographs by Peter David

THE SQUID *CALLITEUTHIS*, VIEW SHOWING THE
DISPARATE EYES

THE SQUID *OMMASTREPHES PTEROPUS*,
IMMATURE FORM

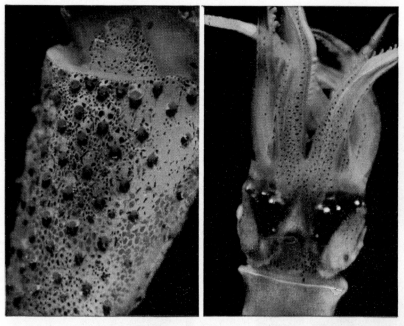

PHOTOPHORES ON THE
SQUID *CALLITEUTHIS*
Magnification about 4 × natural size

PHOTOPHORES ROUND EYES OF
AN ENOPLOTEUTHID SQUID
Magnification about 3 × natural size

All photographs by Peter David

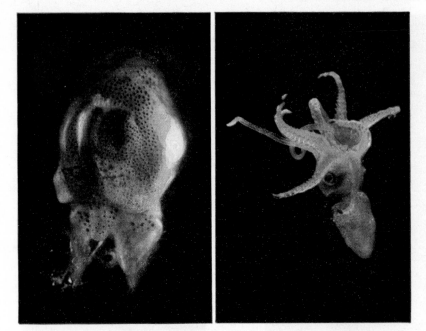

HETEROTEUTHIS DISPAR
Magnification about 2½ × natural size

A NORTH ATLANTIC SQUID,
PROBABLY IMMATURE FORM
OF *HISTIOTEUTHIS*

Great care has been taken with the plates in this section, but the technical processes involved make it difficult to render exactly the colors of the living cephalopods. Squids, especially, exhibit a wide range of colors, including a violet effect.

Color Plate 4

except at the "neck." The fins can make swift powerful strokes
which instantly alter the direction of travel, jets from the funnel
probably aiding in the maneuver. The fins also act as stabilizers
and, with the bunched arms, aid in steering.

Many of the smaller species of squid, such as *Loligo,* cruise on
and on indefinitely,[1] propelled by beats of the strong flexible fins
aided by comparatively weak jets from the funnel. Douglas P.
Wilson thus describes the swimming of the common British squid
(*Loligo forbesii*):

"It is a fine sight to watch a shoal of these elongated creatures
and see their skins shimmering as the tiny spots of color rapidly
expand and contract. In a long tank they have been observed to
move repeatedly backwards and forwards from one end to the
other, never turning round but just reversing. Of two individuals
swimming side by side, one would be moving tail first, the other
head first, at the same moment. Perhaps when they are in the sea
they are equally indifferent as to which end goes foremost."

As squids normally swim backwards when traveling fast, many
of them strand in the shallows, especially at night. When in this
predicament they invariably work their jets at top pressure—with
the funnel pointed seaward, and become even more firmly
stranded!

Henry B. Bigelow reports that short-finned squids often strand
in windrows on the islands in the mouth of the Bay of Fundy, between Nova Scotia and New Brunswick, Canada. La Pylaie, writing of conditions in the early part of the 19th century, refers to reports that squids sometimes stranded in the Bay of St. Main,
Newfoundland, in such vast numbers that they were found heaped
on the beach "up to the height of a man." I understand strandings
on such a scale are unknown now, windrows a foot high being
considered exceptional today.

Bigelow says that for some unknown reason once squids are
aground they seem "forced by instinct to drive farther and farther
ashore." According to him, if a stranded squid is picked up and
thrown out "ever so often into deeper water, it shoots, arrowlike,
back on the beach, to perish there as the tide ebbs."

[1] There are very few references to squids and other cephalopods sleeping. Verrill (1897) claims to have seen a squid sleeping in an aquarium at night and Siegfried G. A. Jaeckel deals briefly with the subject on page 643 of his monograph.

Most cephalopods normally swim backwards. As the eyes are on the side of the head and the visual angle of each eye is nearly 180°, cephalopods can see backwards quite well, but not dead astern.

Paul Bartsch tells me that watching squids catch prey swirling about a submarine light (see page 65) left no doubt in his mind that they knew where they were going. He says: "A human being could be no more precise, but could never equal their speed of action."

Squids, and other cephalopods, have organs of balance in the head called statocysts. These are small membranous sacks with bone-like weights. They indicate to the squid the direction of its movements, and are thus a valuable aid to navigation. The statocysts are more complicated in the swift-moving squids than in the other cephalopods. In some of the deep sea octopuses, such as *Opisthoteuthis*, they are comparatively huge. A study of cephalopod statocysts has been made by R. Hamlyn-Harris.

Some species of squid, especially *Loligo*, travel in large schools. In the spring and early summer the common American squids (*Loligo pealeii*) often form schools of between 10 and 100, or even more. Sometimes a school, pursued by fast-swimming fish, will momentarily shoot out of the water, hydroplaning along the surface.

Some small squids actually glide through the air for considerable distances. The hooked squid (*Onychoteuthis banksii*) has a broad membrane on the outer edges of the third pair of arms, smaller membranes on the other arms, and the fins are wide. These provide a supporting surface when the squid takes to the air. Thor Heyerdahl had exceptional opportunities for observing flying squids in action while he and his companions were crossing the Pacific on the *Kon-Tiki* raft.

"They pump sea water through themselves till they get up a terrific speed, and then they steer up at an angle from the surface by unfolding the pieces of skin like wings. Like the flying fish, they make a glider flight over the waves for as far as their speed can carry them. . . . We often saw them sailing along for 50 to 60 yards, singly and in twos and threes."

The American marine zoologist, George F. Arata, Jr., while on board the U.S. Fish and Wildlife Service ship *Theodore N. Gill*, as she was off the southeast coast of North America, observed the takeoff and flight of a flying squid at close-hand. The squid was about six inches long, but the species could not be determined. Conditions for observation were ideal; a bright, clear summer morning, and a calm sea.

The squid was first seen as it glided over the sea ahead of the ship. After striking the water it remained motionless until the ship was within about ten feet. Then the squid darted to one side, turned and leaped backwards from the sea, a fine stream of water shooting from its funnel. By the time this jet had ceased the fins were spread, and the arms were held close together to form a kind of hood. Arata estimated that the squid reached a height of six to eight feet above the sea, and flew diagonally across the ship's bow for about 50 ft. before making a "belly-landing" on the water. There was no wind to support the flight.

Many other ocean-going travelers have seen shoals of squid take flight. But they have sometimes, probably often, been mistaken for flying fish, especially by observers who are unacquainted with the habits of small squids, and whose knowledge of creatures that leap from the sea and sail through the air is confined to various species of small fish.

There is, however, a characteristic of a school of flying squids which clearly distinguishes it from a shoal of flying fish. Whereas the fish are individualists in the air, and make no attempt at formation flying, the squids maintain the same distance from each other as they sail through the air, and the whole school falls back into the sea together. (Austin H. Clark.)

There are various records of encounters between flying squids and vessels at sea. Nearly every night one or two were found on the deck, or on the roof of the bamboo hut on the *Kon-Tiki* raft. (Rachel Carson.) During his single-handed westward passage across the Atlantic in his yawl *Temptress*, E. C. Allcard was dozing at the steering one day when he was suddenly awakened by numerous bodies smacking into him. He was under bombardment from a school of flying squids. But all such experiences pale before the story told by the old classical writer, Trebius Niger, who says that ships were sunk under the weight of flying squids falling on board! (Quoted by George W. Tryon.)

Even the decks of large ships are sometimes invaded by squids.

When W. H. Rush was on a ship 300 miles off the coast of Brazil, a shoal of hundreds of squids shot out of the water and landed on the deck and in the chains. To reach the deck, which was 12 ft. above the water, the squids had to go over the hammock nettings, so they flew at least 15 ft. high during their aerial excursion.

Even this is not a record. W. J. Rees (1949) has published a paper giving 14 records of specimens of the hooked squid which were captured through landing on ships. Some of these may have been washed aboard during rough weather, but others are known to have flown aboard. Among these was one about seven inches long which landed on William K. Vanderbilt's yacht *Ara* when she was between Madeira and Casablanca. This squid flew 20 ft. above the surface and, coming in over the bow, landed on the bridge!

Although such high-flying squids are probably helped by wind, it is obvious that they must reach high speeds before taking-off.[1] The British marine zoologist, Sir Alister Hardy, once saw a squid (*Ommastrephes pteropus*) about six inches long trying to escape from a small tank on board the *Discovery II*. After several unsuccessful attempts it swam to the middle of the tank and "suddenly shot upwards like a rocket, cleared the edge of the tank and hit the far wall of the deck laboratory."

Bartsch says: "Inch for inch, the squids will compete in swimming power with any other creature that lives in the sea." One very dark night in 1908, when the sea was calm, he was on the *Albatross* in Jolo harbor in the Sulu Sea. He and several others tried to catch small squids (*Uroteuthis bartschi*) by baiting hooks with small fish and bobbing them in the water. But the squids were so fast that they dashed up to the baited hooks, snatched off the fish and shot away.

An electric lamp, enclosed in a glass globe, was lowered into the water and attracted thousands of small fish. They in turn attracted the squids.

"They shot forward or back like a shuttle, with lightning rapidity. Not only that, but they were able to divert their course into any direction with equal speed. Shooting forward, their tentacles would seize a small fish, and instantly they would come to a full

[1] Flying fish are known to travel at 30 or more miles per hour before they finally leave the water.

stop, only to dart backward like a flash at the least sign of danger. Kill, kill, kill; they were bloodthirsty pirates. A bite in the neck, and the fish was done for; but the sport continued, and, likely as not, the fish would be dropped and another seized and dispatched. Never before nor since have I seen anything that appeared to me more beautifully equipped for an aquatic existence than these squids. Frequently—yes, very frequently—their impetuous darts would carry them away above the surface of the sea; flying squids, when the pumping of their siphons produced a popping sound. . . .

"The bright idea to float a pocket net from the beam and have them enmesh themselves in it occurred to someone. This was tried, and we found that our squids possessed an intelligence equal to their lightning movements. Did they enmesh themselves? Oh, no; not one of the thousand or more that composed the school, but they seemed to enjoy shooting through a hole in our seine and it was a comical as well as wonderful sight to see them dart through this opening not more than 18 in. in diameter, like arrows fired from a rapid-fire machine gun. Now and then the whole school would come near the surface and pause, then again it would sink to a depth beyond our range of vision. Then they would line up on the far side of our net, sink below it, and shoot up on our side, to make an assault upon the small fish fry which attempted to escape by breaking from the water.

"We finally did capture some by carefully watching the speedy flight of an individual near the surface and quickly casting our dip net ahead of him. But three nights' efforts of a half a dozen fishermen yielded only a couple of dozen specimens."

Gilbert Klingel had a somewhat similar experience while on a fishing trawler off Chesapeake Bay, Virginia (see page 41).

When the American zoologist and photographer, Paul Zahl, tried to catch some small squids he discovered their lightning-like reaction to danger. From a dock in the Bimini Islands, in the Bahamas, he suspended a light about a foot above the water. He then lay on the dock planks with a net poised to capture anything that came within range.

"Suddenly, as if by sleight of hand, a host of banana-long squid appeared, pulsating close under the light. Their lateral flaps undulated gently; their tentacles, streaming behind, were motionless.

Fascinated, but not to the extent of inaction, I lowered my net slowly to the surface and struck fast and hard. Powered as they are by true jet propulsion, the large-eyed creatures reacted with violent explosiveness. In a flash they were gone, leaving in the net only clouds of brown 'ink.' "

While migration occurs in many species of cephalopod it is most pronounced in the fast-swimming squids, such as *Loligo* and *Illex*. Lukas Tinbergen and J. Verwey found that common European squids (*Loligo vulgaris*) were abundant in the neighborhood of Den Helder, Holland, from April to August, which was their breeding season, but were rare in other months of the year.

The Pacific coast squid (*Loligo opalescens*) migrates inshore in large shoals between April and July. The fishery in California is largely confined to their spawning grounds off Monterey Bay. K. Virabhadra Rao, who was Molluscs Research Officer at Madras, India, has described a somewhat similar migration-fishery for the Palk Bay squid (*Sepioteuthis lessoniana*) off Madras.

In addition to spawning migrations there are movements which are most likely associated with food supply. There is a widespread daily migration among some squids, especially the bathypelagic [1] families such as the Histioteuthidae and Cranchiidae. These squids live in deep waters during the day and come to the surface at night, following the daily migration of plankton and fishes. Incidentally, in the histioteuthids the left eye is several times larger than the right, and it has been suggested that the large eye is for use in the dark depths, and the small eye for the light surface waters (see page 110).

The short-finned squid appears regularly along the northeast American coast from Maine to Newfoundland during the spring and summer, but leaves in the late autumn, although specimens are sometimes taken in offshore waters in the winter. Bigelow believes the inshore migration has nothing to do with spawning, and is probably associated with food. "This squid, like so many of the pelagic [living in the open sea] fishes, is very erratic in its appearance, being here today in hordes and gone tomorrow, perhaps to

[1] Meaning frequenting the deep waters but not the sea-bottom. The vertical migration of vast numbers of such squids has been suggested as a possible explanation of the scattering layer—the sea's "phantom bottom"—which reflects, at varying depths, the pings from ships' echo-sounders before they strike the sea-floor. (Carson.)

reappear in a few days." Writing of the dozen or so migrants that visit the far-eastern seas of Russia, N. N. Kondakov says the squid *Gonatus magister* "cruises in all directions throughout the entire North Pacific." But much more information—especially from recoveries of marked specimens—is necessary before such statements can be accepted without question.

The common cuttlefish (*Sepia officinalis*) in European waters migrates to the north in summer. Normally this does not extend beyond the West Friesian Islands in the North Sea, but in very warm summers cuttlefish go farther north than this.

Migration also occurs among octopuses. Occasionally there are "plague years" in the English Channel, when there is a large influx of adult common octopuses, some living inshore during the whole year. Apart from these years the octopuses normally migrate into deeper water during the winter.[1] The quest for food appears to be the chief reason for all these cross-Channel migrations of adult octopuses. The lesser octopus (*Eledone cirrhosa*) also has seasonal migrations to and from inshore waters. (W. J. Rees (1952), and W. J. Rees and J. R. Lumby.) Adolphe Portmann tells me that in the Mediterranean the lesser octopus has a vertical migration varying between the shallow waters near the shore to waters over 300 ft. deep.

Generally, cuttlefish (*Sepia*) are not so swift as squids. The cuttlebone gives rigidity to the oval body, but this is not as efficient for cleaving water as is the torpedo-like body of the squids. The two long side-fins or frills give stability. A cuttlefish without fins can swim and steer but rolls from side to side. It also tends to drift to the surface, its body being a little lighter than water. Normally the cuttle swims by comparatively slow jets from its funnel, probably assisted by undulations of the fins. In the com-

---

[1] That is, the meteorological winter—the marine winter is some two months later. Sea temperature appears to have little influence on the movements of the common octopus. Lumby, who is a British oceanographer, comments: "The octopus was said to move offshore in October and return in April in order to 'winter' in deep water and avoid the cold. In fact, however, sea temperature in October is very near its maximum and in April very near its minimum."

mon cuttlefish (*Sepia officinalis*) the funnel can be extended about 1½ in. and can be pointed in any direction. (B. B. Boycott, and F. S. Russell and G. A. Steven.)

A cuttlefish can swim forwards, backwards and sideways. According to David H. Tompsett's monograph, *Sepia*, the two fins "work independently, and occasionally it uses one of them for achieving a sideways motion." When turning, the fins undulate in opposite directions, the movement being aided by gentle jets from the funnel. This precision steering enables the cuttle to "turn on a dime," which is no doubt useful in its rocky and weedy habitat. When traveling under full jet-power the fins are folded against the underside of the body. It is then that cuttlefish, like squids, are sometimes killed by piling up on the shore.

The British zoologist, Sir J. Arthur Thomson, says: "Sepias sometimes swim together in little companies, keeping time with one another, and sometimes changing color almost at the same instant."

Octopuses are generally not such fast swimmers as squids and cuttlefish. Joseph Sinel, whose studies were based chiefly on the common octopus (*Octopus vulgaris*) in the Channel Islands, gives the speed of one with a two-foot span as about eight miles per hour. H. J. Baal tells me that common octopuses on migration travel at about four miles per hour, "perhaps faster if they were driven." According to Sinel, each expelled jet drives the octopus six to eight feet. The distance is much greater in squids of comparable size, owing to their more powerful jets and streamlined shape. Some octopuses can shoot a spout of water ten feet into the air. The Italian worker on the Mollusca, Jean Baptiste Verany, saw octopuses in an aquarium hurl themselves backwards out of the water in an arc some 15 ft. long. This was achieved by a particularly vigorous jet, aided by a thrust with the arms.

Sir Arthur Grimble has the following picturesque description of watching small octopuses swimming in Tarawa lagoon in the Gilbert Islands:

"A dozen sprawling, lace-like shapes would suddenly gather themselves into stream-lines and shoot upwards, jet-propelled by the marvellous siphon in their heads, like a display of fairy water-rockets. At the top of their flight, they seemed to explode; their tails of trailed tentacles burst outwards into shimmering points around their tiny bodies, and they sank like drifting gossamer stars back to the sea-floor again."

The adult common octopus nearly always swims backwards when traveling by jet, but the young, for at least a week after hatching, swim backwards and forwards with equal ease. G. E. and Nettie MacGinitie tell me, however, that the very young octopuses they have observed in California—mostly the two-spotted (*Octopus bimaculatus*) and the mudflat (*Octopus bimaculoides*) —always swim backwards. Incidentally, Limbaugh tells me that the speed of these octopuses is one to two m.p.h.

In addition to jet travel, octopuses also swim by powerful contractions of the web-like basal membranes. The octopus *Bathypolypus arcticus*, which has a membrane running about one-third the length of its arms, uses this, in addition to jets from its funnel, in swimming backwards. Verrill observed one swimming at close quarters and records that "the arms and web were alternately spread and closed, the closing being done energetically and coincidently with the ejection of the water from the siphon, and the arms after each contraction were all held pointing straight forward in a compact bundle, so as to afford the least resistance to the motion."

Annie Isgrove says that the lesser octopus uses its web only when sinking. Then the tips of the arms separate like the ribs of an umbrella, and thus stretch out the intervening membrane.

When the common octopus wants to rise quickly from the bottom it thrusts with its arms and web. Other species have been reported to swim for a short distance by beating the arms.

Unlike other cephalopods, an octopus can crawl about the sea-bottom on its arms, and even make brief excursions on shore, occasionally foraging there for food. It is, in fact, typically a crawling animal, and alone among the cephalopods fully lives up to the name "head-footed" by walking on its arms. According to Isgrove, the lesser octopus travels over the bottom with a gliding motion, the body being raised and supported on the suckers of the middle region of the arms. Sometimes the suckers nearer the tips are used, and then the animal seems to be traveling on tip-toe.

Sinel says: "The [common] octopus can proceed at a goodly rate by the simple process of walking, spiderlike, although it more frequently seems to glide along, throwing its long arms as far forward as they will reach and making fast its suckers to the ground, releasing the hold, and repeating the operation as it brings its body up to the advanced point." If it meets a small obstruction on the sea-bottom an octopus will sometimes jump over it, landing on the other side, to quote Guy Gilpatric, "with the lithe grace of a tubful of tripe poured from a tenth-storey window!"

Some species of octopus are the only cephalopods which can live for any length of time on land. As mentioned on page 32, Rudolf H. Fritsch noticed that at night, when they normally seek their food, common octopuses in an aquarium shot water at the walls and at the covering of their tanks. He wondered if this habit were related to their occasional excursions on shore—wetting the ground might make it easier for the octopuses to travel.

Some octopuses can live a surprisingly long time out of water if the atmosphere is humid, for they are very sensitive to dryness. Julius Kollmann says that a small octopus (*Eledone*) was kept on land for four hours and revived when put back in sea-water. Baal tells me that he has known common octopuses, which were to be used for bait, to be kept alive in wet sacks or under the boards at the bottom of a boat for much longer than this. "If they are kept damp and cool they will live for at least 48 hours out of the sea."

There is a wide difference of opinion on the speed at which octopuses can travel on land. Baal estimates that the fastest he has seen a common octopus travel is at a speed of eight yards per minute, or just over a quarter of a mile per hour. But Ronald Winckworth found while hunting these octopuses that they often moved as fast as he could when walking rapidly. Over rough ground he had difficulty in keeping up with them. (Quoted by G. C. Robson, 1925.)

The octopodan habit of occasionally quitting the water and going exploring on land sometimes causes embarrassment to aquarium-keepers. Several such instances are quoted in Chapter V. Lee once transferred an octopus from the aquarium to a large vase of sea-water in his office. He then went out to meet some friends who wanted to examine the octopus at close quarters. When they arrived, a quarter of an hour later, the octopus had escaped from the vase, climbed or tumbled off the table on to the floor, and as they opened the door it was toppling and sprawling along the carpet on the opposite side of the room.

The American conchologist, R. Tucker Abbott, says that an octopus in a small aquarium in Bermuda pushed off the lid of its tank, climbed down to the floor, crawled off a veranda and made for the sea. It traveled about 100 ft., then collapsed and was attacked by a horde of ants.

L. R. Brightwell tells me that at the Marine Biological Station at Plymouth, England he once met an octopus walking downstairs at 2.30 in the morning. It had come from the laboratory, crawling along on "all fours." An even more surprising encounter with a perambulating octopus occurred while Brightwell was on a Channel trawler. The fishermen caught a small octopus and left it on the deck. It walked down the companionway to the cabin and two hours later was found in the teapot!

Gilpatric also had an experience with a wandering octopus, this time in a library. He had a small, newly captured octopus in a bucket half filled with water, which he put on the floor while he talked to the librarian. After a while they heard a noise and looked round. The octopus had climbed out of the bucket, meandered across the room, and was then crawling up the bookshelves. But apparently the exertion and lack of moisture together were too much for it. As Gilpatric and his friend watched, the octopus reached the third shelf, stopped at one of the books, turned color, and dropped dead. Gilpatric maintains that the book where the octopus stopped was one of his own. . . .

Five BEHAVIOR[1]

"I think if you asked any zoologist to select the single most startling feature in the whole animal kingdom, the chances are he would say, not the human eye, which by any account is an organ amazing beyond belief, nor the squid-octopus eye, but the fact that these two eyes, man's and squid's, are alike in almost every detail."

The zoologist's surprise, which the Canadian zoologist, N. J. Berrill, thus expresses, becomes the more understandable as the eyes of man and squid are compared side by side. Both have a transparent cornea, although there are differences [2] because the squid's medium is water, and man's is air. Behind the corneas of both eyes are small chambers filled with liquid. Both have an iris diaphragm, and behind this a lens set in a ring of muscle and ligament. There are dark pigments in both eyes which act as light screens in excessive glare, and both have tough fibrous coats to keep the eyes rigidly in shape.

Other squids have some of the strangest eyes in the whole animal kingdom. The deep-sea *Toxeuma belone* and *Bathothauma lyromma* have eyes on the end of stalks, the eyeballs carrying their own light organs which act as miniature searchlights. The American zoologist, William Beebe, caught a deep-sea squid in which the eyes "were great, glowing globes with small, pink pupils. Most of the eyeball was frosted, and on the upper half were two opales-

[1] I have included in this chapter some information on senses which are, of course, intimately linked with behavior.

[2] To the comparative ophthalmologist there are, of course, other important differences between the two eyes. Jack H. Prince tells me that the light-sensitive retina and connecting optic nerve are quite different in the two kinds of eye. A comparative drawing of a human and a cephalopod eye is given by Sir Alister Hardy.

cent light organs throwing illumination in what I should consider the most blinding direction." Some squids (*Histioteuthis* and *Calliteuthis*) have a huge left eye and a small right eye (see page 110). And the eye of a giant squid may have a diameter of 15 in.! The eye of a 100-ton blue whale, the largest animal the world has ever seen, is only some seven inches across. (For renaming of *Toxeuma*, see page 240).

While following the same general pattern as the squid eye, those of octopuses show great variations. They range from the huge eyes of *Thaumeledone* to the atrophied eyes of *Cirrothauma*. In *Amphitretus pelagicus* the eyes are telescopic. Nearly all octopuses have well-developed eyelids. There is some evidence that if an octopus loses part of an eye it can re-grow it (see page 52).

The eyes of cuttlefish follow the general cephalopodan pattern, but the eye of the pearly nautilus (*Nautilus*) is more simple than that of the other cephalopods. It has no lens, and light reaches the retina direct through a very small opening. Thus the nautiloid eye appears to function on the principle of a pinhole camera. (Arthur Willey.)

The brain behind the cephalopod eye is the most highly developed of any invertebrate. As Gilbert Klingel says: "Alone among the molluscs they have acquired by concentration of their chief nerve ganglia what may be truly considered a brain." It is enclosed in a cartilaginous "skull," and is divided into 14 main lobes governing different sets of functions. One set of lobes controls the jet apparatus, and another set the memory. The optic lobes are the largest of all.

A noteworthy feature of the common squid's (*Loligo*) nervous system is the size of the giant nerve-fibers which conduct messages from the lobe controlling the jet apparatus to the appropriate muscles. In the comparatively slow-moving octopuses these giant nerve-fibers are absent.

Cephalopods have several small structures on the surface of their bodies whose function appears to be sensory. Near the eyes squids have a small pit, and octopuses a papilla (small projection) which are believed to be organs of taste or smell. Some cephalopods have spots, like tiny eyes, scattered over their skin. The squid *Mastigoteuthis grimaldii* has about 30 on its tail-fin. These "thermoscopic eyes," as they have been called, are supplied with nerve-endings, are highly pigmented, and are surrounded by transparent cells. It has been suggested that they are especially sensitive to temperature changes, acting as natural thermometers.

H. Giersberg carried out experiments on the chemical sense of the common octopus (*Octopus vulgaris*), especially in relation to taste. The whole surface of the body appears to be chemically sensitive, but especially the arms and suckers. Sensation is keenest in the rims of the suckers.

In his experiments Giersberg used solutions of meat, fish and crab-juice to test the sense of smell. For taste he used salts and acetic acid (sour), quinine (bitter), and grape and cane sugar (sweet). He found that blind octopuses, which were therefore entirely dependent on their other senses, used their sense of touch much less than that of taste. An octopus that touched an empty crab-shell, and then abandoned it, seized a porous stone impregnated with juice and took it to its mouth. Only after chewing it for some time was the inedible object discarded. Other experiments with blind octopuses are recounted on page 89.

More is known about the behavior of octopuses (*Octopus*) than of any other cephalopod. They are more easily studied in their natural habitat, and they can be kept in captivity with less difficulty than decapods.

Many species live near the shore-line. They make their lairs in rocks, among boulders, in empty shells, or in the recesses of coral reefs. Sometimes they bury themselves in mud, sand or gravel. Often the entrance to a lair is partially closed with large stones or pieces of rock, and generally empty shells, the débris of past meals, are nearby. The French conchologist, P.-H. Fischer, says that they are sometimes found "by hundreds," and J. Gwyn Jeffreys quotes an observer who claimed to have found 2,000 shells outside the lair of a common octopus. Octopuses are not social animals—even during the mating season they "keep their distance" as far as the physiology of reproduction allows—and their lairs are generally well separated.

Rudolf H. Fritsch studied the lair-building of the common octopus in the Zoological Station at Naples where there is always a plentiful supply of these animals. Building took place at night, and only after feeding. Stones of various sizes were put in the octopuses' tanks and they showed a preference for the medium ones. One octopus carried eight stones at once to the building site. Incidentally, I have seen a film in which a common octopus holds stones as a shield against an attacking moray eel.

Normally an octopus piles up the feeding débris outside its lair, but Fritsch found that if insufficient stones were left for it to build with, the octopus used empty crab-shells as well. If no stones were left and the feeding débris were removed, the octopus snuggled into a rounded corner of its tank. When small octopuses were put into round glass-containers "they utilized the corner between wall and water-surface, i.e. the water-surface being used as a wall."

The octopodan fondness for secluded crannies sometimes leads to their capture. Fishermen plant kegs, pots and other ready-made homes where octopuses are abundant. The octopus takes possession and clings to its temporary home even when the fisherman draws it up.

The French under-sea explorer and photographer, Jacques-Yves Cousteau (1954), found an interesting example of this proclivity for utilizing artificial homes when he and his companions were retrieving the cargo of an ancient Greek ship which sank off Marseilles. The cargo consisted chiefly of wine jars which the Greeks called amphorae. In the course of the centuries the stoppers from many of these had been lost, and almost every open amphora that was brought up contained an octopus.

Cousteau says that the Greek wreck had apparently dumped thousands of ready-made homes into a chronic octopodan housing shortage! True to octopodan tradition the amphorae contained pieces of pottery, pebbles, shells and other débris which the tenants had collected. "The wreck has doubtless been 'octopied' for two millenniums." Cousteau (1953) also describes an octopodan "shanty-town" which he says he examined on the flat sea-bottom near Île de Porquerolles in the South of France. A typical lean-to had a flat stone roof propped up eight inches on one side with a stone and a brick.

Other unusual sites are sometimes chosen for lairs, such as bottles and carboys—broken and unbroken—and various débris from ships. One octopus made its home in a pair of overalls—and gave a diver the fright of his life when he started to pick them up (see page 187). According to Salvatore Lo Bianco (1899) a fisherman once found an octopus inside a human skull.

Tests made by the Dutch zoologist, J. A. Bierens de Haan (1926), show that if transparent objects as well as stones are left in an octopus's tank, it surrounds itself with both indiscriminately. It will also crawl between glass plates as readily as between pieces of slate. Bierens de Haan therefore concludes that the octopus does not consciously hide itself.

Octopuses can crawl through almost unbelievably small openings. To reach a desirable lair an octopus will flatten its rubber-like body and ooze through a hole several times smaller than the diameter of its body. Keepers of aquaria containing octopuses have to take special precautions to see that the tanks are almost hermetically sealed against these eight-armed escapologists.

Sometimes this Houdini-like trait proves embarrassing to teuthologists when bringing home their living booty. Berrill says: "I once knew a naturalist who had caught a fair-sized octopus, a foot or so long, and took it into a street-car, safely confined within a wicker basket. Ten minutes later came a scream from the other end of the car, and sure enough the creature had squeezed through a half-inch crack and was sitting on the lap of an hysterical passenger."

Roy Waldo Miner, who was Curator of Living Invertebrates in the American Museum of Natural History, says that while collecting with a companion near some coral reefs in Puerto Rico, West Indies, he captured a small octopus. Its body was about two inches long and its arms spanned a foot. Miner put it in an empty cigar box, carefully tucked in the eight squirming arms, and hammered the lid down with tacks. He then wound some cord round it several times and tied it securely. He put the box into the bottom of a dinghy and continued collecting.

A MUDFLAT OCTOPUS 'LEAPS' FROM ITS LAIR

Woody Williams

Plate 17

A COMMON OCTOPUS GLIDES ACROSS ITS TANK

Franz Thorbecke

Peter David

THE BROBDING-
NAGIAN LEFT
EYE OF THE
SQUID *CALLI-
TEUTHIS* (see p.
73)
Natural size

A MUDFLAT
OCTOPUS AT
REST IN ITS
LAIR IN A
SHELL

Woody Williams

Plate 18

Rotofilm, Hamburg

PORTRAIT OF A HAPPY COMMON OCTOPUS

The ridges over the eyes and the papillae, or pimple-like projections, covering the skin are seen only when an octopus is content (see p. 97)

Plate 19

COMMON CUTTLEFISH AT REST

Notice how well its skin matches the mottled background

Rotofilm, Hamburg

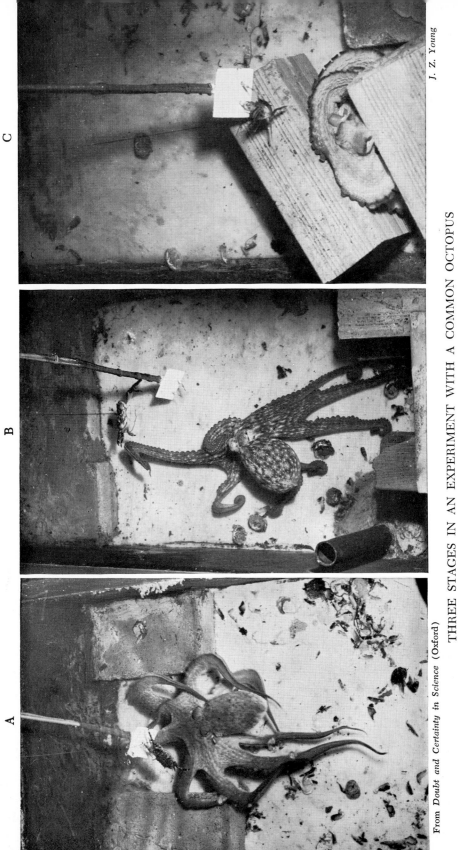

From *Doubt and Certainty in Science* (Oxford)

J. Z. Young

THREE STAGES IN AN EXPERIMENT WITH A COMMON OCTOPUS

A. The octopus rushes forward to seize a crab but receives a mild electric shock from the white plate at the end of the stick
B. When the crab-and-plate are offered again the octopus changes color and approaches with caution
C. After several shocks the octopus refuses to come out, turns pale and tries to blow crab-and-plate away by shooting water from its funnel

Plate 2

When he landed Miner picked up the cigar box, which was still firmly tied, and prized open the lid to show his capture to his companion. The box was empty.

"We felt as if we had been fooled by a trick of parlor magic, but upon looking into the bilge water in the bottom of the dinghy, we saw the octopus calmly peering at us from under the blade of an oar, and quickly recaptured it. Apparently the weird creature had succeeded in pushing the delicate tips of its tentacles through the tightly closed crack below the box lid, and then, getting a purchase outside, had deliberately pulled its rubber-like body through the crack by flattening it to the thinness of paper." How the octopus had squeezed its beak and eyes through the crack is a mystery, but Miner's name is sufficient to authenticate the incident.

C. W. Coates, of the New York Zoological Society, tells me that a collector for the Society in Key West, Florida, once sent ten octopuses to New York in cigar boxes, putting one into each box. Quarter-inch holes were drilled in the boxes and they were tightly bound with fish-line before being put in the shipping tank. The lines tightened in the water, and held the boxes so tightly shut that when they were tested afterwards with a screwdriver it was found impossible to pry up the lids as much as an eighth-inch. Yet every one of the octopuses escaped.

Sam Dunton, a photographer of the New York Zoological Society, captured an octopus at sea and put it in a wire-mesh "cage" with a close-fitting cover. On landing he looked for the octopus and found it had squeezed out of the cage and was sitting, with arms outstretched, over a hole in a walled-off compartment of the boat. One of the crew tried to recapture it with a dip net but the octopus constricted its body, raised its arms over its head, and dropped through the hole. This was the size of a half-dollar piece.

There are various opinions on the "temperament" of octopuses. Klingel found that those he encountered were timid, and other observers also say that the small and medium-sized octopuses are not naturally aggressive towards anything beyond their normal prey. G. C. Robson (1929), however, says "the Octopodinae seem to be solitary, and if it is not reading too much into our evidence, irritable and ferocious." Z. M. Bacq comments: "At the bottom of the sea, an octopus is like a tiger in the jungle."

Several writers refer to octopodan "rages" which they have witnessed. Victor Berge, who caught octopuses in bamboo cages and kept them in tide-pools, says that they "act as if rage were their normal state." He could never keep one in a pool for more than two hours, as it would tear itself to pieces. "I've seen one eating his own arms, dashing against coral, biting himself or anything else. . . ."

Eating their own arms is a well-known octopodan habit, especially in times of stress, and it is known to be a frequent preliminary to death. When excited they appear to be remarkably immune to pain. In the incident recorded on page 180 of a man being attacked at the sea-edge, the octopus climbed on to a rock which, according to an eyewitness, was made so hot by the sun that it was "almost unbearable to naked feet." An Italian fisherman told Guy Gilpatric that if a bonfire is built between an octopus and the sea it will crawl right through it. The fisherman was ready to stage a demonstration then and there but Gilpatric decided to take his word for it. And Roy Campbell claimed that he had known an octopus crawl through a beach-fire rather than go round it.

Wilmon Menard (1948) tells how he speared a small octopus while goggle-fishing in a lagoon among the coral atolls of the Tuamotu Islands in the South Pacific. The octopus made no attempt to writhe off the spear, but crawled with convulsive spasms along the shaft towards its assailant, enlarging the hole in its body as it progressed. Eventually it reached Menard and plastered itself round his arms, neck and chest. As his native companion peeled the creature off he said to Menard: "Oh my! If this bigger *fe'e* [octopus], it pull you and spear into hole. Maybee you no care to live no more, huh?"

Klingel, during his submarine excursions off Great Inagua, often met octopuses. Most of them were very shy, fleeing to their lairs at his approach. He was specially interested in a large octopus with a head "about as big as a football" and arms "about five feet from tip to tip." Such an octopus could be dangerous, but Klingel found that it always avoided him although it was not so timid as its smaller relatives. On the few occasions they met it withdrew to its lair.

Being interested in this octopus, he began to cultivate its acquaintance. But his advances were rebuffed. The octopus always seemed irritated at his approach and went through the remarkable color-changes described on page 98. Finally, Klingel stroked it along the side of its body with a long stick. Immediately the octopus reacted with explosive—but evasive—action. It snatched the pole out of his hand, shot out of its lair, ejected an immense cloud of ink, and departed for less complex parts of the ocean floor.

One day Klingel captured a baby octopus with three-inch arms and put it in a tide-pool where there were plenty of small crabs. It chose as its look-out a place where it had ready command of a corner of the pool, its color matching the background perfectly. Here it would lie motionless for hours—"patience was its most evident virtue"—staring at the life in the pool. I have told on page 40 how squids which failed to capture fish by direct attack, caught them eventually by waiting in camouflaged ambush.

There is an alleged action of octopuses in capturing prey which has become part of octopodan folk-lore. The story goes back at least to Pliny, so it has a history of some 2,000 years. This story is that an octopus will lie motionless beside a shellfish which is too strong to be pulled open, and wait for it to open its valves. As soon as it does, the octopus pops a small stone between them, thus preventing their closure, and making sure of a meal. In modern times the French naturalist, Jeannette Power, claims to have seen the same behavior.

Menard informs me that in the lagoons of the Tuamotu Archipelago he used to watch octopuses through a water-box as they foraged for food. Several times he saw them creep up to an oyster bed and attack the oysters by dropping a piece of coral into their open shells. "Whole beds of pearl-oysters have been ruined by octopuses. Divers always started killing octopuses when they hit an atoll lagoon, when the *rahui* (open season) for diving for pearl shell started."

Scientists are skeptical of this alleged behavior of octopuses because they have been unable to get them to act in this way in experiments. B. B. Boycott (1954) says: "Providing several octopuses on several occasions with various stones, *Pinna* and other large lamellibranchs [shell-fish], I have never been able to confirm this observation." Bierens de Haan (1926) also obtained negative results from similar experiments. Such negative results, however, do not prove conclusively that the story is untrue; most captive animals do not behave exactly as they do in their natural surroundings. Boycott comments: "The story appears to be so widespread that I feel there may be some factual background to it. What it is I can't imagine." Travelers told him that the story is current among fishermen on the north coast of Africa and along the Greek Archipelago, but he has not found any Neapolitan fishermen who believe it.

As with most creatures of the sea, comparatively few observations have been made on the behavior of octopuses in their natural state, but useful information has been gained by watching those kept in aquaria.

There is considerable variety in the behavior of octopuses. This is illustrated by the experience of Charles F. Holder with some octopuses he kept in a tank. He watched their reactions to his arm as, with fingers widespread, he moved it towards them.

"There was the greatest difference in the combativeness of individuals. Some paid no attention to my advance and allowed themselves to be stroked; and one large one I found as readily accepted my gentle scratching between its green eyes as a dog. Others again would advance to meet my hand, throw their arms about it and attempt to drag it beneath the rocks, while one, and the largest, invariably flung itself upon my hand and endeavored to cover it with the fin-like membranes which connect the base of the tentacles."

An octopus seems to get used to captivity fairly quickly. G. E. and Nettie MacGinitie say:

"An [mudflat] octopus (*Octopus bimaculoides*) in the laboratory soon becomes accustomed to being fed and will actually become quite tame in time. One that we had we fed by firmly grasping in a closed hand a piece of fish or clam meat and then putting the hand into the water. The octopus would at once take hold of the hand and insert its tentacles between the fingers so that it could pull out the food. While it was engaged in unclasping the fingers we could lift it out of the water without alarming it."

In some aquaria octopuses will take food from the hands of visitors and, as the MacGinities found, pull at the fingers of a hand which contains food.

Theodore Rousseau, who has made a number of observations on octopuses in their natural haunts while skin-diving, tells me:

"They seem to be animals possessed of an unusual amount of curiosity. If you stay still in the water, they will sometimes come and sit on your foot or hand. This has happened to me on at least three occasions, and I have never been bitten.

"In recent years, on several occasions, I have pulled a small octopus out of a hole in a rock. At first it struggled and ejaculated its ink with great excitement; but gradually it seemed to get used to me and ceased its fighting for freedom. It then floated around almost completely relaxed and even allowed me to scratch its back. In fact, I had the impression that if it had been possible to stay with the animal long enough, it might have become completely tame!"

The American travel writer, Willard Price, records that when he was in Samoa he was taken in a canoe by a native to see an octopus whose acquaintance the Samoan had cultivated for three years. The octopus had its lair in a cleft of a coral reef. The canoe waited over this reef until the octopus came to the surface, and Price saw the native stroke its arms and mantle. The octopus appeared to be quite relaxed. Later it was fed with crabs which the native brought with him.

Julius Kollmann, writing in 1875 of the common octopuses in the Zoological Station at Naples, says that they knew their keeper and "loved" (*liebten*) him. They held his hand with gentle caressing movements of their arms, and would apparently join in the game when he used to tease them with tit-bits, first withdrawing and then slowly releasing the food.

In addition to their "feelings" for their keeper, these octopuses showed their character in other ways. They lived at peace with each other, and with two lobsters which were put in the tank with them. But they strongly resented any newcomers, whether of their own kind or not. Several times additional octopuses of the same species were put in the tank, but the result was always the same: the interlopers were killed and eaten. Hunger had nothing to do with the killings, as the octopuses were well fed.

Then one day a newcomer of a quite different kind was placed in the fatal tank, and what followed has become a classic in the literature of octopodan behavior. In another tank in the Station there were four turtles, some fish and an outsize lobster. One of the turtles fancied the lobster for a meal, and unwisely took the offensive. The lobster got the turtle's bony head in one of its massive claws and crushed it like nut-crackers splintering a walnut.

It was decided that Samson should be removed to another tank . . . that containing the octopuses. They were immediately hostile. They formed a wide arc round the giant newcomer and drew menacingly near, swinging threatening arms and only withdrawing when the lobster raised its heavy claws. Slowly the octopuses retreated, and it seemed that they had lost interest in the unwelcome stranger.

The lobster apparently thought the same, for it lowered its guard, retired and settled down to rest. In a moment one of the octopuses was upon it, and sucker-clad arms completely encircling it, the lobster was held defenseless. A watchful attendant immediately came to the rescue and "released the lobster from the bundle which looked like eight raging snakes."

An uneasy truce lasted for an hour or so and then the attack was renewed. Again an octopus got its arms round the lobster and the animals rolled round the floor of the tank in a vicious clinch. Suddenly the octopus swam away dragging the lobster with it. But the lobster had won the bout. It had managed to get the thick basal part of one of the octopus's arms into one of its claws and was exerting great pressure—pressure that had already cracked a turtle's skull. But although the arm was compressed almost to paper-thinness the lobster could not tear it off.

As the octopus swam jerkily about, unable to wrench its arm from the vice-like claw, the lobster was banged against the rocks on the floor of the tank. It was apparently this rough treatment that eventually made it let go, and lobster and octopus retired to opposite ends of the tank. The lobster sat quietly in a dark corner, its claws ready for action at the first sign of hostility, and the octopus clambered on to a stony ledge, where it began a ceaseless play of its arms. The arm which had been almost wrenched off moved as freely as the rest.

From then on it was war to the end between lobster and octopus. Throughout the next days one or another would frequently attack, and the keeper had repeatedly to come to the rescue of the lobster. Yet even in their implacable hostility the octopuses seemed to follow an ancient code of chivalry. Never more than one octopus attacked at a time. While it was fighting the common foe the others remained passive.

During one violent bout the lobster suffered a severe loss: a claw was wrenched off. To save further conflict the lobster was moved once more, this time as the severely mauled loser. It was put in an adjoining tank, separated from the den of octopuses by a cement partition which protruded slightly above the water-level.

And that should have been the end of the story. But no-one reckoned with what transpires deep in the octopus brain. The same day one of them, and my guess is that it was the one which nearly lost an arm, climbed out of its tank, crossed the dividing cement wall, and again grappled with the lobster.[1] Handicapped by the loss of a claw it was doomed. In little over half a minute the octopus had literally torn it apart and started to eat it.

This is not the only occasion on which an octopus has gone exploring from its tank. In May 1873 the stock of young lump-fish (*Cyclopterus*) in the Brighton Aquarium began slowly to diminish for no apparent reason. Almost daily there was one less fish in the tank, and no clues to what had happened. Then one morning the mystery was solved: one of the aquarium officials found an octopus in the lump-fishes' tank.

This octopus had somehow discovered that the fish were in an adjoining tank, and had thereafter raided it almost nightly, always returning home by morning. This, incidentally, does not indicate an intelligent attempt to avoid detection, as it is the octopodan habit to retire during the day to the lair. On the morning of its discovery, however, it had apparently stayed to "sleep off" its midnight feast.

The incident provoked Tom Hood, Jr., to write *The Straying 'Topus—A Legend of the Brighton Aquarium*, of which it will be sufficient to quote the first verse:

> Have you heard of the Octopus—
> 'Topus of the feelers eight—
> How he left his tank o'po'pus
> Lump-fish to disintegrate?

[1] According to Bierens de Haan, the action was not necessarily intelligent. It may have been that the octopus extended an exploratory arm over the wall, touched the lobster and then went after it.

But this was not the end of the story. After the octopus had been replaced in its tank, a careful watch was kept to see if it would repeat its nocturnal wanderings. Lee says:

"So acute are these creatures in their perceptions, so quick of sight, and so sensitive to the light of even a distant lantern, that our suspected pirate would not start on a buccaneering expedition whilst anyone was cruising in the building. He seemed to know that he was watched; and for about a week remained quietly at home."

Then one night *two* octopuses climbed out of the tank; the previous offender and another. They went in opposite directions, avoiding the next-door tank on either side, and entered those beyond. But this time the enterprise was singularly unrewarding. One octopus found itself in a tank of outsize crabs, and the other was put to flight by a giant lobster.

The MacGinities comment: "Octopuses penned in an aquarium are never quite satisfied. They escape not because they want to go foraging, but because they want to get to a more comfortable place."

Surprising as it sounds, octopuses can be hypnotized. The Dutch zoologist, J. ten Cate (1928b), proved this with the common octopus. It was not an easy subject, but when it succumbed it was completely passive. After trying various methods ten Cate found that the most effective was to hold the octopus in one hand with the mouth upwards, and with the arms and body hanging downwards. The great difficulty was to prevent the arms from touching his hand or arm, as this completely broke the spell. But when he was able to prevent such contact, and to hold the octopus in the required position long enough, it was hypnotized perfectly. It breathed easily, and the arms hung limply, with no trace of movement.

When the octopus was thus hypnotized an arm could be lifted, and when released it fell as lifeless as a piece of rope—as great a contrast with the normal behavior of an arm as could possibly be imagined. The octopus could be thrown from hand to hand and showed no more reaction than if it had been a football. A heavy pinch with surgical nippers, or even more drastic treatment, was required to awaken it.

Compared with many other animals few scientific experiments

have been made on the psychology of octopuses. Before dealing with this work it is necessary to point out that the restraints and artificial conditions necessarily imposed by the experimenter frequently affect the behavior of an animal. Many animals, for example, either cannot or will not exert their full strength when confined or controlled, and the same may well be true of their mental powers. Yet despite the handicaps of such work experiments with animals are essential in the study of their psychology. At least they show what an animal *can* do, even if in the wild state it can do much more.

Until the beginning of this century our knowledge of how animals behave was due almost entirely to the anecdotal method— to what people said they had seen animals doing. Some of these anecdotes gave a true account of what had actually happened, but many did not. The evidence was frequently distorted or exaggerated, not because the reporters were lying but because of the inherent difficulties of making accurate observations, especially by those untrained in such a discipline. Most people—including scientists themselves occasionally, see, for example, page 117—are prone to equate what they *think* they see, and sometimes what they *want* to see, with what actually happens. That they are not the same is demonstrated every "sunrise" and "sunset." We think we see the sun moving round the earth; actually it is the earth which moves, rotating on its axis.

Another drawback of the anecdotal method is that all too often it confuses observation with interpretation. An observer may well give an accurate account of what he saw an animal do, yet give a wholly false reason why it was done. The most frequent example of this is the tendency to ascribe greater intelligence to animals than they do, in fact, possess. It was for this reason that Lloyd Morgan, one of the pioneer workers in animal psychology, formulated his now famous rule: "In no case may we interpret an action as the outcome of the exercise of a higher mental faculty, if it can be interpreted as the outcome of the exercise of one which stands lower in the psychological scale." (Frank A. Beach.)

All this is not to say that the anecdotal method has no place in natural history. Far from it. Only a minute fraction of the animal kingdom has so far been subjected to scientific examination and controlled experiment. If naturalists had accepted nothing until it had received the accolade of laboratory verification, they and their subject would long since have died of inanition.

For whole areas of zoological knowledge—speed in Nature, for example—we are largely dependent on anecdotalism. Evidence of unusual behavior is nearly always obtained as a result of chance observation.

Sometimes anecdotalism has pointed the way to surprising discoveries. The intriguing bird behavior known as "anting" was first brought to the attention of 20th-century ornithologists by an Australian schoolboy recounting that he had seen a starling putting ants under its wings. (See my *Animal Wonder World.*) And it would have been impossible to write this book on cephalopods without making considerable use of the anecdotal method.

The great value of experiments is that they are repeatable. This means that every experiment can be checked and re-checked, either with the same or with a different animal. If necessary the experiment can be filmed and then studied at leisure again and again by a whole brigade of experts. Moreover, in experimental work variations in procedure can generally be introduced to eliminate possible alternative explanations of an animal's behavior.

Why do zoologists take such trouble over their experiments? Because nothing but the highest standard of accuracy is sufficient when seeking the truth about living creatures and their behavior. And each hard-won fact which such experiments yield, trifling though it may seem in itself, helps us to understand the kingdom of Nature a little better. It should also be remembered that such studies, although seldom undertaken for economic reasons, have sometimes proved of great practical value to mankind. (V. B. Wigglesworth.)

J. Z. Young (1955), in a broadcast talk on his work, said:

"The problem in the case of the memory systems of the brain is to know where to begin. Nervous systems are so immensely complicated and the things that they do and remember are so intricate that it seems impossible that we shall ever understand them. One of the means that biologists use when faced with a complicated process is to find an animal in which conditions are relatively simple. This was one of the reasons that led my colleague, Mr. Boycott, and me to study the memory systems in octopuses. Actually, as we shall see, they are capable of remembering quite complicated things. Nevertheless, study of the parts of the brain with which they do it has given valuable hints about the way memories are carried in our own brains."

The British zoologists, Young and Boycott, have carried out what are, I believe, the most thorough series of experiments on octopuses. The work was done at the Zoological Station at Naples on the common octopus.

In one series of experiments Boycott (1954) arranged a simple maze in a tank. An octopus was shown a crab, and then led round two corners and given it. Each octopus was given three practice runs. Then it was shown the crab at the first corner only, and thereafter it was on its own.

The first octopus to be tested went straight through the maze and got its crab at once. Another started well, and went hesitatingly through on its first run and got its crab. Thereafter it attacked the corner where it was shown the crab, but never went round the second corner where the free tit-bit was waiting. Two other octopuses always attacked the corner where the crab was shown and never attempted to go round the second corner and get it. Yet another octopus learned to turn the first corner and then got stuck, either staying there for several hours or going back. It would continue only if it were given another glimpse of the crab at the second corner. In their various experiments Boycott and Young repeatedly noticed considerable differences in the behavior of octopuses of the same species.

In other experiments a sheet of glass was placed part-way across a tank and then a crab was shown behind it. Each octopus tested went straight to the glass and attacked it again and again, trying to get the crab behind it. They did not learn that to attack the glass was useless, and they never went straight to the edge where, of course, they could have got to the crab with ease. To do so would mean losing sight of the prey, and such a course of action seems beyond the powers of the octopodan mind.

Similar results were obtained by Bierens de Haan (1926 and 1948) using wire-netting instead of glass. The octopuses made no attempt to go round the netting, but continually reached through it, trying to get the crab direct. But in similar experiments carried out by F. J. J. Buytendijk (1933) one octopus, after many direct attacks, suddenly crept round the netting and seized the crab.

Bierens de Haan comments: "This shows how the endowment for the solution of this problem may vary in animals of the same species; probably in this case the task lies at the limit of their ability."

In other experiments Bierens de Haan (1926) put a crab in a glass jar and placed it in a tank with an octopus. It rushed towards the glass, the color changes flashing over its skin indicating its excitement. But when it got to the glass it persistently pushed against it and made no attempt to reach into the open top of the jar. Even when one of its writhing arms accidentally went over the edge the octopus continued to attack from the outside. It was only when an arm again went over the edge and accidentally touched the crab that the octopus followed its arm into the jar and seized the crab. Bierens de Haan says that an octopus never deliberately put an arm over the top to pick the crab out.

F. K. Sanders and J. Z. Young found that the common cuttlefish (*Sepia officinalis*) also attacked a glass jar containing a prawn. The cuttles repeatedly shot out their tentacles in attempts to seize the elusive prey. They required from 20 to 30 hours to learn that these prawns were unattainable fare for cuttlefish. Presumably they became discouraged through the pain caused by their tentacles hitting the glass. As far as I know these are the only scientific experiments on the intelligence of decapods of which there is any detailed record.

In experiments with the octopus *Eledone moschata*, Serge Mikhaïloff taught them to respond to the switching on of lights. At first an octopus was touched with a piece of wire and at the same time a colored light was switched on. The animal responded by expanding its dark chromatophores, thus darkening all over. For 16 days the training continued, then on the 17th day the light was switched on, but the octopus was not touched with the wire. It darkened all over. One octopus responded to the light for 81 days after it had been trained.

Joseph Sinel believed that the common octopus can remember for several days at least. He offered some large oysters to several hungry captive octopuses. They tried for hours to open them without success. A week later the same oysters were again offered, but this time the octopuses merely glanced at them, and did not even extend an exploratory arm. M. J. and J. Wells found that common octopuses which had learned not to take lamellibranch shells filled with sealing wax, would not touch them again if offered during the next 36 hours. With some octopuses the memory lasted longer.

In their experiments the Wellses used the reward and punishment technique—food for a right choice, a mild electric shock for a wrong choice. It was found that both blind and normally sighted octopuses could readily distinguish objects by touch which they were unable to differentiate by sight.

The experiments showed that blind common octopuses could distinguish between objects which had only slight external differences. They could, for example, be trained to distinguish between small Lucite (transparent plastic) cylinders where the only difference was vertical grooves cut roughly an eighth- instead of a quarter-inch apart. But they could not be trained to distinguish between a pair of similar cylinders when one had vertical grooves and the other circumferential, both sets of grooves being spaced the same distance apart. Apparently octopuses recognize objects by their general surface texture and not by the particular pattern of the texture. Summarizing these and other experiments the Wellses say:

"From the results of experiments in which blind animals were trained to discriminate between members of pairs of objects, it is concluded that octopuses can discriminate by touch between objects which differ from one another chemically or physically.

"Octopuses can distinguish by touch objects which differ only in the proportion of irregularities on their surfaces. They cannot learn to discriminate between objects which differ only in the arrangement of such irregularities or in the orientation of these relative to the form of objects."

Boycott and Young (1955a) have carried out a number of experiments on the learning capacity and memory of the common octopus. They thus define their use of "learning" and "memory":

"An animal may be said to have learned when its behavior in a given situation can be shown to be dependent on previous experience of the same or a similar situation. An essential requirement for such behavior is that there should be some feature of an animal's organization that allows for the persistence of a condition or set of processes within the animal corresponding to the occurrence of a particular set of attributes in the environment. We shall refer to the arrangements established as a result of a particular change in the environment as a *memory* of that change; here considering only neural memory. (Young, 1954.) The presence of a memory is known at present only by the fact that the behavior of an animal when certain attributes recur differs from the behavior before their occurrence."

Such definitions may sound pedantic but it must be remembered that in the study of animal behavior terms need to be clearly defined. Otherwise the same words may be used to describe different behavior—and that way lies confusion.

Boycott and Young (1955 and 1956) used a similar reward and punishment technique to that employed by the Wellses. They found that by this method octopuses can be trained to respond to various objects, or learn an elementary "lesson." In numerous experiments it was proved that an octopus can learn to distinguish between a small and a large square, a rectangle shown horizontally and vertically, a white circle and a black one of the same size, and a black cross and a black square.

In one series of experiments (1950 and 1955a) a crab, tied by a black thread, was lowered into a tank at the opposite end from the octopus to be tested. It was found necessary to move the crab about at the end of the thread as otherwise the octopus was unlikely to attack, although the crab was in full view.[1]

After the octopus had thus been fed a few times, a new factor was introduced. First a small, square, white plate on the end of a stick was placed beside the crab, and the octopus was unable to get its tit-bit without touching the plate. This did not act as a deterrent, but then the plate was electrified and when the octopus next touched crab-and-plate it received a mild electric shock. It reacted in the manner typical of a baffled octopus. It turned pale, moved quickly back to its lair, and pumped jets of water in the direction of the crab-and-plate.

About two hours later the crab-and-plate were again offered for

[1] Food is often ignored because it is still, whereas sometimes an octopus will attack a disturbance in the water. One octopus attacked a place where the water was agitated 15 times. (Marie Goldsmith.) Another octopus failed to recognize a crab suspended on a string in mid-water and moved slowly towards it. When the crab touched the octopus it tried to blow it away with a jet from its funnel. Eventually the crab clambered over the octopus, but it was only when it touched a sucker that the octopus was galvanized into action and seized it. (Bierens de Haan, 1929.)

two minutes. But this time, instead of rushing from its lair and flinging itself on to them as it had done in previous trials, the octopus behaved very differently. It came cautiously down the tank with arms outstretched and put them half-way round the crab-and-plate, "presenting a picture of an intense internal strain." The desire for the tit-bit urged the octopus on, the memory of the shock held it back. While resolving this conflict it swayed backwards and forwards, hesitatingly put out an arm to seize the crab, and then withdrew it. In some trials the octopus returned to its lair and then came back for another bout of indecision.

After two or three attacks and consequent shocks the painful memory won.[1] Although the octopus continued to take the crab when offered alone, it lost all interest in attacking crab-and-plate, and when they were offered it merely leaned out of its lair to watch the proceedings. If the crab-and-plate were shown near its lair the octopus changed color and shot violent jets of water at it. (See Plate 20.)

The experimenters now went a stage further. They took an octopus that was thoroughly trained not to attack the crab when the white plate was shown, anesthetized it and removed, or put out of action, the memory lobes—the *lobus verticalis* and *lobus frontalis superior*—situated at the top of the brain. It was found that up to 70 per cent of the area could be removed without affecting normal functioning. (Boycott, 1957.)

An hour after the operation the octopus was again shown the crab-and-plate. It acted as if it had never had a shock from them in its life! It came hurriedly out of its lair, seized them without the slightest hesitation, got a shock, and almost immediately came back for more. The painful memories of the past were practically eliminated. Time and again the operated animal seized crab-and-

[1] "The great rapidity with which the conditioning is established may perhaps be an indication that the situation is not very remote from those normally occurring in the life of the animal. The stings of anemones associated with hermit crabs produce in the octopus a reaction very similar to that given by the electric shock. An octopus that has been stung in this way afterwards reacts to the hermit crab and anemone by a cautious approach similar to that we have seen to the white plate." (Boycott and Young, 1950.)

In other experiments Boycott and Young (1955b) trained octopuses to attack crabs but not fish and *vice versa*. But an operated octopus could not even distinguish between a crab and a fish!

W. K. Taylor has invented an electronic "octopus" which "learns" by the reward and punishment technique. (Young, 1955.)

plate during the two-minute periods as though it was the first time it had ever seen them. One octopus continued attacking for 35 days, when the experiment was ended. "Even at the end of a day on which it had received 15 shocks it emerged as readily as ever to attack the crab and white square." (Boycott and Young, 1955a.)

Apart from their memory the octopuses which had the operation appeared quite normal. But with the removal of a piece of brain the size of a large grain of rice they virtually lost their power to remember.

NOTE: There is an apparent contradiction between the facts that (a) octopuses sometimes disregard what appears to be severe pain (see page 78), yet (b) react strongly to the discomfort of a mild electric shock. The explanation appears to be that in (a) the octopuses are either so excited or near death that pain is ignored or not perceived, and in (b) these conditions are absent, and the shock, therefore, has its full effect on behavior.

Commenting on autophagy M. J. Wells tells me: "In my experience animals only do this if already damaged—they start gnawing parts where the skin is broken, for example—so it is quite likely that the nerves from the parts being eaten are already moribund when the creature starts eating itself."

CHROMATOPHORES IN VARIOUS STAGES OF EXPANSION
AND CONTRACTION

The chromatophores, or pigment cells, change the appearance of the squid so quickly that it looks at times as if colored smoke is drifting across its body. This common American squid was photographed while trapped in a tide-pool

PHANTOM SQUID FORMED BY THE INK OF *ALLOTEUTHIS SUBULATA*

As the ink is ejected the squid changes color and darts away on another course. If undisturbed, the ink retains its shape for about ten minutes. This photograph shows the ink after being discharged from a pipette

A MASTER OF COLOR CHANGE—THE COMMON CUTTLEFISH

Plate 22   *Above:* Swimming freely
Below: Half-buried on a sandy bottom, a barely-seen mass the same color as the sand

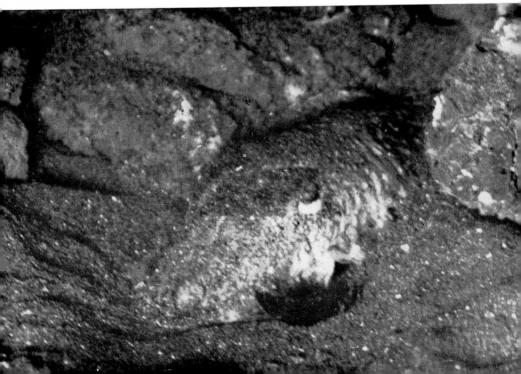

A   B

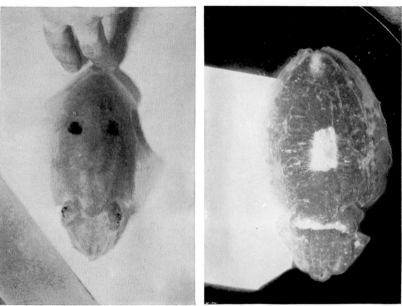

By permission of the Zoological Society of London

THE COLOR CHANGES OF THE COMMON CUTTLEFISH
(see p. 103)

A. Black spot pattern   B. White square pattern
C. White square pattern showing papillae, or pimple-like projections, on the right side of the mantle. Each papilla has a bright white tip
D. White stripe pattern

C   D

William Holmes

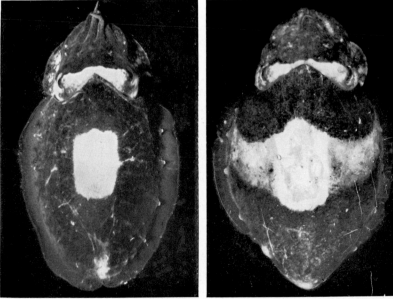

Plate 23

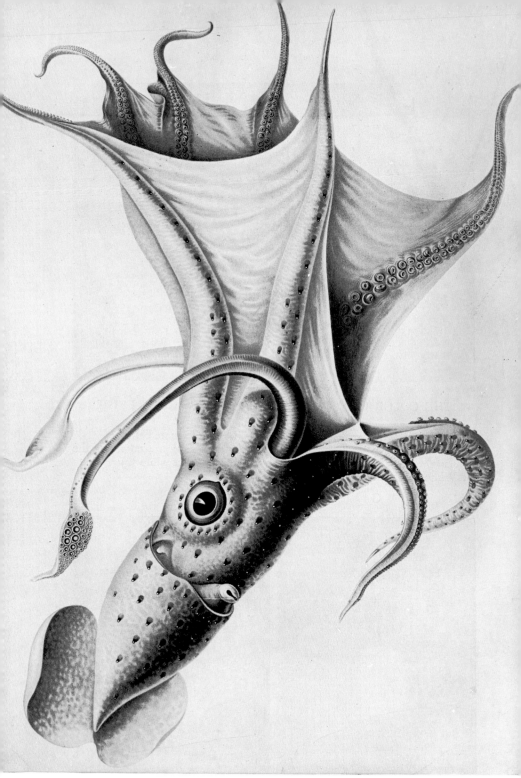

Carl Chun (1910)

HISTIOTEUTHIS BONELLII

This squid, whose overall length is about three feet, is covered with nearly 200 photo-phores, or luminescent spots

Plate 24

Six COLOR

Cephalopods are not generally considered to be colorful animals. It is therefore all the more surprising to find that they surpass even the famed chameleon in the speed and variety of their color changes. These scintillating displays are due to mechanisms which are unique in Nature, as in no other animals are color changes brought about by muscular action. Briefly, the color comes from tiny pigment cells which expand and contract on an iridescent pearly-white background. The movement of the cells is controlled by muscle-fibers.

The pigment cells, which are round and have elastic walls, are embedded in the skin, beneath the thin, transparent, outer layer. They are called chromatophores, and in cephalopods they are larger and more complex than in any other class of animal. They are generally much more numerous on the dorsal, or upper, side of the animal, and some are found on organs inside the body, such as the walls of the ink sack.

The chromatophore contains a fluid carrying granules of pigment which, on expansion of the walls, colors the surrounding area. The central membrane which holds the pigment is capable of great distension. Attached at regular intervals to the circumference there are between 4 and 24 muscle-fibers. These are very long, and extend far into the neighboring tissues, where they are firmly embedded.

When the muscles are extended the chromatophore is contracted, the elasticity of its walls causing it to shrink almost to invisibility. The area occupied by its pigment is then so small that it does not directly affect the general background color of the animal. This, of course, varies considerably with different species.

93

Approximately these colors are: in the common octopus (*Octopus vulgaris*) grayish-white on the ventral, or under, side, and yellow on the dorsal; in the common squids (*Loligo*) white; and in the common cuttlefish (*Sepia officinalis*) creamy-gray. The multitude of chromatophores in the skin, contracted to pin-point size, appear as a background of very fine stippling.

When the muscles contract the chromatophore is expanded into a very thin, flat disk, and its pigment tints the surface. Each chromatophore is independently controlled, as is the degree of expansion. This varies from 2 to 60 times the diameter of the contracted chromatophore, so that in some cephalopods chromatophores will expand from pin-point size or less to that of a pin-head—a relative increase from a quarter to a 3½-ft. wagonwheel!

The colors of the chromatophores vary with the different cephalopods, and even in the same species. Brown, black, red, yellow and orange-red are the usual pigments, but there are many variations of these basic colors. The dark chromatophores are largest, the yellow ones smallest. No cephalopod has chromatophores with all these colors, three different pigments being the usual equipment. But some cephalopods, by expanding all the chromatophores, can present a tolerable imitation of a rainbow.

The numerous muscle-fibers controlling the chromatophore can transform it from complete contraction to complete expansion with a rapidity unparalleled by any similar mechanism in the animal kingdom. These muscle-fibers seem to be practically immune to fatigue, for A. V. Hill and D. Y. Solandt found that their response was undiminished even after they had been stimulated for 30 minutes with mild electric shocks delivered at a rate of 30 per second.

The actual speed of the change has been timed photo-electrically by Hill and Solandt. In the cuttlefish (*Sepia*) the expansion of a contracted chromatophore—quarter to wagonwheel—took two-thirds of a second.[1] It is this speed which enables color changes to sweep over the surface of a cephalopod with a rapidity and variety more like that of an animated electric sign than of an animal—and a cold-blooded mollusc at that. In fact G. H. Parker (1930), an authority on color change in Nature, uses this analogy in speak-

---

[1] By applying electric stimuli direct to the muscle-fibers of the common European squid (*Loligo vulgaris*) Emil Bozler obtained single contractions in from a half to a seventh of a second.

ing of the intricacy of the cephalopod chromatophore. He says the color changes "must involve a complexity of communications and of controls such as are present in the modern electric sign over whose surface an ever-changing design may be made to pass."

Numerous investigations have been carried out on the working of the chromatophores. (See references in Parker.) Their reactions to a wide variety of drugs—including tetrahydrobetanaphthylamine!—have been observed.

But the chromatophores are not the only agents in producing color. Many cephalopods possess in the skin, and inside parts of the body, reflectors called iridocytes, or iridophores. Some lie above and others below the chromatophores. These iridocytes are tiny cells containing an interlocking chain of reflector platelets. The minute mirrors are doubly refractive, and when light falls on them there is a play of colors—an iridescent shimmer, suggestive of the glow of pearls. (A detailed study of iridocytes in the common cuttlefish has been made by Wilhelm Schäfer, 1937.)

Such then is the color equipment of many species of cephalopods—the pigment cells, the mechanism for lightning change, the reflecting and iridescent apparatus. What controls the color changes? The ultimate controlling force is the central nervous system. As soon as the nerves connecting the chromatophores with this system are cut, the chromatophores are completely paralyzed, although under artificial stimulation they will function again. If the nerves controlling the chromatophores on half of the body are cut, that side will show no flicker of color change, however intense the play of color on the other half may be.

Messages initiating the color changes come primarily from the eyes. As soon as the cephalopod sees something which attracts its attention its color alters, the hue depending on the nature of the stimulus. A cephalopod with only one eye shows less vigorous reaction on the "blind" half. The loss of both eyes still further reduces the changes, but some stimulus is still received from the suckers. Even a blind cephalopod which has also lost these shows some color changes—if put on its back, for example. (Enrico Sereni, 1930.)

The squids as a whole do not exhibit such marked color changes as octopuses and cuttlefish. The common European squid is either a pallid white when swimming undisturbed, or a uniform reddish-brown when excited. Complicated color patterns appear to be beyond the power of its chromatophores.

But other squids show greater variety of color change. The short-finned squid (*Illex illecebrosus*) has been observed when hunting mackerel to drop to the sandy bottom, change color, and become almost invisible. Normally, when swimming, the squids were thickly spotted with red and brown, but when darting among the mackerel they looked pale and almost translucent. (A. E. Verrill.)

Even a whole school of squids can become almost invisible in a moment. J. A. Stevenson was watching a school of the common American squid (*Loligo pealeii*) which was trapped in a pool near the shore, when a large rock was thrown into the water. Every squid sank like a stone, and when the ripples had died away the pool appeared to be empty. Only close inspection showed that all the squids were lying motionless on the bottom, their color merging with the background. The squids stayed like this, absolutely motionless, for at least five minutes after the rock was thrown.

William Beebe once caught a scarlet two-inch squid (*Symplectoteuthis oualaniensis*) in a net "and in the length of time it took to lift it to my eyes, the net appeared empty, until a slight sag in the mesh showed where there lay a squid of pearly whiteness." Of another squid he caught Beebe says: "When it quieted down it pulsated slowly, while the colors came and went over the body in such a way that new adjectives will have to be coined adequately to describe it—reds, blacks, browns, yellows, rolling, surging, springing into vision as the pigment spots contracted or expanded, a living, liquid palette."

On page 54 I have recounted an incident which shows how squids combine their power of color change with ink discharge and speed, to outwit an attacker.

If a squid is resting undisturbed and a finger tip is gently passed along its side, a wave of creamy white marks its passage. Then this narrow band flickers into an independent color display, which lasts for a minute or more, before the stripe disappears in the gen-

eral pulsation of the chromatophores which is characteristic of the
squid when resting.

Octopuses, like other cephalopods, are born with chromatophores. Henry Lee studied octopus embryos under a low-power
microscope. He saw a young octopus in its transparent envelope
and watched ". . . the bright orange-brown color in the pigment
cells of its skin flashing, dying out, and re-appearing in another
place, like sparks in tinder. And I was astonished to see that the
little creature within the unbroken membrane was already endowed with the power of assimilating its color to that of its surroundings. When light was reflected upon its surface, and through
its translucent body, from a piece of white paper laid on the mirror
of the instrument, it became pallid and colorless: on a bronze
penny being substituted for the paper, it assumed a darker hue;
and (which was still more remarkable) on its being disturbed by
a slight compression or agitation of the egg, its surface became
suffused with the red flush of anger and irritation which charac-
terizes the adult under provocation."

Joseph Sinel, who handled hundreds of common octopuses, records that their skin is very elastic. Normally it lies smooth and
even, but it can also be raised in little ridges. A fairly high ridge
is raised over each eye. Such wrinkles are seen only when the octopus is at rest and undisturbed. At such times the general tint is
a purplish-brown, but a constant play of slight color changes flows
over its body—gray, brown and purple.

"When highly content, as after a meal, and perched, as it is fond
of perching at times, upon an eminence, the papillae [pimple-like
projections on the skin] are erected, and these are always of an orange color. Oftentimes the whole body will be marked off in irregular, honeycomblike patches, or more like crocodile-skin. First
some of the patches are purple, others orange, then these colors

are reversed. When danger threatens, or even when the hand is moved towards it, as if to strike, the animal winces, and turns to an ashy gray."

Occasionally the two halves of an octopus's body are colored quite differently. James Hornell was watching a common octopus moving over the rocks in an aquarium, its skin showing a pattern of dappled brown, when suddenly one side of its body, including the four arms, "paled almost to snowy whiteness." The dividing line between the two colors on the dorsal side was as exact as if drawn down the middle with a ruler. Hornell could see no cause for the sudden change, which lasted about five minutes. On several subsequent occasions, by long and careful watching, he observed the same division of color in other common octopuses, but it was a comparatively rare occurrence. As described on page 95 a similar phenomenon can be induced artificially. Incidentally, it has also been observed in other cephalopods and other animals—in one instance a chameleon was seen to be red on one side and green on the other.

It is possible that the octopuses Hornell saw changing color on one side of the body only, were exhibiting part of what has been called by J. Z. Young the "dymantic," or fright, response posture. When an octopus is frightened or otherwise disturbed—as when undecided whether to attack or escape—it sometimes pales on the side of the body nearer the unpleasant object. In the full dymantic response the octopus turns pale all over, and positions its body so that it appears at maximum size. (B. B. Boycott, 1954, and personal communication.)

No other animals can color their skins with the portrait of their emotions as can cephalopods. Gilbert Klingel records the kaleidoscope of color which passed over the skin of a large octopus he studied during his submarine excursions off Great Inagua.

"It always seemed irritated at my presence. Its nervousness may have been caused by fear, for it certainly made no pretense of belligerency, and it constantly underwent a series of pigment alterations that were little short of marvelous. Blushing was its specialty. No schoolgirl with her first love was ever subjected to a more rapid or recurring course of excited flushes than this particular octopus. The most common colors were creamy white, mottled vandyke brown, maroon, bluish gray, and finally light ultramarine nearly the color of the water. When most agitated it turned livid white, which is, I believe, the reaction of fear. During some of the changes it became streaked, at times in wide bands of maroon and cream, and once or twice in wavy lines of lavender and deep rose. Even red spots and irregular purplish polka dots were included in its repertoire, though these gaudy variations seldom lasted for long."

The chromatophores are, of course, the source of the octopodan power of camouflage. The octopuses most richly endowed with chromatophores are those which live in shallow waters. Some of the octopuses of the deep seas are jet black, and others (*Cirroteuthis*) have no chromatophores. They are also absent in the nautiluses (*Nautilus*), the most primitive of cephalopods.

Klingel once caught a baby octopus, spanning seven or eight inches, and kept it for several days in a tide-pool. Here it made unceasing war on the small crabs and fishes. It would lie in wait for its prey literally for hours, its skin matching exactly the creamy-brown rocks of its pool.

The Australian zoologist, William J. Dakin, observed a small octopus in a white dish filled with sea-water. The octopus was practically white. Dakin touched it, and immediately it flushed into a fairly deep brown, but "variegated like a sandy surface covered with bits of shell and weeds."

Some octopuses can change the texture, as well as the color of their skin, and thus match their background even more closely. Guy Gilpatric says that the skin of the common octopus can be made to resemble the surface of a rock, seaweed or rusty iron, and match the texture of sand or ooze. E. V. Cowdry has published paintings of the various color changes of the common octopus.

A small octopus (*Octopus hummelincki*), that lives where attached *Sargassum* weed grows, is covered with tiny flat filaments, or cirri, which are branched at the tip. Gilbert L. Voss watched one of these octopuses at Long Reef in the Florida Keys, and found that the filaments had the same general color and appearance as the surrounding vegetation. "In the water, which was stirred by wave action, the animal appeared to be covered by a dense growth of marine algae waving with the motion of the water."

Voss believes that this octopus is found only on coral reefs overgrown with brown algae. He noticed that its main color patterns were brown or grayish-white. "The first color pattern noted corresponds in a striking degree to the colors exhibited by the surrounding algae and the granular grayish-white mottlings of the second phase imitated the white calcareous sedimentation found in small areas throughout the reef."

As the chromatophores are in operation before the octopus is born, so they continue to work for a while after it is dead. The muscle-fibers actuating them function for some hours, and their contraction and expansion cause the *post mortem* color changes. Lee compares them with "the flashing and dying out of sparks in tinder."

This curious play of color after cephalopods are dead has been studied by various biologists. Pieces of skin, rich in chromatophores, have been taken and observations kept on their various changes. It is almost as if, for a brief time, they had an independent life of their own. Generally, the skin is quite pale at first, but after a few hours it darkens, and waves of light and dark tints may pass over it. Eventually the tissue dies, and the skin blanches completely. (See references in Parker.)

Charles F. Holder (1909) kept several argonauts (*Argonauta*) in captivity and was able to observe one of them closely. Waves of color—rose, yellow, green, and various tints of brown—constantly flowed over it. Each time water was inhaled or expelled waves of color passed across its body, thus giving a continuous "heat-lightning effect."

One of the most remarkable color displays is that of the common cuttlefish. The British zoologist, William Holmes, made a detailed study of this aspect of its behavior, basing his observations on the cuttles in the aquarium and open-air tanks of the Marine Biological Station at Plymouth, England. He found the variety and complexity of the color patterns were greater than those of any other cephalopod he knew.

The cuttlefish's chromatophores lie in three layers: bright yellow nearest the surface; orange-red in the middle; and dark at the base, varying with different animals from brown, brown with a reddish tinge, to almost black. These colors overlap when the chromatophores are expanded, and consequently various compound colors can be produced, such as green and gray. These, plus the iridocytes, provide the cuttle with an extensive wardrobe, with changes to match almost any background,[1] or to register any emotion. I believe even if it were placed on a Scottish tartan it would present a tolerable imitation of that multi-hued cloth!

A. Kühn and R. F. Heberdey have studied the reactions of the cuttle to different colors. If placed on green, a color which is not directly represented in its repertoire, the cuttlefish contracts its orange chromatophores, and those containing yellow and black combine with the green-hued iridocytes to give a passable imitation of a green-surfaced animal. But against a yellow or red background, the yellow and orange chromatophores are fully expanded to fill the spaces between them and the black chromatophores. This action completely excludes the green hue of the iridocytes.

On white, gray, or black backgrounds, the red and yellow chromatophores remain contracted, and the degree of shading is determined by the amount of expansion of the black chromatophores against the generally whitish background of the skin. Red or blue are beyond the powers even of the cuttlefish—but such pure colors are rare in its natural habitat.

When the cuttle is at rest slight waves of color are continuously pulsating over its skin. Its general pattern is striped, and has been compared to that of a zebra, dark brown alternating with grayish-white. Although the stripes are not uniform in shape or size, the details of the pattern on any one cuttlefish are always the same. Whenever the pattern appears each stripe occupies exactly the same position.

This zebra pattern undoubtedy helps to camouflage the cuttlefish in its natural environment. It is a well-known principle of camouflage that a strongly contrasted pattern of stripes, or other markings, helps to break up the outline of the animal, and thus

---

[1] "Although its powers in this respect are not equal to those of the plaice when subjected to critical tests, under normal conditions it can mimic its surroundings very effectively." (David H. Tompsett.)

makes detection more difficult. (Hugh B. Cott.) Moreover, the cuttle often swims among beds of seaweed on the ocean floor, and the striped pattern would have obvious concealment value against such a background. Cuttles swimming together in small schools have been seen to change color almost instantaneously.

If a cuttlefish is turned on its back its normally white underside darkens immediately to blackish-brown, the chromatophores expanding instantly to camouflage the dangerously conspicuous belly. When resting on sand a cuttlefish assumes a mottled pattern of very light and slightly darker browns. It partially buries itself in the sand and throws some on its back, thus making detection even more difficult. Cuttles appear to have a strong preference for a sandy bottom and if placed in a tank without sand they are restless.

The Australian conchologist, Joyce Allan, watched some small Australian cuttlefish (*Solitosepia liliana?*) swimming slowly about an aquarium tank containing variously colored objects. As the cuttles passed over dark, reddish-brown rock they matched its color perfectly. A few inches away was some dead coral. Passing over that they turned a light gray, then, in turn, light brown for sand, green-brown for weeds, and back again to the reddish-brown of the rock.

Holmes several times tried the experiment of putting a cuttlefish into a perfectly black tank with a close-fitting lid. "When the animal is left in such a tank for a few minutes, with the lid closed, it is only with the greatest difficulty that it can subsequently be seen by the observer, even by the light admitted by partial removal of the lid." As more light was let into the tank the cuttle gradually became less dark. The ability thus to turn almost black would be an obvious advantage when, in its natural habitat, the animal was under rocks or in a rock crevice.

Black backgrounds are sometimes found in the cuttlefish's environment, but white would rarely occur—pure white virtually never. Yet when a cuttle was put in a white tank it grew progressively paler until eventually all that could be seen was the iridescent light reflected from the iridocytes.

Holmes also tried the experiment of putting a cuttlefish in a black tank with a square of white porcelain lying on the bottom. The cuttle responded by going black except for a white spot at the posterior end of its back and a bold white square in the middle, and a white band across its head. Sometimes, instead of the square, a white band appeared across its back (see Plate 23).

Holmes found that cuttlefish in an open-air tank, with black sides and light-colored shells or stones on the floor, also made the white square pattern. But in wholly light or dark surroundings the pattern was not made.

Under different stimuli cuttlefish produce other displays. Lukas Tinbergen has described the varying color changes that sweep over the body during courtship and mating. The female coloring is rather drab compared with the male's, the chief colors being deep brown and a near-white. The male's "love dress" undergoes various changes, in some of which the coloring is brilliant. The light stripe in his zebra pattern may be white, yellow or orange-brown, and the dark stripe deep purple or black. Circles appear round the eyes and a stripe between them. Deep purple stripes appear along the sides of the large fourth arms.

When a cuttlefish is about to attack its prey it undergoes quite a different color change. Its arms fan out and a brilliant color display flickers over them and the dorsal surface.

Cuttlefish react in various ways to danger. If disturbed in a corner or behind stones, a cuttle often makes no attempt to escape, but exhibits a warning or frightening coloration, a protective device well-known in Nature. (Cott.) The body flattens and expands, the pupils dilate, and a black crescent forms beneath each eye. The mantle pales except for two intensely dark spots, and the edges of the fins turn black.

If a cuttlefish is slightly disturbed in the open, as by a hand touching the water, it reacts by raising little pimples in its skin, each with a bright white tip formed by the iridocytes. If further disturbed, as by touching, color changes flash over its surface. A succession of what Holmes called "terrifying" patterns are displayed, each lasting a few seconds.

Almost invariably the first pattern consists of two black spots on the dorsal surface. They always appear in the same place, each a little to either side of the middle line.[1] Then the rest of the sur-

---

[1] Voss tells me that one of the color patterns of the squid *Sepioteuthis sepioidea*, which superficially resembles a cuttlefish, consists of "two dark spots, one on either side of the midline and at about the mid-point of the body."

face rapidly and completely pales, while the black spots become accentuated.

"Thus for a moment the two black spots stand out most vividly on the background of the iridescent white animal. The total pallor is never maintained for more than a few seconds, but its transitoriness makes it the more striking. Often this is followed by the animal's contracting its mantle violently and shooting away by the action of its siphon, and this movement is accompanied by a color change which makes it amazingly difficult to follow, even to the human eye. For while at one moment one's eyes are fixed on a white animal with two black spots, at the next it seems to have disappeared, for its rapid movement is accompanied by total darkening of its body, by full expansion of all chromatophores.

"This complete color change, most deceptive to a human observer, must be even more effective in nature in deluding predators. The color of the animal on darkening in this way is different from the darkness shown in a black tank, in that, in the present instance, the animal has a purplish tinge due to the expansion of the orange and yellow chromatophores, which does not take place in a dark environment.

"If further irritated, the animal may respond by a total paling of the whole of its body, and upon this background may appear longitudinal black stripes, at the base of the fins and along the middle of the back. These lines flicker vividly over the pallid back, and then suddenly disappear, to be followed perhaps by a reappearance of the black spots, another total darkening, or a brief reappearance of the zebra pattern. All this time the animal darts about rapidly, as if to avoid the irritation, and its final action when it cannot do so is to eject a cloud of ink. Then at once it becomes motionless, and hides below the black cloud which it has produced, and its color can be observed no more."

Seven LUMINESCENCE

"In October 1902 we were one night steaming outside the slopes of the coast banks of Norway, and for many miles we could see the squids moving in the surface waters like luminous bubbles, resembling large milky white electric lamps being constantly lit and extinguished."

Whether this spectacle which Johan Hjort thus describes was due to luminous organisms in the sea around the squids, or was the result of their own display, is questionable. But there is no doubt that cephalopod luminescence is one of the most extraordinary sights in Nature. Bioluminescence, as such natural production of light without heat is called, has reached its highest development in cephalopods, particularly among the small squids. About one-third of all the known species of squid are luminescent. Of these 120 or so species the great majority live in the deep sunless seas.

E. Newton Harvey, the American authority on bioluminescence, says: "It is highly probable that no true octopus is luminous although a few references occur." Igor Akimushkin, however, tells me there is a hitherto undescribed species of *Tremoctopus* that lives in the open sea of the Northwest Pacific, in which the females have luminous organs on the dorsal webs of the arms. M. M. Slepzof, who observed these octopuses from a ship at night, told Akimushkin that: "The arms of an octopus, quietly swimming near the surface, extended and then folded and accordingly the reddish light twinkling around them became weaker or flashed. The luminous females were 'courted' by the males deprived of photophores."

Harvey, in his monumental work *Bioluminescence* (it has a bibliography of some 1,800 titles from 20 countries), says that there are three main ways in which the light is produced—bacteria, secretion, and photophores or luminous organs.

Some cephalopods which live in shallow water have glands beneath the mantle near the funnel in which live luminous bacteria. These glands are equipped with both lens and reflector, and appear to be for the sole purpose of producing light. So, as these cephalopods shoot backwards through the water, they have a built-in rear-light, complete with magnifying optical system, which "burns" light-giving fuel for hours on end without recharging! Yata Haneda, the Japanese zoologist, tells me: "The light is 'continuous' yet 'controlled' by a thin film of ink about the glands."

The light-giving bacteria have been minutely studied by biologists in various countries, especially by Giuseppe Zirpolo and Teijiro Kishitana. These bacteria are quite different from the ordinary luminescent species which live on the skin of other marine animals. Some, at least, appear to be specially adapted for their strange life in tiny pockets of the cephalopods, and live as symbiotes—organisms of different species living in partnership. (See references in P. Buchner.)

The light emitted by the bacteria is rather pale. Madoka Sasaki saw the so-called lantern "squid" (*Sepiola birostrata*) "discharging a faint cobaltish light," and Johannes Schmidt several times saw a *Spirula* emitting "a pale yellowish green light, which from the normal position of the animal in the water is directed upwards. In contrast to the light displayed by so many other marine organisms (Crustacea, etc.), which flares up and fades away again, the *Spirula's* little lamp burns continuously. We have seen the lamp showing uninterruptedly for hours together." The *Spirula's* bead-like light-organ has a diaphragm above it which apparently shuts the light off and on.

According to Paul Girod (1882), in the mating season female cuttlefish (*Sepia*) show bright luminescence while swimming at the surface. "Males, lurking among the rocks at the bottom of the sea, rush on to her like luminous arrows." The luminescence probably comes from luminous bacteria on the cuttlefish.

The best-known cephalopod which produces light by secretion is a tiny "squid," about the size of a man's thumb-nail, named *Heteroteuthis dispar*. It is generally regarded as a deep-sea species, but more specimens have been trawled between 400 and 500 ft. than in deeper hauls. (W. J. Rees and G. E. Maul.) As *H. dispar* has both an ink sack and a luminous secretion it probably lives both above and below the threshold of light.

These little squids are found in the Mediterranean, and are sometimes caught in the whirling currents of the turbulent waters of the Strait of Messina, home of Scylla and Charybdis of ancient dread. Held in the powerful whirlpools of the Strait, the squids are sucked up from the depths and can be caught in the surface waters. Sometimes they are cast ashore, with many deep-sea animals. It was in this region that Paul A. Zahl took his wonderful series of color photographs of deep-sea creatures, including *H. dispar*.

The light-giving secretion of *H. dispar* is a form of mucus which comes from a gland near the ink sack. The gland stores the secretion, of which there is an abundant supply, in a reservoir from which it is squeezed by muscular contraction.

When the squid is undisturbed there is usually no luminescence, but the moment it is touched it shoots out a stream of mucus. As soon as this meets the oxygen in the water it blazes with a chain of brilliant bluish-green points of light. Werner Meyer, describing a display he observed in an aquarium at the Zoological Station at Naples, says, when irritated, the squid "shot rapidly through the water, and spurted through its funnel a luminous secretion which floated in the water as separate globules, these being drawn out by the currents into shining threads, a pyrotechnic display which it was able to repeat many times. The light of the secretion and of the light organ itself had the same pale greenish hue which we observe with our glow-worms."

Ulric Dahlgren gives the following more detailed description of the display. He says that when gently struck with a glass rod as it swims in the aquarium ". . . the animal throws out of its siphon several little masses of mucus which show no light at the moment of ejection, but almost instantly, as the oxygen of the water begins to work on them, show a number of rod-shaped particles of a brilliantly luminous matter embedded throughout the very delicate mass. As the mass continues to expand this light continues to glow brightly for as much as three to five minutes, after which it rather suddenly dies out. In color the light is the usual blue-green of luciferine [the substance causing the luminescence] when burning outside the body. The animal can repeat this process for a number of times, when it appears to have exhausted its supply of luciferine, and it is not possible, apparently, to keep it in captivity for a long enough period for the supply to be restored."

For many years *H. dispar* was the only cephalopod known to produce luminescence by secretion, but there are at least two other squids which discharge "liquid fire." Haneda says that he caught in a trawl in Suruga Bay, Japan, some specimens of *Sepiolina nipponensis* which measured about four inches over-all. Haneda found that this squid has a luminous organ on the ink sack. When the squid is disturbed, this organ pours a luminous secretion into the funnel which discharges it as a bright bluish light.

The third squid with a luminous discharge was first seen three-quarters of a mile below the surface. In 1953 Jacques-Yves Cousteau and Georges Houot dived to 4,000 ft. in the Mediterranean in the French Navy's bathyscaphe *F.N.R.S.3*. When they were down some 3,500 ft. a squid, about 1½ ft. long, appeared in the beam of the searchlight. It shot out a blob of what looked like white ink, but when the light was switched off the secretion glowed phosphorescently. As they watched, two other squids ejected luminescent white clouds. (Technically, *Heteroteuthis* and *Sepiolina* are sepioids, see page 5.)

The third way in which cephalopods produce light is by small luminous organs called photophores, these being rendered luminous by minute chemical reactions. The actual source of the light is an enzyme-catalysed reaction, luciferase acting on luciferin.

The surface of the photophore is covered with a layer of chromatophores which acts as a diaphragm. Normally the chromatophores are expanded and cover the photophore. When they contract light is emitted. Whether or not light is always present in the photophore is not known. Harvey thinks it is possible that contraction of the chromatophores and stimulation of the light cells occur simultaneously. The color of the light can be varied by chromatophoral control in some squids, such as *Histioteuthis* and *Mastigoteuthis*.

Some of the photophores are simple, others are highly complex. According to S. Stillman Berry (1920) they range from "the lump of photogenic tissue which forms the proximal photophore in the tentacle of *Lycoteuthis*, through almost innumerable intermediate types, to the astonishingly complex bull's-eye lanterns of *Abraliopsis* and the mirrored searchlights of the Histioteuthidae." Some photophores are as complicated as the squid's eye. They have reflector mechanisms, pigment cups, lenses, mirrors and color screens. Among the 22 light organs of *Lycoteuthis diadema* there are 10 types of photophore (see Plate 25).

The number of photophores and their distribution on the body varies with the species. Some squids have less than 20, others have 100 or more. The New Zealand squid, *Nematolampas regalis*, measuring only a few inches over-all, has nearly 100 photophores, most of them comparatively large. It has 5 on each eye, 10 within the mantle, and 70 on the arms and tentacles. Unfortunately, this squid has never been seen alive. *Histioteuthis bonellii*, a Mediterranean squid measuring about three feet over-all has nearly 200 photophores three-tenths-inch long and almost as wide. In *Vampyroteuthis infernalis* some of the photophores are less than one-thirtieth-inch in diameter.

Some squids have photophores only on the eyes and the tips of some of the arms. In others, such as *Abralia*, they are spread over almost the whole body—head, eyes, round the eye-sockets, mantle, arms, funnel and fins.

In *Vampyroteuthis infernalis*, which has numerous photophores, the two at the end of the body near the base of the fins have "eyelids" which can be opened or shut at will (see Fig. 1). Some squids, such as *Abraliopsis*, have transparent "windows" in their skin which allow the light from the photophores to shine through.

Those squids, such as *Pyroteuthis*, which have photophores inside the body, have transparent mantles, and the luminescence can be seen glowing through the covering tissue. Berry says these squids have "a belt of fiery jewels" in the middle of their body. Altogether a dozen genera are known to possess internal photophores.

Photophores occur very frequently on the eye, especially the lower half. In some squids (*Taonius*) almost the whole of the lower half of the eye is covered by one or two large photophores.

The tiny *Nematolampas regalis* has five photophores on each eye, and *Pterygioteuthis giardi* has thirteen. Some of the most bizarre of deep-sea squids, such as *Toxeuma belone* and *Bathothauma lyromma,* have photophores on the balls of eyes which are at the end of stalks. So these squids are permanently equipped with the optical system of a range-finder complete with built-in miniature searchlights! (See Plate 5.) (For renaming of *Toxeuma,* see page 240.)

A remarkable, and so far unexplained,[1] development of ocular photophores occurs in *Histioteuthis* and *Calliteuthis.* In both genera the left eye is relatively enormous compared with the right, the surface area being in the ratio of about 4:1. The difference is so great that the already disproportionately large head appears so unbalanced that, as Berry says, it "would seem to render it a physical impossibility for the animal to propel itself in a straight path without recourse to spiral movement or some violent sort of counter twisting."

This extraordinary asymmetry extends, quite inexplicably, to the photophores themselves. The small right eye has a well-developed circlet of photophores surrounding the eye-sockets, but in the Brobdingnagian left eye they are widely separated and distorted, some are rudimentary, and others are atrophied or missing altogether (see Plate 18 and Color Plate 3).

Few naturalists, and still fewer laymen, associate loveliness with cephalopods, yet the beauty of natural luminescence reaches its highest development in the displays of squids. The first man to see and record the display of a luminescent squid appears to have been Jean Baptiste Verany. In his *Mollusques Méditérraneens,* published in 1851, he records that he often went down to the beach at Nice to see what the fishermen brought in. One day in 1834 he saw a damaged specimen of *Histioteuthis bonellii.* He was so impressed with its brilliant coloring that he offered the fishermen a handsome reward for another specimen, either alive or in good condition.

"Shortly afterwards I was summoned and shown a specimen clinging to the net, which I seized and placed in a vessel of water. At that moment I enjoyed the astonishing spectacle of the brilliant

---

[1] Gilbert L. Voss has suggested to me that the small eye may function in the surface waters and the large eye in the dim light of the deeper seas.

spots, which appeared upon the skin of this animal, whose remarkable form had already impressed me; sometimes it was a ray of sapphire blue which blinded me; sometimes of opalescent topaz yellow, which rendered it still more striking; at other times these two rich colors mingled their magnificent rays. During the night these opalescent spots emitted a phosphorescent brilliance which rendered this mollusc one of the most splendid of Nature's products."

When Carl Chun was in the Indian Ocean on the *Valdivia* Expedition in 1899 some small squids (*Lycoteuthis diadema*) were brought up from a great depth. Two of them were kept alive for a short time in iced sea-water. They were studied and photographed. They had five photophores on each eye, two on each tentacle and others were distributed within the mantle cavity, which is transparent. Chun (1903) says:

"Among all the marvels of coloration which the animals of the deep sea exhibited to us nothing can be even distantly compared with the hues of these organs. One would think that the body was adorned with a diadem of brilliant gems. The middle organs of the eyes shone with ultramarine blue, the lateral ones with a pearly sheen. Those towards the front of the lower surface of the body gave out a ruby-red light, while those behind were snow-white or pearly, except the median one, which was sky-blue. It was indeed a glorious spectacle."

Sir Alister Hardy, who has seen great numbers of sea animals, says of one of these squids which he saw just after it had been caught on the *Discovery:* "It is one of the most beautiful animals I have ever seen."

One of the most thoroughly studied of all luminescent cephalopods is the Japanese *hotaru-ika,* or fire-fly squid (*Watasenia scintillans*), which measures about four inches over-all. The reason it is so well-known is because, although it is a deep-sea species, it comes to the surface to breed in Toyama Bay in the Sea of Japan each year from April to June. Although so small, this squid has three comparatively large photophores on the tips, and numerous tiny photophores on the rest of two of its arms. There are also five tiny photophores on each eye, and literally hundreds scattered over its mantle, the females having more than the males.

The fire-fly squid flashes its light periodically, like the insect after which it is named, but the emission periods are more variable and last longer, sometimes half a minute. The eye, mantle and arm photophores can flash in unison or separately. Moreover, the photophores on the arm tips can also flash separately or altogether. Their light is brighter than that of the eye and mantle photophores, and shines so brilliantly that Chiyomatsu Ishikawa says "one sees only two effulgent bodies moving in the dark water, like the glow of an electric contact, and the lively oscillations of the invisible arms produce a very weird effect." Berry says that the effect of the numerous photophores on the tentacles of *Nematolampas* must be to extend "a string of fiery beads far in advance of the animal."

Harvey saw a net in the water filled with fire-fly squids, their arms flashing in bursts of brilliant bluish light—"a startling display of fireworks." The Japanese zoologist, Shozaburo Watasé, after whom the squid is named, records that at night the tiny photophores on its mantle "shine with a brilliant light like that of the stars in heaven." He adds that when seen under the microscope the light from the photophore of a living animal "is so brilliant that it seems like a sunbeam shot through a tiny hole in a window curtain."

What is luminescence for? In view of the diverse and intricate mechanism for its production what vital purpose does it serve? Harvey (1950), writing generally of bioluminescence, says:

"The use of the light has frequently baffled zoologists . . . who can suggest the use of light to a luminous bacterium, an organism 1/25,000th-in. in diameter with no nervous reactions of a higher form, or the use to a protozoan, living at the surface of the sea, blown hither and thither by the wind? One is forced to the conclusion that in their case the light is merely fortuitous, a chance phenomenon, accompanying some of the necessary organic chemical changes proceeding in the organism." (See also Hardy.)

Can a purpose be suggested for luminescence in cephalopods? A complete answer cannot be given because the deep-sea habitat of most luminescent squids makes direct observation almost impossible. Any answers, therefore, must be tentative and deductive.

It has been suggested that the luminous discharge of *Heteroteuthis dispar* [1] may serve to baffle pursuers. The sudden bursting

---

[1] Like its fellows of sunlit seas, it also has an ink sack and when disturbed often ejects a small amount of dark ink.

of a series of brilliantly colored "rockets" in the darkness of deep seas would certainly be disconcerting to normally sighted enemies, although where it is permanently dark there may be other ways of detecting and hunting prey.

What of the cephalopods whose luminescence comes from photophores? It might be that the sudden flashing of the lights would disconcert enemies, but the luminescence could also guide them to their prey.

Two other theories have been suggested. One is that the luminescence is an aid to recognition, and is of particular value in the breeding season. Many species of squid are known to have their own photophore pattern. The lights may help the animals to locate each other—this is almost certainly so with *Spirula*—and may also be a source of sex attraction. The periodic flashing of the firefly squid, and the fact that the color of the luminescence sometimes differs in opposite sexes of the same species, may be significant if this theory is correct.

The other theory is based on the fact that not only squids, but also euphausiids (small shrimp-like animals) and deep-sea fish, have photophores near their eyes. As already mentioned, among squids photophores frequently occur on the lower part of the eyes. The position of the lights thus enables them to act as miniature searchlights. Perhaps, as the French zoologist, Louis Joubin, suggests for *Histioteuthis*, their function is to illuminate the animals' surroundings, and possibly to act as a lure for their prey.

Voss suggests that this is how *Chiroteuthis lacertosa* uses the photophores on the tip of its very long tentacles:

"In an animal apparently poorly suited for swimming, and living in the darkness of the deep sea, it would appear that the extremely long tentacular stalks might be for lowering the long, well-armed clubs below the body where the luminous organs would attract planktonic animals within reach of the tangle of hooked suckers which in turn might act like a "jig" used by fishermen [see page 144 and Plate 26]. Such an adaptation might easily be a very efficient food catcher and no other explanation seems plausible."

Whatever its precise purpose may be, cephalopod luminescence is one of the most striking characteristics of these altogether remarkable animals.

Eight REPRODUCTION

Aristotle was the first writer to put on record a reasonably accurate description of the broad outlines of the cephalopodan reproductive system, but his findings were practically ignored, or disbelieved, for the next 2,000 years. It was not until the middle of the 19th century that the true nature of cephalopodan reproduction was re-discovered and described in some detail. But even today our knowledge of their sex-life is very inadequate except for a few of the easily accessible species.

The breeding season varies considerably with the species and habitat. In American waters cephalopods breed chiefly from early spring until late summer, although some breeding occurs throughout the year. In British waters cephalopods breed in the spring and summer, but in the Mediterranean many species breed throughout the year except between November and January. Not much is known about the number of times cephalopods breed. The subject is dealt with by Lukas Tinbergen and J. Verwey and Salvatore Lo Bianco.

Although there are wide variations, the general sex pattern is the same for all but a few highly specialized species, such as the deep-sea *Vampyroteuthis infernalis.* In the others, one or more of the arms of the male is modified into a sex organ called a hectocotylus, or hectocotyle (see Plate 26). This is used to plant the fertilizing sperm cells on or inside the female, although G. C. Robson (1926) suggests that in the decapods the hectocotylus may be for holding or stimulating the female rather than for transferring the sperm. Apart from the argonauts and related octopuses, the sperm cells are contained in either one large or a number of small tubes called spermatophores.

The arms which develop into the hectocotylus vary with the different species. In the lesser octopus (*Eledone cirrhosa*) and common octopus (*Octopus vulgaris*) it is the third right arm. In the common squids (*Loligo*) and cuttlefish (*Sepia*) it is the fourth left arm. But sometimes more than one arm is affected. In the nautiluses (*Nautilus*) four of the small inner arms develop into a cone-shaped organ, called the spadix, which acts in the same way as a hectocotylus.

In most of the octopuses with hectocotylized arms a fold of skin forms a thin groove or channel for the transmission of the spermatophores. In the lesser and common octopuses the extremity of the arm becomes spoon-shaped. In the squids the suckers at the end of the arm become smaller or disappear and their pedicles grow longer. In the common cuttlefish (*Sepia officinalis*) the only change is the suppression of some rows of suckers at the base of the arm. But in *Rossia macrosoma* the suckers disappear over nearly the whole length of the arm and a membrane, with abundant mucous glands on the inside surface, takes their place. (Tables of the variations throughout the Cephalopoda are given by William E. Hoyle.)

There are three main ways in which the hectocotylized arm carries the spermatophores to the female. In the squids and cuttlefish the slightly modified arm merely takes them from the external genital organ and passes them to the female (but see p. 136). In most of the octopuses the hectocotylized arm is inserted near the female's oviduct, and then the spermatophores travel down the arm and ejaculate the sperm mass into her. In the argonauts and a few related octopuses, the thin worm-like end of the hecto-cotylized arm breaks away completely and remains in the female.

It is in these cephalopods, and especially in the argonauts, that the vagaries of the cephalopodan sex-life reach their ultimate bizarre development. There are six species of argonauts, with similar sex mechanisms, but I am concerned here with the common argonaut, or paper nautilus (*Argonauta argo*).

At the beginning of the 19th century nobody knew how the argonauts reproduced themselves. And although the females, with their pearly-white shells, were fairly well-known nobody had ever described a male. The solution of these twin problems forms a famous chapter in natural history.

In 1827 the Italian zoologist, Stefano delle Chiaje, discovered a small body attached to a female argonaut. He concluded that it was a parasitic worm. Two years later the French zoologist, Georges Cuvier—or, to give him his full name, Baron Georges Léopold Chrétien Frédéric Dagobert de Cuvier—received five more specimens for examination. He also concluded that they were parasites, and moreover that they constituted a genus new to science. Because they resembled a cephalopod arm, about five inches long with 104 [1] suckers, he named the genus *Hectocotylus*, meaning "the arm of a hundred suckers." (Cuvier and Valenciennes.) And that is the name which has been accepted throughout the scientific world for the specialized mating arm of cephalopods.

The name of Cuvier was sufficient to assure most scientists that this description was correct, and the strange little worm that made its home with the argonaut was added to the zoological and parasitological lists. But as more information about argonauts became available some scientists began to doubt the diagnosis.

Among these was the Swiss zoologist, Albert Kölliker, and in 1845 and 1846 he published papers in which he gave the results of a detailed study of the alleged parasitic worm. He pointed out that a microscopical examination of its skin showed that it contained chromatophores, the complex pigment cells which are characteristic of the Cephalopoda, and suckers similar to those on the female argonaut. He also discovered that the "worm" had a small cavity in which he found sperm cells uncommonly like those of a cephalopod. Kölliker was hot on the scent of the true nature of Cuvier's "parasitic worm." Then he made a bad mistake, and through it forfeited the honor accorded to men of science who make brilliant discoveries and solve long-standing problems.

Remember at this time the two problems which baffled zoologists about the argonaut were: How do they reproduce them-

---

[1] Actually the total varies considerably; some argonaut hectocotyli have about half this number.

selves? and Is there a male? Kölliker thought that at one stroke
he had solved both problems—Cuvier's "worm" was none other
than the long-sought male, and it entered the female to fertilize
the eggs.

It is impossible not to sympathize with Kölliker. His painstaking examination had shown the likeness between the "worm" and
the female argonaut, and also the cephalopodan nature of the
sperm cells. Moreover, there are parallels, undoubtedly known to
him, among other invertebrates of a similar strange sex mechanism. In the wheel animalcules (Rotifera), for example, the diminutive male lives parasitically on the female.

On further examination Kölliker (1849) professed to find, and
actually drew and described, the digestive, circulatory and respiratory organs of what he had convinced himself was the male
argonaut. These on an organism which, as was subsequently
shown, does not eat, has no heart and does not breathe! Kölliker's
jump to an egregiously wrong conclusion after such careful preliminary work, and his subsequent blindness to valid criticism of
his cherished theory, is a salutary lesson to all scientists.

The truth is that Kölliker tried to solve two problems when he
had the material to solve only one. What Cuvier described as a
parasitic worm, and Kölliker as a male argonaut, was the modified
sexual arm of the male which breaks off and stays in the female.
Kölliker's mistake has been practically forgotten, but Cuvier's
error is perpetuated for all time in the word "hectocotylus." Kölliker admitted his error in 1853 in a note appended to a translation of Müller's paper. The volume in which this appears contains
translations of other papers about the hectocotylus controversy.
A detailed account of the whole story has been given by F. J. Cole.

The second problem was solved in 1853 when the German zoologist, Heinrich Müller, published the first description of the
male argonaut. While working at Messina he examined several
very small argonauts which had no shell, and were a different
shape from any he had seen before. On careful examination he
found there was a little sack among the arms. And each sack that
was opened contained a coiled hectocotylus. Müller had found
the male argonaut.

It is not surprising that it evaded detection for so long. The
male argonaut is a Liliputian animal with a thimble-shaped body

whose mantle is rarely more than a quarter-inch long, with head and arms about as long again. The female's body measures up to six inches across, with the arms two or three times longer than this. The shell of such a large specimen would be about 12 in. across, but most of those taken are much smaller than this. The rounded body of the female sometimes has a diameter about 20 times greater than that of the male—a difference roughly equal to that between a pea and a football. To complicate matters still further, the female sometimes carries the male around in her shell.

In the male argonaut the sperm duct reaches into the hecto-cotylus, which is the third left arm. This, as Müller described, forms a sack enclosing the hectocotylus. Eventually the sack bursts as a result of the violent movements of the hectocotylus, which then unwinds. The base is a sperm reservoir, the middle has a forest of 50 to 100 tiny suckers, and the end consists of the long, thread-like male organ. The hectocotylus is richly supplied with nerve ganglia. Its total length varies, but is sometimes about five inches, or some ten times as long as the male argonaut itself (see Plate 27).

Eventually the hectocotylus breaks free from the arm on which it has grown and is then capable of considerable independent movement. Delle Chiaje watched one swim and crawl about in water for many hours. Müller says hectocotyli are difficult to investigate "since they are for the most part very restless, and wind and twist about in the most determined manner." And the Italian zoologist, Pasquale Pasquini, tells me: "The autotomous hecto-cotyli survive for a long period swimming, reaching the female and fixing in the [mantle] cavity." Small wonder that Cuvier called them worms!

Very little is known about the mating. It has been suggested that the males are parasitic but this view is generally discarded today. Gilbert L. Voss tells me that he has in his collections several male argonauts, all of which were taken in plankton hauls independently of females. He comments: "I do not believe that there is justification for considering the males parasitic in any case. All of the records in the literature are from free-living planktonic specimens, liberally recorded by Chun, etc. This of course does not mean that they cannot be parasitic, but it does seem doubtful."

The only other cephalopods which are fertilized by similar autotomous, or detachable, hectocotyli are the octopuses *Ocythoë* and *Tremoctopus*. These are related to the argonauts, but they have no shell and there is not the great difference in size between the sexes. The length of their hectocotyli varies, but Robson records that in the Natural History Museum in Paris there is one from a specimen of *Ocythoë tuberculata* caught at Nice which measures about 16 in. over-all. And the whole body of the male rarely spans more than 10 in., although the females are much larger.

According to P.-H. Fischer, these hectocotyli, like those of the argonauts, can move independently. He says that when detached from the male's arm the hectocotylus swims under its own power and fixes itself by its suckers on to the female at the mantle cavity.

Apart from these octopuses with autotomous hectocotyli, nearly all other male cephalopods fertilize the females by sperm cells contained in spermatophores. The size, shape and construction of these tubes vary with different species, but the general pattern is roughly the same—and a remarkable pattern it is.

After the sperm is secreted it passes into a thick-walled sack. Here an "assembly-line" of numerous chambers, or glandular pouches, pours various secretions on the sperm cells, and wraps them in tube-shaped membranes—the spermatophores. There is a "nervous mechanism that sees to it that each secretion is started and stopped at the proper time to make the whole a complete, well-formed complicated machine." (Drew, 1919.) Microphotographs of spermatophores have been taken by Guy Fort (1941), and Bernard C. Cotton. (See Cotton, Verco and Cotton, and Plate 34.) The spermatophores pass into a temporary reservoir called Needham's sack, where they lie until the external genital organ ejects them into the grasping hectocotylized arm.

The spermatophores lie in the organ parallel to each other, all with the same end pointing outwards. In the common American squid (*Loligo pealeii*) 20 to 40 may be held at one time, and 400 may be stored in the reservoir. Spermatophores in this squid, and most of the other cephalopods, are produced continually throughout the breeding season.

In the common American squid the spermatophores are about half an inch long and one-fortieth inch wide at the broadest part.

But in other cephalopods they may be either larger or smaller than this. In the giant squid (*Architeuthis physeteris*) they are about 3½ in. long. The longest known appear to be those of the large Pacific octopus (*Octopus hongkongensis*), some of which are nearly four *feet* long when unrolled.

The sperm cells are held together in a thin membrane by a mucous secretion. This sperm mass occupies about two-thirds of the total length of the spermatophore. Attached to the top of the sperm mass is a small rounded gland, called the cement body, containing a glue-like fluid, which sticks the sperm mass in position inside the female. Running from the top of the cement body to the end of the spermatophore is a spiral filament. The top of the spermatophore is surrounded by a cap to which a long thin thread is attached.

Many writers have wrongly referred to the spiral filament as the spring which discharges the sperm mass. Its actual function appears rather to be the slowing down of the ejaculation at a critical stage. Drew says: "The part played by the spiral filament seems to be largely, if not wholly, that of keeping the tube from collapsing with the pressure, but there may be some elastic force that aids in the evagination." The spiral filament is absent from the spermatophores of at least one species (*Rossia australis*). (Cotton, 1938.)

Covering the whole length of the spermatophore are two elastic membranes, the outer one tough, the inner one soft. The outer membrane shrinks as it enters Needham's sack, and remains under tension. There is a small gap between these membranes and the sperm mass. One end of the spermatophore is dome-shaped, and the other, which terminates in the cap, is narrow.

How does the sperm mass break free from the spermatophore? As the hectocotylized arm of the male grasps the spermatophores from the external genital organ there is a pull on the long thread connected to the cap. This action loosens it and partly ruptures the tightly-fitting, elastic, outer membrane. As this breaks the sperm mass is pushed out, and part of the membrane comes with it and acts as a reservoir. The cement body bursts and its glue-like contents coat the outer covering of the sperm mass. Thus as it enters the female it is automatically cemented into position. The male holds the spermatophores in position until the ejaculation of the sperm mass is complete.

The whole action, from the seizing of the spermatophores by the hectocotylized arm to the cementing of the sperm mass, is very rapid, taking in the common American squid about ten seconds. Sperm cells are discharged very slowly. Emission begins at once but sometimes lasts 24 hours.

This is a simplified description of an intricate process. The details have been taken primarily from the paper by the American zoologist, Gilman A. Drew (1919), on the formation, structure and ejaculation of the spermatophores of the common American squid. This is a most detailed account of 40 pages and numerous drawings. To that paper all subsequent students of the cephalopod spermatophore are deeply indebted.

Although hectocotylus and spermatophore follow the same general pattern in nearly all cephalopods, there are considerable differences in other aspects of their sex-life.

Émile G. Racovitza (1894a and b) made a detailed study of the mating behavior of the common octopus based upon observations in an aquarium at Banyuls-sur-Mer, France. The animals remained some distance apart. The male first caressed the female with the tip of his hectocotylized arm, and then inserted the tip into her mantle cavity beside the funnel where it stayed for over an hour. During this time the female remained quiet except for spasmodic movements, and the male's arm moved slightly as the spermatophores traveled down its longitudinal groove. The Swiss zoologist, Katharina Wirz, tells me that the mating of the common octopus may last several hours, or even a whole day.

The general shape of octopus eggs is that of a grain of Patna rice, but their size and the number laid vary considerably with the different species. The common octopus lays eggs which are only an eighth-inch long, but those of the mudflat octopus (*Octopus bimaculoides*) measure half an inch, and are among the longest octopus eggs known. A mudflat octopus weighing about half a pound lays some 600 eggs. Long eggs are relatively slender. The eggs of *Eledone*, while comparatively short, have considerable mass because of their grapelike shape.

The smallest cephalopod eggs appear to be those of the argonauts, measuring about one-thirtieth-inch. They are laid in bunches attached to a thin stalk. The stalks are fastened to the knobbed prow of the shell and the eggs are incubated inside (see Plate 27). The eggs of the pearly nautilus (*Nautilus macromphalus*) are, as far as I know, by far the largest laid by any cephalopod. Arthur Willey (1897) says that the complete egg, including the two casings which enclose the ovum, and the two outer capsules, is about 1¾ in. long. The eggs are laid singly. Most of the little knowledge available on the reproduction of these rarely studied cephalopods is contained in Willey's monograph published in 1902.

F. H. Gravely watched the spawning of a lesser octopus in the Port Erin Aquarium in the Isle of Man. She produced one to four egg clusters nearly every day for about a month, laying generally in the morning and evening. Such continuous egg-laying was probably exceptional, due to the artificial conditions.

The eggs measured about three-tenths-inch and were pear-shaped, white and opalescent. But such lack of color is abnormal. The end narrowed into a stalk which was joined to the common stem of the cluster. The number of eggs in a cluster ranged from about 25 to 50. (Under normal conditions some 800 eggs are laid altogether.) The egg clusters were attached either to the glass or concrete sides of the tank by a glutinous disk on the main stem.

The eggs of the common octopus are translucent, and are individually attached to a common stalk or strand, round which they cling like a miniature bunch of bananas. The length and number of the egg clusters vary with the age and condition of the octopus. A young one lays from 12 to 30, each about three inches long, but a mature octopus may lay 50 clusters each about five inches long. There are sometimes about 1,000 eggs on such a cluster, so this means that 50,000 eggs are occasionally laid in about two weeks by one common octopus. Exceptionally many more than this may be laid. The French zoologist, J. H. Heldt, counted the number of clusters laid by an octopus in an aquarium at Salammbô, Tunisia. There were 192, and if laid end to end they would have stretched 11½ meters, or over 37 feet. She estimated that the total number of eggs was about 150,000.

F. G. Wood, Jr., Curator of the Marineland Research Laboratory in Florida, tells me that he has obtained an even higher figure for a common octopus that spawned in one of their tanks. Wood carefully counted the number of eggs in individual clusters and then calculated from all the clusters laid the total number of eggs. He found that some clusters had 1,000 eggs, and the total number of eggs laid was 180,000.[1] "Most, if not all, of these could normally be expected to hatch, but we know that on the average only one or two of the baby octopuses produced would reach maturity." Many octopuses die in the act of spawning when distended with ova.

Generally, octopuses lay their eggs inshore, attaching them to rocks, stones, sea vegetation and débris. The egg clusters are fixed to such supports by a glue-like secretion and hang down in small bunches (see Plate 28).

When a common octopus is about to spawn she seeks out a sheltered rock-hole or similar hideout to deposit her eggs. The elasticity of her body enables her to squeeze into narrow openings, and the narrower the opening the greater the safety for the eggs. Henry Lee once found an octopus and her eggs inside a two-gallon carboy which had been dredged from the English Channel. The neck of the carboy was two inches in diameter — the octopus had a body about the size of a large grapefruit, some six inches in diameter. Joyce Allan states that an Australian trawler's net brought up a petrol tank of a crashed airplane which contained an octopus surrounded by a large mass of eggs.

[1] Writing in July, 1959 he tells me that another has laid about 328,000 eggs. Even such a figure is far from Nature's record for the number of eggs laid in a season. G. E. and Nettie MacGinitie made a careful calculation of the number of eggs laid by the foot-long marine snail *Tethys*. During the laying periods 41,000 eggs were deposited per minute. In 4¼ months 478 million eggs were laid, and if placed end to end the egg strings would have stretched for about one-third of a mile! (Joseph Bernstein.)

Morris M. Wells found on some sandy flats on the Florida Gulf Coast a small octopus (*Octopus joubini?*) with two egg clusters in the shells of an oyster. The octopus had thrown her arms back over her body and the suckers were fastened to each valve of the shell, which she held tightly closed. After a heavy storm at sea, Wells collected about 20 shells containing eggs, and 15 of them either contained an octopus or one was nearby.

The deep sea octopuses (Cirromorpha) do not leave the depths to spawn. When submarine cables have been lifted octopus eggs have sometimes been found attached to them. Two sets of eggs were found on a cable hauled up from a depth of about a mile. (Robson, 1932 and A. E. Verrill.)

The octopus guards her eggs vigilantly. The American zoologist, W. K. Fisher, records the following example of devoted brooding. One July a small octopus, which was christened Mephista, deposited about 40 clusters of eggs on the ceiling of her lair in the Hopkins Marine Station at Pacific Grove, California. The eggs were always laid at night. Mephista cradled them in her arms and from then on she was oblivious of almost everything else.

If food was dropped nearby she squirted jets from her funnel at it or, momentarily disengaging an arm from the improvised egg basket, she picked it up and dropped it farther away. When someone picked up the discarded morsel and dropped it near her again Mephista flushed brick-red, seized the objectionable tit-bit, crawled jerkily a few paces across the floor of her tank and *hurled* the food away from her. But she ate during the night as only part of the food was left in the morning.

In mid-September, some ten weeks after the eggs were laid, the baby brood burst forth from the confining egg capsules and went out to make their own way in the watery jungle. But Mephista seemed unable to return to the non-maternal world of everyday existence. She continued to brood, though all that was left were the empty skins from which her offspring had fled.

Day after day Mephista performed the now useless task of protecting what she should have discarded. Now entirely without food, and noticeably thinner, she stayed at her meaningless post, fondling the empty husks. Thus one morning she was found, still on guard but no longer alert—one with the shriveled skins for which she had vainly given her life.

Denis L. Fox records another instance of devotion to maternal duties. A small octopus in the Scripps Institution of Oceanography deposited her eggs on the wall of her tank. One day this tank was emptied for regular cleaning operations. As the water drained away the male octopus sank lower and lower, endeavoring to keep his body covered with water. But the female refused to leave her post where she continued to guard her eggs, and clung there for the 15 to 20 minutes which it took to empty and refill the tank.

During her waterless vigil her eyes were closed, and at intervals of three to five minutes she "took in a great spasmodic gulp of air through her inhalant siphon, while her body and tentacles quivered." When she was again covered with water she breathed in and out rapidly for a short while, but soon resumed the normal rate.[1]

Lee had a common octopus at Brighton Aquarium which laid her eggs in a recess of the rock-work, close to the glass of the tank, where she could be easily observed.

"Her body just filled the entrance to it, and she further strengthened its defenses by dragging to the mouth of her cavern two dozen or more of living oysters, and piling them one on another to form a breastwork or barricade, behind which she ensconced herself. Over this rampart she peered with her great, sleepless, prominent eyes; her two foremost arms extended beyond it, their extremities coiling and writhing in ceaseless motion, as if prepared to strike out right and left at any intruder. . . ."

The vigilant mother would not allow any other octopus near the nest.[2] When undisturbed she would cradle clusters of the eggs in the expanded membranes of one of her arms, caress and gently rub them, and shoot water at them from her funnel. This care and fondling of the eggs has also been observed with other octopuses. The common Pacific octopus (*Octopus apollyon*) keeps the eggs scrupulously clean by almost constant activity. The female manipulates the egg clusters with her arms, working the suckers

[1] Respiratory rates I have gathered from various sources are: *Eledone* 6 per minute at rest and 16 when excited, common octopus 34 while brooding, common cuttlefish 55 at rest, common Japanese squid (*Ommastrephes sloanii pacificus*) 30 at rest and 65 when swimming and a small ommastrephid, in a tank just after being caught, about 40.

[2] Gilbert Klingel says that a common octopus in an aquarium has been observed to kill another octopus that pestered her by continuously coming too close to her eggs.

round them like miniature vacuum cleaners and sometimes shooting jets of water among them.

Such solicitude is not for incubation purposes, as Aristotle appeared to think, but to protect the eggs from injury, aerate and keep them free from parasites, and to prevent them from being devoured—possibly by their own father. Louis Joubin says that the young of the deep sea octopus *Vitreledonella richardi* are incubated in the mantle cavity, apparently in a pouch of skin. The blanket octopus (*Tremoctopus violaceus*) also incubates its eggs between membranes at the base of its arms. (Adolphe Portmann, 1952.)

Incidentally, contrary to the belief of many zoologists, it is possible to hatch octopus eggs without the parent. Voss tells me: "The eggs need to be placed in an aquarium directly under the water jet so that they are thoroughly agitated and oxygenated. They will hatch out rather easily and nearly every egg will live."

The female's devotion to her eggs is such that her health often suffers. Quite frequently when her maternal duties are finished she dies.[1] Aristotle observed that often the female common octopus will fast entirely during her weeks-long vigil. Lee thought that Aristotle was mistaken, but in this rare instance the naturalist of Brighton was wrong and he of Stagira was right, as later observations have proved. Some brooding octopuses eat a little, but others fast entirely. G. E. and Nettie MacGinitie inform me that the mudflat octopus can fast for 4½ months.

These authors say: "We have never seen an octopus caring for eggs show any interest in food, except as something to be removed from the vicinity of her eggs." When they put some food into the tank of a common Pacific octopus it squirted it over the side with a jet from its funnel. Until the MacGinities stopped the supply the floor round the tank was covered with water and rejected food. They also noticed that nothing that would decay was ever left near the eggs.

Lee took an egg cluster from the tank of a common octopus and watched the eggs develop. Under a low-power microscope a

[1] Wood comments: "In our experience, which covers observations on dozens of female octopuses that have spawned in our [Marineland] tanks, we have never known one to survive the hatching of the last eggs by more than a week or so. . . . I think there is little doubt that females of the common octopus always die after hatching."

young octopus could be seen moving "in the fluid contained in each transparent granule, the bright orange-brown color in the pigment cells of its skin flashing, dying out, and reappearing in another place, like sparks in tinder."

Lee found that the time from the laying of the eggs to the emergence of the young was 50 days, the same time that Aristotle gave. But the period varies, eggs often hatching in from four to five weeks. The MacGinities tell me that the large eggs of the mudflat octopus require from 4 to 4½ months to hatch. Temperature plays an important part in the time needed for hatching—eggs hatch more quickly in warm water. There is sometimes an interval of about ten days between the hatching of the first and last eggs in the clusters of a single octopus.

The new-born young are well developed and resemble the adults much more than most molluscan larvae. Octopuses hatched from small eggs with little yolk do not resemble the adults so closely as young from large eggs. Where there is plenty of yolk the young emerge as miniature adults.

Cephalopods, unlike the majority of molluscs, have no "veliger" stage, in which the larva has a velum, or locomotor organ, not found in the adult stage. Because of this some biologists maintain that the term "larva" should not be applied to immature cephalopods, the general definition of a larva being a self-supporting immature form of an animal differing markedly from the adult in structure. Despite the absence of a velum, however, there are several other ways in which newly hatched cephalopods differ from the adults. In larval forms of different species there are outsize chromatophores, usually concentrated on the head which is relatively huge; diminutive fins located at the extremity of the body (in squids); four fins instead of two (in Vampyromorpha) and bristles on the skin (in octopuses). Sometimes the difference between larva and adult is so pronounced that the larval form has been regarded as a different animal and given its own name. In larval ommastrephids the two tentacles are united, forming a tube-like appendage (*Rhynchoteuthis*), and in the chiroteuthids there is a long "neck" between head and funnel containing an oesophagus, aorta, and cephalic vein (*Doratopsis*) (see Plate 5). Portmann (in press) says: "It remains to be elucidated if this larval form can attain, exceptionally or regularly in certain species, sexual maturity." [1] In view of such striking differences from the adult forms it seems reasonable to refer to new-born cephalopods as larvae, although the comprehensive term "young" is often applied, being sanctioned by usage.

New-born common octopuses are about the size of an adult flea, some eighth-inch long, and when irritated they assume nearly the same reddish-brown color. They also have orange and strawberry colored chromatophores. The young octopuses are covered with tiny bristles, or spines, which appear to be sense organs, probably for conveying information on currents. Later the bristles develop into the small warts which cover the skin of the adult. At this stage the arms are little more than conical excrescences, with hair-fine points arranged round the head like a tiny coronet. New-born lesser octopuses have much longer arms.

Little or nothing is known about the behavior of the young in many species, and much still remains to be learned about the early phases of cephalopods which are otherwise well-known. More is known about the behavior of octopus young, especially of the common octopus, than about the young of other cephalopods. Generally, cephalopods hatched from small eggs with little yolk are planktonic (carried with the currents) for the first weeks or months after hatching. Cephalopods hatched from large eggs probably do not have a planktonic phase.

Conflicting views have been expressed about what happens to newly-hatched common octopuses. The work of W. J. Rees and J. R. Lumby has, however, shown that they are planktonic for the first few weeks after hatching. Young common octopuses have been taken in plankton hauls in various parts of the English Channel. This evidence shows that before the young settle on the bottom they are carried with the currents for up to two months after hatching, and may become dispersed over a wide area. Octopuses hatched on the south side of the Channel off the coast of France may spread over most of the Channel, and some found off the English coast may have drifted there.

Voss, who is especially interested in larvae and their develop-

---

[1] "There is no call for speculation here, for there is no evidence to suggest that development is abnormal; fewer adults than larvae are taken in expedition nets, but this is true also for most bathypelagic squids of similar size and merely reflects man's inability so far to devise suitable nets to capture them as adults." (W. J. Rees, 1958.)

ment and who has an extensive collection of larvae of many species, thus summarizes the position as seen by zoologists today:

"In *Octopus* and closely related genera there are two types of reproduction or development. One is by means of large eggs, such as is found in *Octopus briareus* [the briar octopus] and *O. joubini* [Joubin's octopus] where the eggs may reach a length of around 12 to 14 mm. [about half-inch]. Species of this type lay fewer eggs, usually in a single layer, attached beneath rocks, etc. The young octopus when it hatches out is well developed, about as long as the egg, has a well developed ink sack, and the arms are developed enough for feeding and crawling. In other words, by size and development, it is already equipped to fend for itself and it immediately takes up a normal life on the bottom, to the best of my knowledge never becoming a swimming form.

"The second type of *Octopus* has very small eggs only a couple of millimeters [about one-tenth inch] in length, laying them in festoons. When the young hatch out they are too small to be developed enough to take up a bottom life, but rise to the upper layers of the water and spend several weeks as members of the temporary plankton. This is what happens to *O. vulgaris*. In all of my searchings in our waters, despite having taken numbers of *O. briareus* and *O. joubini* on the bottom, I have never taken one in the plankton, from either deep or shallow water. Conversely, in the Florida Current [the southern part of the Gulf Stream] where the water is about 1,200 ft. deep, I have taken large numbers of *O. vulgaris* in the plankton but none of the large egg larvae. The larvae of *O. vulgaris* are definitely planktonic in the early stages, only settling out and dropping to the bottom much later on. As is usual with so many larvae, they also seem to have the ability to delay their settling out time for a considerable period of time if unsuitable terrain is present.

"In most of the *oceanic* squids and octopuses, perhaps in all of them, the larvae are planktonic for a period of time from a few days to perhaps a month. At this time they differ in most cases quite remarkably from the adults as for instance the *Rhynchoteuthis* stage of the ommastrephids, the *Doratopsis* stage of the chiroteuthids, the *Macrotritopus* stage of *Scaeurgus*, the early stage of *Vampyroteuthis*, etc. The best works for a summary of these various larvae are those of Pfeffer (1912) and Naef (1923). In the shore forms such as *Loligo, Sepia, Rossia,* etc. the larval form may either be lacking or of very short duration. The yolk sack is usually absorbed before hatching."

As already mentioned, the reproductory mechanism of *Vampyroteuthis infernalis* differs in several ways from that of other cephalopods. The male has spermatophores but no hectocotylus. The female has a receptacle in front of each eye in which, in mature animals, spermatophores are sometimes found. It is believed that the male places them in the pocket, but as he has no hectocotylus this is probably done with the funnel. The eggs are spherical and have no stalk. They have been taken in deep-sea nets and must therefore be left to float until they hatch. (Grace E. Pickford.)

Common cuttlefish (*Sepia officinalis*) generally mate during the spring and summer in shallow waters. At these times the females, the luminescence of their skins glowing brightly in the darkness, swim at the surface at night. The males flock towards them. When Paul Girod was collecting specimens off the coast of Roscoff, France, he saw males rush on to a female "like luminous arrows."

When cuttlefish are sexually roused their bodies are patterned with zebra-like markings, the males being more brightly marked than the females. The males display the large, conspicuously marked, fourth arms. If the "love dress" is presented to a male he returns the display, but if it is presented to a sexually ready female she either remains quiet or swims away. There is rivalry and sometimes fighting between the males, and the females pick and choose among those that offer themselves. A male often pursues a female that has spurned his advances. Mating is impossible without the full co-operation of the female.

Lukas Tinbergen, the Dutch zoologist who studied the common cuttlefish in the breeding season, says:

"Paired *Sepia* usually swim close together, the male following the movements of the female exactly. Only the approach of another *Sepia* will make the male leave its position and place itself exactly between the female and the third *Sepia*. If the female changes direction the male follows at once; if the male changes direction the female seldom follows, but the male returns almost immediately to the female."

Prior to mating there is some "love play" with the arms. Two males sometimes indulge in preliminary sex rites.

In mating, the arms are intertwined and male and female remain in close embrace for two to five minutes, after which the female slowly frees herself. Mating is repeated several times in a few days, often but not always between the same pair. During the embrace the male's hectocotylized arm places spermatophores on the sperm receptacle of the female—a groove on the inner side of the membrane surrounding the mouth. It is not, of course, easy to see exactly what happens. From his observations Bott thinks that the male's hectocotylized arm forms a bridge between his funnel and the female's sperm receptacle, over which the spermatophores flow to her.

The German zoologist, Georg Grimpe (1926), watched cuttlefish lay their eggs in the Zoological Station at Naples. Each egg was laid singly through the funnel, and was passed to the sperm receptacle where it was fertilized. Meanwhile glands poured an indiarubber-like solution into the funnel and this covered the egg with a tough capsule. It was darkened by ink from the ink sack. After each egg was laid the cuttlefish flushed the funnel and outer organs by expelling several powerful jets of water.

Cuttlefish eggs, which are about a quarter-inch long, look like small black grapes or, as Aristotle says, black myrtleberries. In fact, in Mediterranean countries they are called *raisin de la mer*, or *uva di mer*. Some of the eggs apparently miss the douche of ink and show up white against the orthodox black eggs. The German zoologist, Richard Bott, who studied the egg-laying in aquaria, tells me that he thinks the white eggs are laid when the cuttle has little ink—as, for example, just after using a lot in defense.

It is difficult to determine how many eggs are laid by a cuttlefish as they are often deposited in different places and at different times, and frequently several females lay their eggs in the same place. Bott advises me that the number laid in a season varies between 100 and 300. A. Jullien kept numbers of gravid female cuttlefish in wicker enclosures in shallow water near Toulon. He found that they laid from 260 to 300 eggs in two or three days. Sometimes they were laid closely packed in a single layer. But the more usual method is to attach the eggs to a blade of sea grass, a twig or a marine plant.

The way the eggs are threaded on to these supports has puzzled many who have seen them but were unaware of the mechanism involved. When laid, the egg has a flexible indiarubber-like stalk. With its large fourth arms the cuttlefish twines the end of this stalk round the support and welds it back on itself close to the egg. When it hardens the stalk is thus formed into a solid ring, with the support running through the center. Sometimes the stalk of one egg is fastened round that of another, and sometimes this process is repeated until the whole egg mass hangs together without any central support.

Bott comments:

"When depositing eggs the male stays by the female and accompanies her to the place of affixing the egg, and then returns again to the place of repose. But if the male is taken away from the female, the female will continue by herself to deposit eggs. The male is soon ready for mating with another female."

Cuttlefish frequently indulge in community egg-laying when suitable supports are available. Lee once saw a submerged branch of a tree, over 2 ft. long and 14 in. wide across the tips of the twigs, covered with single rows of cuttle eggs. In parts of the Mediterranean creels containing branches of aromatic-smelling mastic are sunk near the shore to entice cuttlefish to lay their eggs in them. Achille Russo says that by June a creel is often covered inside and out with a mass of eggs: there may be some 7,000 weighing 15 pounds. The creels set in one small area may be the nursery of 50 million embryo cuttlefish!

Lee thus describes the young cuttlefish.

"The young *Sepia* when born is much larger than a baby octopus or squid. It is about the size of a rather small horse bean [about half-inch long]. When about half developed, the little animal has the head and eyes disproportionately large, but gradually acquires a greater resemblance to its parent. If the black integument be removed, as one would skin a grape, it may be seen moving in the fluid which fills the egg. Cut down to the little living grape-stone under water, and away it will swim, with all its

wits about it, and in possession of all its faculties, with as much
facility and self-possession as if it had considerable knowledge of
the world.[1]

"It sees and avoids every obstacle, and if you take it out of the
water, in your hand, the precocious little creature, not a minute
old, and not sufficiently matured to leave the egg naturally, will
spurt its ink all over your fingers. You may tame an old cuttlefish,
and it will learn to know that you are a friend, and intend to do it
no harm; but the youngsters regard everyone but their mother as
an enemy."

The common squids breed chiefly in the spring and summer,
although some eggs can be found throughout the year. Squids often migrate to inshore waters for the breeding season, and sometimes great shoals are discovered on the communal spawning
grounds.

Fishermen sometimes encounter schools of mating squids when
fishing at night, and at least one zoologist has witnessed this spectacle. One evening in July 1951 John S. Garth was on the *Velero
IV* anchored in 15 fathoms at Emerald Cove, Catalina Island, California. He saw a school of Pacific coast squids (*Loligo opalescens*) milling in compact formation on the surface directly under
the night-light hung over the ship's side. The squids were mating
and were oblivious to all else. Even when touched with a long-
handled dip-net they were not alarmed. Normally a squid would
flash away long before a net reached it but now the crew scooped
them up and dozens were landed on deck. Several mating pairs
were still interlocked when they were tipped out of the net, and
at least one pair continued their embrace until separated by hand.

Garth continued to watch the school as it milled about the ship.
The squids were swimming leisurely in a tight circle with the
ship's light as the center. They swam fin foremost but when a
male selected a female he reversed direction and grasped her
round the middle. Often a second male would cut in, and some-

[1] "When first hatched the tiny cuttles are beautiful little creatures, transparent
and spotted with various colors. They soon become actively engaged in catching
copepods and other little animals in just the same way as the adults catch prawns."
(Douglas P. Wilson.)

times two rivals grasped a female simultaneously. Then a skirmish broke out.

"In attempting to escape the female would break the surface and the pursuing males would eject water with a whoosh that was clearly audible, as well as the stream being visible to the eye. The successful male would often retire quickly to the depths with his prize, but in the absence of a rival the mating was completed quietly on the surface."

Garth was able to make careful observations on the color changes of the mating squids.

"Selecting a spot on the outer edge of the circle, where there were fewer individuals per cubic foot, I watched one colorless individual being approached by another, equally colorless individual. As the second grasped the first there was no color change, but as the [arms] moved along the barrel-shaped body of the female until they reached the lower middle portion, the color came. At first it was a pale flash, then several strong, rhythmic impulses, then finally brilliant red-brown color which clearly silhouetted the [arms] of the male against the body of the female like fingers, four on a side. The color lasted as long as the embrace, or at least for as long as I could keep any one pair in sight.

"After watching the males color for several matings of different pairs, I called the attention of others, who verified this essential of the process. The blushing rarely appeared while two males were vying for a female, but only after one or the other was successful in establishing physical contact. Where couples broke apart early in the process through some disturbance, usually an attempt by another male to cut in, the color quickly left the detached male. No mating pairs were observed in which the coloring failed to take place. It was significant that while the animals are capable of turning their entire bodies dark red, and often did so on being landed on deck, those completing their mating in the water failed to color anything but the [arms]. In making these observations it was assumed that the male was the aggressor and the one that colored."

The eggs were apparently deposited on the bottom immediately after fertilization, for when the ship's anchor was raised the next morning there were several gelatinous egg-capsules attached to it. They were about six inches long and resembled "elongated teardrops." As sand grains were found adhering only to the thin end of the capsules it is probable that this end was inserted into the sand. The capsules were almost transparent and the developing eggs could be clearly seen. (This account is based upon Garth's report, a copy of the manuscript of which was kindly sent to me by the Allan Hancock Foundation, Los Angeles.)

The sexual activities of the common American squid have been described by Drew (1911). He kept squids, which were caught in the nearby fish traps, in glass-sided tanks at the Marine Biological Laboratory at Woods Hole, Massachusetts. Although the squids did not live for many days, enough were caught and observed while copulating and egg laying for Drew to describe these actions in considerable detail.

When the squids were sexually roused they swam about in a peculiar way.

"The female in swimming seems to be nervous or excited. She throws short but rapid puffs of water from the funnel, moves the tail fin very rapidly and, leaving the arms quite limp, spreads them apart and frequently throws them to one side. This gives the arms a jerky or trembling motion not shown in ordinary swimming. Except during the most rapid movements of the female, the male solemnly swims by her side, an inch or two away, but parallel, and with his head in the same direction. He frequently manipulates his arms, spreading them apart, commonly with the two dorsal [upper] arms elevated nearly or quite to a perpendicular position, and the third arms spread far to the sides."

The male squids did not all respond in the same manner to the sexual displays of the females. Sometimes one male followed a female for hours, while the other males in the tank completely ignored her. Drew also observed males that were so excited that they followed squids of both sexes indiscriminately. Three times he saw a male insert spermatophores into the mantle cavity of another male, which protested vigorously.

These squid mate in two ways. The first method is generally employed when the eggs are not yet ripe for laying. A male and a female squid face each other from a distance of a foot or more. Suddenly the male darts forward and seizes her, and their arms intermingle, each grasping the other. The male then sweeps his hectocotylized arm past the end of the funnel and takes a batch of spermatophores from the external organ which momentarily protrudes into the funnel. As many as 40 spermatophores may be taken at one time.

The spermatophores are thrust between the lower arms of the female and held there by the male for a few seconds until the sperm mass is discharged. The whole action, from the intermingling of the arms to the discharge of the sperm mass, lasts about ten seconds. The sperm mass is attached to a depression on the outer buccal membrane. Sperm cells are slowly emitted and enter a nearby cup-like receptacle.[1] Here they are mixed with a secretion and remain inactive, possibly for some weeks. Subsequent matings may result in the attachment of additional sperm masses. The sperm does not become active until the eggs are laid, when it fertilizes them.

In the second method of mating the male grasps the female from below, generally when they are both swimming, and always, as far as Drew could see, from her left side. As soon as his arms have a firm grip, the male seizes a batch of spermatophores and inserts them into the female's mantle cavity close to the funnel. Here he holds them until the sperm mass is ejected and becomes attached near the opening of the oviduct, where the eggs are released into the funnel.

There is no special receptacle here for the sperm and it escapes rapidly into the water. But there are such vast numbers of cells in the sperm mass that although they pour out "like smoke from a chimney," Drew believed they may not all escape for two or three days.

The same pair may mate several times in a few hours. A very vigorous male may be so ardent that he actually kills the female. "Even after the female has become entirely inactive and apparently dead the male may copulate with her several times. In one case, a male that had been several days without food, after copulating with a weakened female, retained his hold and killed her by eating a considerable hole through the mantle."

The eggs may be fertilized in the oviduct, in the mantle cavity, or between the arms. But as far as Drew's observations went he

[1] In the common Japanese squid there are about 30 tiny receptacles arranged in a circle on the buccal membrane.

found evidence of only the last two methods. "In no case did eggs taken from the oviduct show evidence of fertilization although many sperm reservoirs that were giving off active sperm were attached to the walls of the oviduct and to surrounding organs."

The tiny eggs, seldom more than one-twelfth-inch long, are extruded in strings of jelly measuring about three feet. Two kinds of jelly are used: one which is fairly soft and directly surrounds the eggs, and another which forms the thick, tough, outer covering and acts as a protective sheath.

The number of strings laid at a time varies considerably. Drew observed one female lay only one, but another laid 23 in 95 minutes. For two or three minutes after the string of eggs is extruded the female holds it in her arms, which are continually moving. She then turns her body almost vertically and, with the tail fins moving rapidly, she bounces along the sea bottom on the tips of her arms.[1] This peculiar motion is repeated until finally she grips some protruding object, such as a stone or shell. She remains in close contact with the support for two or three seconds, and then fastens the string of eggs. The outside jelly is soft and sticky at this time but it hardens rapidly.

Drew gives the following instance of the strength of the instinct which governs this act. One female in a tank was disturbed several times and ejected six of her egg strings directly into the water. But each time, immediately after the ejection, her arms arranged themselves as if the egg string were lodged between them. The successive phases of the orthodox depositing of an egg string were followed in dumb show. She even drew down tightly to an object as if to attach the string she had never held between her arms. Then she rested until the next string was formed. But with each of the six she lost, the orderly sequence of her actions was never interrupted, though their loss rendered all her subsequent actions useless.

Egg strings are usually deposited in the same place. Often they are attached to those already laid by other squids, or to nearby objects. This explains the very large egg clusters which are sometimes found. Drew says that they are occasionally discovered in

[1] The imprints of the arms of egg-laying squids on the bottom of primeval seas have been found etched in rocks 60 million years old! (Barnum Brown.)

fish-traps. N. J. Berrill found a large circle of eggs grouped round an old tire. Sometimes these clusters are so large that they will not go into a ten-quart pail.

Generally, squids' eggs are laid well below the surface. Berrill found that some egg strings he kept in a tide pool, which was continually freshened by the tide, failed to hatch. But the main mass from which he had taken this sample thrived. The only difference in the conditions was that the water covering the eggs in the pool was of insufficient depth to protect them from the ultraviolet rays of the sun. These rays, striking almost directly on the delicate embryos, killed them.

In February 1953 a local fisherman told marine zoologists at the Scripps Institution, La Jolla, in Southern California, that he could not raise a net, which he had set two days before, because it was so heavily laden with squids' eggs. When divers, headed by zoologist John A. McGowan, went down with aqualungs to the submarine canyon off La Jolla—chiefly in Sea Lion Gulch—they were able to make observations in the actual spawning grounds of a large shoal of Pacific coast squids. During one dive McGowan saw a dozen large egg masses, one of which had an estimated diameter of 40 ft. "These masses seemed concentrated along the edges of the canyon, some of them being on the more gentle slopes and shelves of the canyon wall itself. One such mass, situated on a fairly steep slope, was followed from a depth of about 70 ft. down to a depth of 114 ft. and appeared to continue on down even farther." McGowan tells me that observations made by Conrad Limbaugh in the same area in December 1955 showed that an estimated 220 acres of the sea floor were covered by eggs.

The cylindrical egg case of the Pacific coast squid swells considerably as sea-water seeps into it, and as the mass extends a small cavity is left surrounding each egg. A case that is four inches long when first laid may swell to ten inches within a few days. Each case contains about 100 eggs, and a single female may lay 10 to 20 cases, or from one to two thousand eggs.

Many more eggs, however, have been counted in one of the "sea-mops" of the common European squid (*Loligo vulgaris*). In this species the egg cases are all attached to a common center, and the completed mass looks like a mop head. Johann Bohadsch, who was a Professor of Natural History in Prague in the 18th century, laboriously counted the eggs embedded in one of these masses. There were 39,766. Lee checked this figure by counting the eggs in ten of the cases and then weighing them and the remainder. He thus reached an estimated total of 42,000. He added that he had never seen these egg masses attached to anything and he believed that they were left floating in the sea. They are, however, generally attached to vegetation, such as sea-weed, which may be floating. Wood tells me that he has known a squid (*Sepioteuthis*) attach her eggs to the shell of a live conch (*Strombus*) living in the same tank. The squids of the open seas, such as some of the Ommastrephidae, apparently leave their eggs floating freely in the water.

Spawning is the climax of the lives of the smaller species of squid. As they approach the inshore spawning grounds nearly all the squids cease feeding. McGowan found that the female Pacific coast squids that were examined at La Jolla had completely empty guts, and those of the males contained only a few shreds of mantle epidermis that had apparently been torn from the females.

There is a striking contrast between the fat glossy animals with thick firm mantles that arrive at the spawning grounds, and the spent creatures which have performed their supreme biological function and are waiting to die. The females lose up to half their weight; their mantles become thin and limp, and sometimes they are extensively mutilated. The males do not lose so much weight, but their arms are scarred and the edges of their mantles become ragged from encounters with other squids.

McGowan records that the squids he saw on one of his dives "were all very pale and there were large shreds of epithelium hanging down from their mantles. Those collected had a loose flaccid consistency of the body unlike the firmness characteristic of squid caught in open waters during other seasons of the year." The sea-bottom for about 100 yards was littered with dead and dying squids.

Practically nothing is known of the breeding behavior of the giant squids (*Architeuthis*), but one interesting piece of evidence is available. Some children, on holiday in Jamaica towards the close of the last century, were playing on the beach when they discovered a rare piece of zoological treasure-trove. Not knowing what it was they reported to their father that there was "a great big sausage" on the beach. The father, fortunately for zoology, was W. K. Brooks, Professor of Zoology at Johns Hopkins University. He hurried down to the sea to inspect the "big sausage" and found that it was a giant squid's egg case "five or six feet long and with a diameter as great as that of a galvanized iron pail." (Quoted by E. W. Gudger.)

Once a squid has deposited its eggs it has no more interest in them. The jelly of the egg case protects the embryo from fungoid growths, and it is also distasteful to most animals. The MacGinities fed strings of squids' eggs to sea anemones and the whole mass was regurgitated an hour or two later. The embryos then continued their development as though nothing unusual had happened in their young lives. But the iron-stomached starfish (*Patiria miniata*), that will eat almost anything, did digest a string of squid's eggs—although it took 72 hours to do it.

The eggs of the smaller species take four to five weeks to hatch. Berrill, who watched them developing under a microscope, says:

"I doubt if there is anything more entrancing and more beautiful than a newly hatched squid. It sounds hard to believe, but everyone who has seen one has had the same response as I. It is minute, dartingly active, almost all eyes, but above all it is covered with innumerable tiny patches of color—red, yellow, green, black, not in a set pattern but each flashing large and small, a scintillating jewel of tiny life."

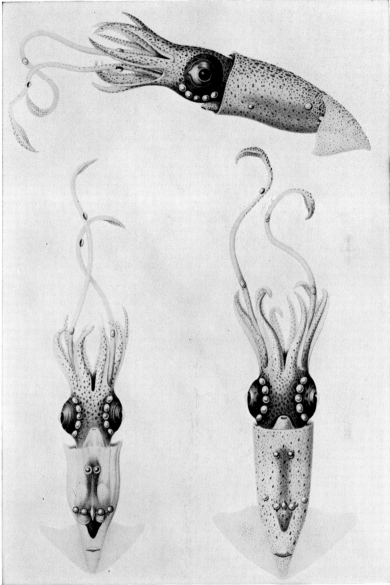

A JEWEL OF THE DEEP SEA

Three views of the squid, *Lycoteuthis diadema,* called by Chun 'jeweled wonder-torch'. About half natural size

Plate 25

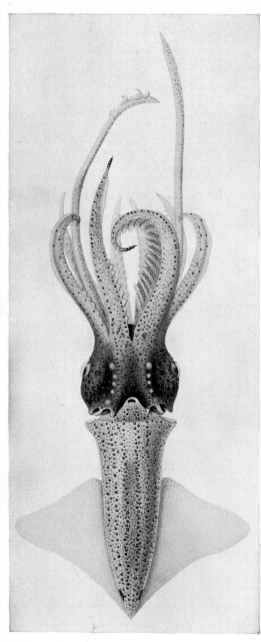

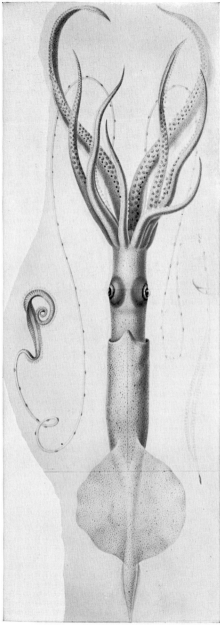

Carl Chun (1910)

THE SQUID *ABRALIOPSIS MORISII*
The illustration shows the clawed suckers,
the hectocotylus and photophores. About
3× natural size

THE SQUID *CHIROTEUTHIS
IMPERATOR*
The tentacles are studded with photophores. About one-quarter natural
size

Plate 26

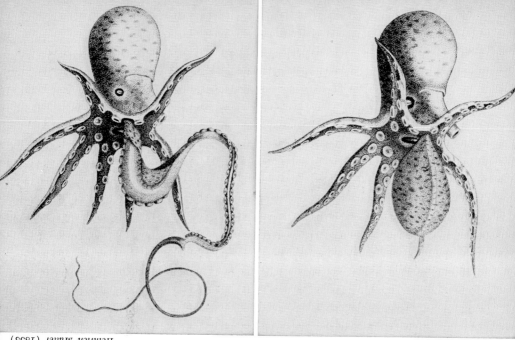

Plate 27

MALE ARGONAUT

Left: Showing sack containing the hectocotylus. *Right:* Showing the hectocotylus un-rolled. About 6× natural size

Heinrich Müller (1853)

A LIVE FEMALE ARGONAUT WITH AN EGG CLUSTER

The photograph was taken while the argonaut was anesthetized. The membranes holding the shell are contracted more than in the natural state, and normally the eggs are almost hidden in the shell. The photograph is, I believe, unique. About half natural size

G. Tregouboff

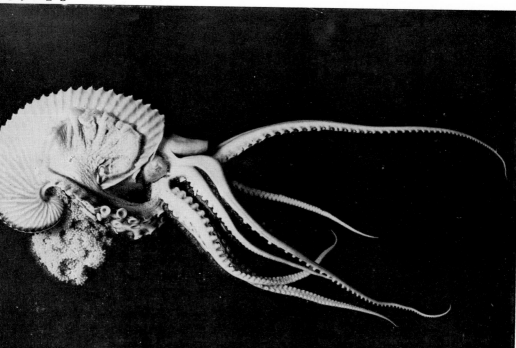

Marine Studios, Marineland, Florida

A FEMALE COMMON OC-TOPUS BROODS HER EGGS

The egg clusters hang from the roof of the lair in bunches. A common octopus at Marineland once laid 496 clusters containing about 300,000 eggs

Plate 28

CUTTLEFISH EGGS LAID ON A SEA PLANT

The eggs are threaded on to the support by a flexible india-rubber-like stalk. About twice natural size

Rotofilm, Hamburg

COMMON CUTTLEFISH MATING
The female is on the left

Plate 29

A FEMALE LAYING A GRAPE-LIKE CLUSTER OF EGGS

Richard Bott

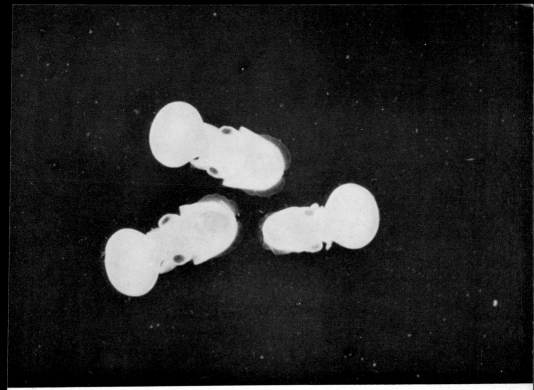

The egg sack is not yet absorbed. About twice natural size

LARVAL CUTTLEFISH

Plate 30

About 3× natural size

A GROUP OF LARVAL COMMON OCTOPUSES

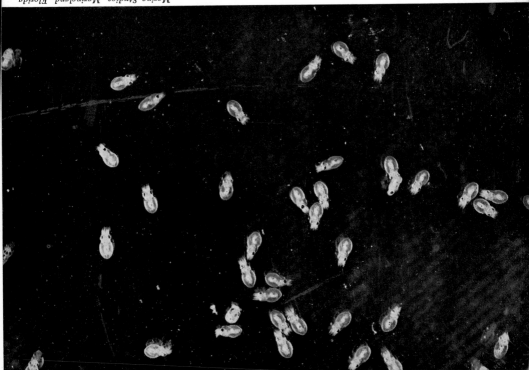

A SHOAL OF MATING PA-
CIFIC COAST
SQUIDS

They swarmed
round a ship an-
chored off Cata-
lina Island, Cali-
fornia, and were
so oblivious of
their surround-
ings that they
were scooped up
in long-handled
nets

University of
S. California

Allan Hancock
Foundation

Plate 31

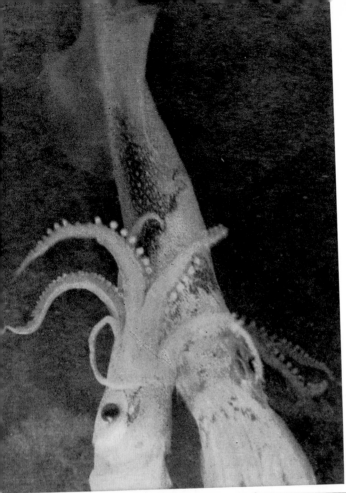

PACIFIC COAST SQUIDS MATING

Two frames from a film taken by Conrad Limbaugh when aqualung-diving among the squids in a submarine canyon off La Jolla, California. I believe these photographs are unique.

Top: A male grasps a female with his arms

Below: Two males struggle for possession of a female

University of California, Scripps Institution of Oceanography

Plate 32

Conrad Limbaugh

Nine FISHING

Angling for large squids ranks with the greatest game-fishing in the world. Very few people have done it. Without a fair-sized yacht and good modern equipment it would be futile and dangerous to try. The 1940 Michael Lerner Expedition had both, and, off Peru, American big-game fisherman Lerner and his companions baited swordfish hooks, and cast them into waters swarming with some of the most dangerous invertebrates alive—the Humboldt Current squids (*Ommastrephes gigas*).

They fished at night when the squids rise to the surface. The sea around the yacht was lit with meteor-like trails as the squids hurtled to and fro in the phosphorescent waters. Now and again the sea exploded in a soundless blaze of light as a large squid broke the surface. When scraps of fish were thrown overboard a horde of squids rushed in to seize them. The watchers thought uneasily of the fate of a man in that cruel sea.

Lerner and his companions caught no squids the first night. They had bites in plenty. They lost hooks, line and tackle. The cabin was drenched and stained with blackened water shot from the squids' funnels. They decided to try again the next night with different tackle and better protection from their quarry's liquid artillery.

When Lerner and his men next took station at the rails they looked like marine ghosts. Their heads were enveloped in pillow-cases, complete with eye-holes, which they had donned to protect their faces from the squids' ink. Instead of the one or two swordfish hooks, each rod was now armed with a bundle of hooks tied to a leader of the toughest steel wire obtainable.

As soon as Lerner's bundle of baited hooks hit the water the squids rushed to seize it.[1] The rod whipped, the line darted to and fro, then went straight down and lay limp and still. Then it suddenly shot up to the surface, zigzagged for a moment, and in a final phosphorescent explosion went limp for good. Lerner reeled in. The extra-tough steel leader was bitten off just above the hooks.

These squids were cannibals. As soon as one was hooked the others swarmed in for the kill. It made fishing difficult, but at last one was hooked and a quick lunge of the gaff brought it aboard. It measured nearly nine feet overall, and weighed more than 100 pounds.

The night's fishing was an education in the rapacity of large squids. Their appetite was insatiable, whether for bait and scraps thrown from the yacht, or for their own kind when hooked. As one squid took the bait a much larger one shot up and grabbed it. Before it could make off with its prize one of the fishermen gaffed it and landed the two squids together. Sometimes squids would bite lumps out of their gaffed companions. One gaffed squid wrapped its arms tightly round the pole and chopped big pieces out of the wood with its beak. (David D. Duncan.)

Since the Michael Lerner Expedition fished for these large squids, John Manning and Lou Marron have taken them while on expeditions for the Marine Laboratory of the University of Miami. They reported some of their adventures to Gilbert L. Voss, who has kindly told me some of the highlights.

The Humboldt Current squids grow to an overall length of some 12 ft. (mantle about 6 ft.) and weigh up to 300 pounds or so. Manning says the discharge from the funnel of these squids "is about like a blast from a fire hose." They were seen both by day and night, and would take any bait. Manning jigged (see page 144) for them with a two-foot iron pipe with several large hooks welded to one end. The pipe was wrapped in white cloth and lowered on wire which was never cut by the squids.

Commercial fishermen, who catch them for food and bait, hunt the smaller squids, especially *Loligo*. There are various methods of

---

[1] When E. Allen Petersen was in these waters one night he trailed a hook baited with a white rag. It was seized by squids several feet long. Later, on one of the Lobos Islands off the Peruvian coast, he saw dozens of these squids dead on a beach.

catching them. In the early days of the squid-fishery at Monterey, California, a skiff carrying a blazing torch would be rowed about the bay at night until a shoal of squids had been attracted to the boat. Then two other boats would set a purse seine—so-called because it can be pursed or drawn into the shape of a bag. This was about 180 ft. long and 18 ft. deep, and would trap a large number of the squids intent on following the torch-carrying skiff.

This primitive and laborious method was practiced until 1905, accounting for about 100 tons of squids a year. In that year the lampara net was introduced, and for many years [1] the fishermen using them had complete control of the squid-fishery. The lampara net has a large central, or bagging section, relatively short wings and no purse line. These nets are capable of taking up to 20 tons in a single haul, and the total catch of squids has increased many times since they were introduced. Nineteen thousand tons have been taken in a year.

When they are caught in nets with other sea animals, squids are sometimes landed with fish or crustaceans fixed in their mantle cavity. Apparently, as the net is drawn tighter, the catch mills wildly about in the constricted space, and sometimes a fish or other animal plunges into the gaping mantle cavity. The same phenomenon sometimes occurs when cuttlefish are caught in nets. The Italian zoologist, Elvezio Ghirardelli, comments: "In the Adriatic Sea *Gobius paganellus* [the rock goby] is frequently found in the mantle cavity of cuttlefish." He thinks this may happen naturally. "It is possible that these fishes, finding no other hiding place, enter the mantle cavity."

J. Grivet says that at La Rochelle, France, the fisherwomen regularly examine the squids for fish, which bring a higher price than the squids. Grivet lists over 20 species of fish, from sprats (*Clupea sprattus*) to a small dogfish (*Scyliorhinus caniculus*), which have been found in the mantle cavities of squids.

One of the most widespread methods for catching squids is jigging. H. J. Squires has sent me the following description of the jig used by the local fishermen to catch the short-finned squid (*Illex illecebrosus*).

---

[1] While the lampara net is still standard equipment on the smaller boats, since the Second World War many of the larger boats have been using modern types of purse seine.

"It is a lead weight shaped somewhat like a small squid but painted red, and with one end fitted with a circle of barbless hooks which are not painted. When the squid are plentiful, the 'jigger' is merely dangled over the side of the boat just below the surface of the water. When the squid rush at this moving object, the fisherman captures several with a deft sweep of a hand net. In this way he is kept busy dipping squid that rush at the jigger and does not bother to hook any. When the squid are scarcer, the jigger may have to be lowered a few fathoms, and jigging with occasional quick jerks may hook any squid that comes near, whereupon it is hauled into the boat."

Squires tells me that in jigging for squids to be used for trawl-baiting, the catch for each boat is about a thousand. One fisherman sometimes takes 1,200 an hour when the squids are plentiful. When fishing to supply a refrigerating plant, the catch for each boat runs into tens of thousands.

There are several variations throughout the world of the jigging technique. Greek fishermen often use the bone of a cuttlefish surrounded with hooks. Some of the South Sea Islanders use a jig made of wood with pieces of overlapping cowrie-shells at one end. When the fisherman jerks the line the bright shells move as if alive. Eventually a squid is attracted and shoots out its tentacles to capture the jig, only to be trapped in the openings between the shells. Before it can disentangle its tentacles it is quickly hauled aboard.

James Hornell (1918 and 1950) says that in the Palk Strait, between Southern India and Ceylon, where squids are abundant, they are caught by netting and jigging. For jigging the fishermen plant stout Y-shaped look-out posts in shallow water. A cross-bar joins the two limbs of the Y, and provides a seat for the fisherman. Leaves are heaped around the base. The fisherman sits on the cross-bar, holding a slender pole, 12 to 15 ft. long, terminating in 5 or 6 jigger hooks arranged in a circle hidden in the heap of leaves.

The leaves attract the squids, especially females seeking a support for their eggs. As soon as a squid is over the leaves the fisherman jerks the pole upward, impales the squid on the hooks and hauls it in. The fishing is usually done in the morning, the men sitting on their look-outs for four or five hours at a time. At Ariyakundu there are usually a hundred or so of these devices in use during the squid season, which is from April to June.

K. Virabhadra Rao has also published an account of the squid-fishery in this area. He says that the fishery is for the Palk Bay squid (*Sepioteuthis lessoniana*), which measures about 18 in. over-all. Some 15 tons are caught in the district each year. According to Rao, the jigging method described by Hornell was obsolete by 1954, and squids are now caught only in nets.

Strangely enough, the common Japanese squid (*Ommastrephes sloanii pacificus*), the most valuable commercial squid in the world—some half a million tons are caught in Japanese waters every year—is not taken in nets, but individually. Isao Taki tells me that a hook is baited with an imitation fish or shrimp made from wood and feathers. Fishing takes place at night, a strong light being used to attract the squids. The line is dropped among those swarming under the light, and as soon as a squid clings to the hook the fisherman quickly draws it in. By this method a skilful fisherman can catch thousands of squid in a night.

Arthur Willey (1902) has described how the natives fish for nautiluses (*Nautilus*) in New Britain. They bait six-feet-long basket-traps with small soft-skinned fish which they capture by exploding dynamite in the midst of a shoal. The fish are tied by fibers to the inside of the trap. Heavy stones are tied to each end and it is set, by paying out rattan cable, at depths between 180 and 420 ft. The traps are lowered in the evening or at night, and are generally raised before morning. Willey saw 15 nautiluses caught in a night from several traps.

He was more successful than the natives when, instead of a fish, he baited a trap with a cooked exoskeleton of a lobster wrapped in coco-nut fiber. When the trap was raised it contained 10 nautiluses. Willey believed the reason for his success to be that the nautilus catches its prey primarily by smell, whereas the other cephalopods pursue their quarry by sight. The nautilus has only a pinhole-type eye, whereas other cephalopods have exceptionally good eyes.

The American zoologist, Bashford Dean, says that nautiluses are caught regularly in fish-traps in the Southern Philippines. The best catches are made in the deep water of the strait between the islands of Negros and Cebu.

Sir D'Arcy Wentworth Thompson, renowned both as classicist and zoologist, has shown how the methods used in fishing for cuttlefish (*Sepia*) in the Mediterranean have changed very little in 3,000 years. This was evident to Thompson when he read a little-known paper by Achille Russo on the cuttle-fishery of Catania on

the east coast of Sicily. "What they do in Catania today is precisely what ancient authors, and Oppian in particular, describe."

The Catanian cuttle-fishers use a baited, conical basket-trap woven from a fine rush. Some 40 of these traps, at intervals of about 35 ft., are tied to a cable made of woven rushes and laid near and parallel to the shore. The cable is buoyed at each end, and weighted in the middle with stone sinkers. The first cable is laid in very shallow water early in the year, and others in deeper water until April. The traps are raised daily for removal of the catch and then re-baited. The cable of traps is not raised for good until the end of the cuttlefish season.

Every detail of this method of cuttle-fishing was described by classical writers thousands of years ago. Oppian describes the basket-traps and the rushes used to make them. Silius Italicus compares the trap to a military ambush, and Plato tells how the traps are used night and day. Oppian says that the traps are laid in the spring, describes the care the fishermen take in putting them down, and records that they are baited with tamarisk (*Tamarix*) and arbutus (*Arbutus*). (All references from Thompson.)

Mediterranean fishermen also place creels containing mastic (*Pistacia lentiscus*) near the shore to entice female cuttlefish. The males follow the spawning females and after the eggs are laid the fishermen make good catches. And over 2,000 years ago Aristotle wrote: "The sepia lays her spawn near to land, in the neighborhood of seaweed or reeds or any off-sweepings such as brush-wood, twigs, or stones; and fishermen place heaps of faggots here and there on purpose." Incidentally, in the Palk Strait fishermen plant branches of *Cassia* to lure spawning squids. (Rao.)

The charms of the female cuttlefish are used in another way by the Catanian fishermen to capture the males. They put a hook through a female's mantle, and adjust the line so that the cuttle-fish swims about six feet below the boat. As they row slowly along males swim up to the captive female and cling to her. The fisher-men then lift them into the boat with a landing-net, disentangle them, and set the decoy to work again. All this is described by Op-pian, except that in his day it was apparently the custom to use de-coy males as well. Writing of this method of fishing as practiced in Malta, Hornell (1931) says he was told that not more than six males could be caught by the same decoy. The Japanese anchor a female near the shore and shoot a seine round males that gather near her. (Henry Lee.)

Cuttlefish are also caught by jigging, and with torch and trident. Again both methods are described by Oppian. In this, if in nothing else, time has stood still for 3,000 years or more for the cuttle-fishers of the Eastern Mediterranean.

Modern Mediterranean cuttle-fishermen also use artificial lures. A piece of cork or light wood, about six inches long, is painted white and ornamented with pieces of glass or mirror. The lure, at-tached to a line, is moved about in the water, and seems to have a strong attraction for cuttlefish. When it is seized the fisherman quickly hauls in his line and the cuttle, intent on holding on to the lure, is often caught at the surface before it has time to let go. (Hornell, 1950.)

Another technique which has remained unchanged for 3,000 years is the fisherman's way of making an octopus release its hold. When an octopus decides to hold fast to its rock lair it can be re-moved only with great difficulty—unless a special technique is used. Bernard Gorsky says an octopus "sticks like a limpet" and "one prods a greyish, heaped up, static mass which seems soldered to the rock. . . . Two of us were obliged to abandon one which remained as firmly attached to the rock as if it had been part of it, although we had harpooned it several times."

But what the modern spear-fisherman could not do by brute force his ancient Greek brother achieved easily by guile. He merely offered the octopus a pinch of pungent-smelling fleabane, whereupon it immediately let go. The same ruse is successful to-day, except that American tobacco often replaces the fleabane. (Nicolas Apostolidès, and William Radcliffe.)

Some of these methods are used to catch squids, cuttlefish and octopuses, but on the whole there is little duplication. A remarkable variety of techniques is used to capture octopuses. They range from putting salt on their tails—almost!—to offering a live man as bait.

In California the small mudflat octopus (*Octopus bimaculoides*), which rarely spans more than 20 in., is the chief quarry of the shore-line hunter. Equipment consists of a quart jar, a syringe, a supply of salt, and a sack for bringing home the catch. The octopuses are hunted in bays and lagoons when the tide is far out, and their lairs are accessible. The lair is generally a hole under water. If inhabited, it has a smooth, worn appearance, and cluttered about the entrance is the débris of recent meals.

But is the octopus there and how can it be captured? The answers lie in the salt.[1] A syringe-full of concentrated saline is pumped into the hole, and if it is occupied the reaction is immediate. The octopus violently expels water through its funnel, and a cloud of bubbles rises to the surface. The hunter knows his quarry is at home.

He waits, and soon a slim exploratory arm emerges from the hole, and feels around. If nothing untoward is encountered the octopus follows, seeking escape from the suffocating brine. Immediately it appears the hunter makes a grab. A moment's delay and the octopus is out of reach, a jet-propelled streak shooting towards the other side of the pool. (J. Charles Davis, 2nd.)

Two thousand miles to the north, when Indians flourished in British Columbia, a very different method of octopus hunting was

[1] Bluestone—blue vitriol—was used but is now forbidden by law in California. In large amounts it kills marine life indiscriminately. Vinegar is occasionally used to persuade the octopus out of its lair. F. Burnett says that in the Cook Islands, in the South Pacific, divers take a handful of slaked lime and empty it within the entrance of a suspected octopus lair. If they have guessed right, the lime, diffusing through the water, quickly brings the beast out, when it is caught and killed.

practiced. Writing in 1866 John Keast Lord tells how the Indians captured the large octopuses they found in the coastal waters.

"Paddling the canoe close to the rocks, and quietly pushing aside the wrack, the savage peers through the crystal water until his practised eye detects an octopus, with its great rope-like arms stiffened out, waiting patiently for food. His spear is 12 ft. long, armed at the end with four pieces of hard wood, made harder by being baked and charred in the fire; these project about 14 in. beyond the spear-haft, each piece having a barb on one side, and are arranged in a circle round the spear-end, and lashed firmly on with cedar bark. Having spied out the octopus, the hunter passes the spear carefully through the water until within an inch or so of the center disk, and then sends it in as deep as he can plunge it."

The Indian then uses the side of his canoe as a fulcrum and levers the octopus to the surface. Keeping it well away from the canoe, for it would be dangerous if it got too near, the Indian picks up a long, unbarbed spear with a razor-sharp tip. With this he stabs the octopus again and again. Eventually the arms and suckers lose their grip and the octopus can be drawn safely into the canoe.

Large octopuses are also speared in the Mediterranean. Herbert Wendt spent a night with some octopus hunters in a Greek caique. A primitive acetylene lamp was rigged over the bows to illuminate the prey, and a fisherman held a five-pronged harpoon at the ready.

As soon as an octopus was seen the fisherman instantly flung the harpoon, and its barbed prongs held the animal fast. The octopus was brought to the caique, shaken free of the harpoon, and dropped on the bottom of the boat. Thomas Spratt and Edward Forbes describe a somewhat similar method of fishing with torch and spear for cuttlefish in the coastal waters of the Aegean.

Joseph Sinel, writing in 1906, says that in the autumn on the north coast of Jersey large numbers of common octopuses (*Octopus vulgaris*) swarm on the surface, and "men armed with long bamboo rods, with large hooks at the end, station themselves on outlying rocks, and simply hook them out as they pass. I have seen many tons' weight caught in one locality by this method, and being used to manure the land." I understand, however, that octopuses are no longer caught in this wholesale way in Jersey.

Another method, used in the Channel Islands and on the north coast of France, is to gaff the octopuses in their lairs. In both these areas there is a wide tidal range, and during the low water of the spring tides many octopuses remain in their retreats, awaiting the return of the tide.

As soon as a lair is found the gaff is thrust in, and if tenanted, the octopus is hauled out. It is generally killed on the spot by the octopus fisherman's trick, practiced the world over, of "turning the cap." He pushes hard at the end of the globular body and thus forces gills, hearts, and viscera out through the opening at the "neck." Another way is to turn the arms back over the head and bite down hard between the eyes. This severs the main nerve center and death is instantaneous.

Spotting cephalopods on the sea floor is often difficult because of the ripples on the surface. Correspondents have told me that fishermen as far apart as the Gulf of Tunis and Cuba overcome this difficulty in the same way. They sprinkle a few drops of oil on the water, thus smoothing the surface so that they can spot the quarry below. It should be remembered that a few drops of oil smooth a surprisingly large area of water.

Hornell (1950) says that in the Cook Islands and other Polynesian groups, a diver goes down to the sea floor equipped with two sticks, one with a point, the other with a gaff hook. The pointed stick is used to prod among likely holes in the rocks, and if an octopus is disturbed the gaff quickly follows and drags it out. Then, like his fellow octopus hunters half a world away, the Polynesian "turns the cap."

In the Bay of Naples, renowned for cephalopods for centuries, fishermen use half a dozen methods to capture octopuses (*Octopus*). Branches of mastic are put in the shallows to attract the females. The fishermen search the sea floor through a glass-bottomed bucket and when an octopus is sighted they spear or net it. If an octopus is spotted in its lair a jig is used, sometimes baited with a crab. The jig is dangled in front of the octopus which, attracted by the crab or the moving bundle of hooks, seizes it and is caught with a quick jerk. Arturo Palombi, the Italian authority on sea fisheries, tells me that octopuses are also caught with a *polpara*, composed of a four-inch leaden cylinder encircled with seven or eight large hooks baited with live crustaceans.

At night the Neapolitan fishermen search the shallow waters with lamps and spear any octopuses they find. B. B. Boycott says: "It is popularly supposed that fishermen use these lights to attract octopus, but they deny that this is so, asserting that octopus are neither attracted nor repulsed by their lights."

Most of the octopuses caught off Naples are obtained with the *nassa*, or the *mummarella*. The *nassa* is a basket resembling an English lobster-pot which the octopus can enter but not leave. It is baited with crabs and set on the sea floor at depths down to 250 ft., depending on the season. These traps are left in the water almost continuously during calm weather, being hauled up periodically to remove the catch, then rebaited and set again.

The *mummarella* is an earthenware pot, generally unbaited, several of which are tied at intervals along a rope staked to the sea floor. They provide ready-made lairs for octopuses, which always seek a hole or crevice as a home to which they return after their foraging excursions. The pots are raised daily, when octopuses which have made a home in them are captured.

By the use of such varied methods Naples, and its world-famous Zoological Station, are supplied with octopuses all the year round. Sometimes specimens of the common octopus are captured weighing up to 35 pounds, which is very heavy for this species.

Across the Mediterranean, off the coast of Tunisia, octopuses are caught by the African version of the *mummarella*. Earthenware drainpipes are also used, placed side by side, sometimes stretching for over half a mile across the sea floor.

According to W. Kirby Green, the most successful octopus fishery in this area is among the Kerkenah Islands. The fishermen plant the butt ends of palm trees close together near the shoreline to form long lanes and labyrinths. When the tide ebbs—some three feet in this area—hundreds of octopuses are left in pools inside the artificial enclosures where they are collected by the fishermen. They are strung together in bunches of 50 and, according to Green, eight to ten such bunches are secured daily throughout the season—January to March—by a crew of four men. (Quoted by Lee.)

In Japan many octopuses are caught by a variation of the Neapolitan's *mummarella*. The Japanese octopus fisherman fastens a cord to an earthenware pot and lowers it into the sea, making the other end of the cord fast to a small buoy. When the pot is raised it frequently contains an octopus, which is grabbed before it realizes where it's going.

In the Palk Strait the fishermen use the large shells of the five-fingered conch (*Pteroceras lambis*) to trap octopuses. The fingers and apex are broken off, and the shells are then strung on a long line and lowered on to the sea floor in about six feet of water. Seven to nine hundred shell traps are attached to one of these lines, which are lifted each morning. Hornell says that every village on the Indian mainland facing the southern end of the Strait has these lines, and two to three hundred small octopuses are sometimes caught at a time.

When Paul Bartsch was in the *Albatross* off the Philippines in 1908, he saw one evening a torchlight procession going from a village to a sand spit near a reef. As soon as the procession reached the sand it broke up, and the torch-bearers appeared from a distance to be indulging in a wild dance.

Intrigued by the sight a party from the ship lowered a boat and rowed to the reef. There they found a group of men and boys, clad only in G-strings, each carrying a long torch made of dried bamboo, and a bolo (a long, single-edged knife) or a spear. The torches, some measuring about 12 ft., and 6 in. in diameter, were carried over the left shoulder with the lighted end in front. The right hand held the weapon.

Thus equipped the warriors were on an octopus hunt. The light of the torches revealed numbers of octopuses which had left the crevices in the reef to go hunting in the shallow water. As soon as one was spotted a quick jab of bolo or spear impaled it. The hunter then picked it off and strung it on a length of rattan, which soon resembled a string of outsize squirming onions.

Bartsch found that on the island of Guam the natives catch octopuses in an entirely different way. They go out in a canoe to the inside of a reef where they tie a large holothurian, or sea-cucumber, to a line with a sinker, and lower it among the crevices of the reef. For some unknown reason an octopus cannot abide the presence of a holothurian, and if one enters its lair the octopus leaves immediately. A native is waiting in the bow of the canoe and as soon as he sees the octopus he spears it. "It is quite a picture to see these fishermen as they work in the very teeth of the pounding surf with a craft so frail that one constantly wonders how they manage to keep it from being dashed to pieces."

If the Guam octopuses are repelled by sea-cucumbers, others in the South Seas are antagonized by rats. There is a widespread legend in Polynesia that the octopus has a grudge against rats. The British artist and travel writer, Robert Gibbings, says that an octopus will attack a rat on every possible occasion, frequently coming to the shore-line at night to seize them. And, like the Guam islanders, the Polynesians make use of this octopodan antipathy to catch them.

Few fishermen in Central Polynesia are without a rat lure. They are made of a cone-shaped stone, about three inches long, on which are tied pieces of shell to simulate the rat's back. A length of palm-leaf midrib is tied on the underside to represent the tail. Each day the lure is used, fresh strips of coconut leaf are tied on to the "tail" to make it look more realistic. With a fishing-line attached the lure is now ready for action.

"When taken out to a place known to be a haunt of the octopus, the lure is lowered quietly to the bottom and moved slowly along; by varying the direction of the pull, it is made to progress with a dancing motion; according to the fishermen, the octopus, as soon as it sees this rat-like thing intruding upon its domain, is beside itself with anger, remembering all the rat's gross insults; furious, it rushes out and seizes the rat in deadly embrace, intent upon its destruction! When this happens, the fisherman either dives and seizes the octopus, or, more usually, he hauls the lure and the clinging octopus to the surface, alongside the canoe; so determined to kill the hated rat is the octopus that the fisherman is able to gaff it before it has time to relax its grip and make its escape." (Hornell.)

Gibbings says that he has seen the rat lure used many times in Samoa, and he has often been in a canoe when octopuses have been caught with it. He adds: "And many times afterwards, even on islands a thousand miles away, I have heard the same story." Willey (1897) found that the natives on Lifu in the Loyalty Islands also used a rat lure to catch octopuses. He confirms the widespread native belief that octopuses have "a special grudge" against the rat. But any small moving object would probably attract the octopus just as well.

Philip Snow tells me that in Fiji, women, who do the bulk of the fishing, sometimes catch small octopuses in the outer reef. The octopuses are first detected by treading on them, and then the women either reach down or dive for them. They are killed by "turning the cap."

Some of the largest octopuses in the world live among the island reefs of Eastern Polynesia. Wilmon Menard hunted them among the coral ledges of Port de Papeari on Tahiti. His companion was a native octopus-hunter, and they were both armed with 12-ft. spears with iron shafts to which ropes were attached.

When an octopus lair was discovered the hunter retreated a short distance and then played weird tunes on his *vivo*, or nose flute.[1] This lured the octopus towards the hunter. As soon as it was within striking distance the spears were thrown. The fishermen held on to the ropes until eventually the octopus tired and was landed.

Menard was present on the Rimaroa atoll when a large octopus, spanning some 18 ft., was killed. The entire male population of the atoll joined in, and under a barrage of spears, machetes and clubs the beast was killed. Menard's leg bore a reminder of the battle for months. During the mêlée he momentarily got too near the octopus, and in a flash it whipped an arm round his calf. He severed the arm and peeled it off. But his skin came off as well, and it was months before the ugly red patch healed completely.

The most dramatic method of octopus-hunting is undoubtedly that of the Gilbert Islanders whereby one man deliberately offers himself as living bait. I am told by the Office of the Resident Commissioner for the Gilbert and Ellice Islands that this method "is not now [1955] practised nor is it believed to have been a common practice." But Sir Arthur Grimble, who spent nearly 20 years in the British Colonial Service in the islands, has left a vivid description of it, and I am indebted to his account for what follows. Incidentally, Menard tells me that in the Tuamotu Group, northeast of Tahiti, a swimmer will sometimes seize an octopus on the sea bed and bring it to the surface by hugging it to his chest and stomach.

---

[1] "I found that a sweet-potato whistle, or ocarina, worked just as well. Another method we used to attract the creatures was to beat two stones together just below the surface, near their hiding-places, or to lower two red-spotted crab-shells on a string in front of the underwater cave."

One man was nearly drowned when he thus attempted to catch an octopus which had a firm grip on some coral. It took several men with knives to cut him free. "It is only when an octopus has nothing to anchor his [arms] to that such a feat can be accomplished." (See also page 185.)

The quarry of the Gilbert Islanders is the octopuses, some spanning ten feet, that lurk in the crannies of submarine cliffs. The natives work in pairs: the bait and the killer. One swims down to the beast's lair and deliberately offers his body—always taking care to have one hand covering his eyes; an octopus sucker on the eyeball can cause permanent blindness.

Occasionally the octopus declines the human bait and withdraws farther into its rock fortress. But usually it strikes, and the sucker-clad, whip-like arms embrace the brown body and begin to draw it towards the beak.

Every move has been watched by the other native staring down through the pellucid water from the reef above. If he strikes too soon the octopus may escape, or, worse, it may grapple him as well. If he waits too long, the beak may have buried itself in his partner's neck. But with the sea-hunting traditions of centuries, and long practice from childhood, a Gilbertese can think like an octopus, anticipating its every move. At the right moment the killer dives. Keeping at arm's length, with a wary eye for a stray arm, he seizes his partner and jerks backward with all his might. The surprise wrench tears the octopus from its anchorage. The human bait gives a powerful scissors-kick and shoots to the surface, still gripped by the octopus. He turns on his back, the killer forces the octopus's head backwards, and plunges his teeth between its eyes. He bites downward with all his strength until his teeth sink into its brain and it dies instantly.

In what bids fair to become a classic of octopodan lore, Grimble has described how he once acted the part of the human bait for a Gilbert Islander. He had been watching some young Gilbertese catch an octopus, and when they brought in their trophy he spoke to them. Seeing his interest, and themselves regarding the octopus hunt as a harmless game, they invited him to try his hand at the easy part—the bait. Grimble was horrified, but was still more so of appearing afraid. Years afterwards he wrote this, possibly somewhat romantic, account of those curdling moments.

"I hope I did not look as yellow as I felt when I stood to take the plunge; I have never been so sick with funk before or since. 'Remember, one hand for your eyes,' said someone from a thousand miles off, and I dived.

"I do not suppose it is really true that the eyes of an octopus shine in the dark; besides, it was clear daylight only six feet down in the limpid water; but I could have sworn the brute's eyes burned at me as I turned in towards his cranny. That dark glow—whatever may have been its origin—was the last thing I saw as I blacked out with my left hand and rose into his clutches. Then, I remember chiefly a dreadful sliminess with a Herculean power behind it. Something whipped round my left forearm and the back of my neck, binding the two together. In the same flash, another something slapped itself high on my forehead, and I felt it crawling down inside the back of my singlet. My impulse was to tear at it with my right hand, but I felt the whole of that arm pinioned to my ribs. In most emergencies the mind works with crystal-clear impersonality. This was not even an emergency, for I knew myself perfectly safe. But my boyhood's nightmare was upon me. When I felt the swift constriction of those disgusting arms jerk my head and shoulders in towards the reef, my mind went blank of every thought save the beastliness of contact with that squat head. A mouth began to nuzzle below my throat, at the junction of the collar-bones. I forgot there was anyone to save me. Yet something still directed me to hold my breath.

"I was awakened from my cowardly trance by a quick, strong pull on my shoulders, back from the cranny. The cables around me tightened painfully, but I knew I was adrift from the reef. I gave a kick, rose to the surface and turned on my back with the brute sticking out of my chest like a tumor. My mouth was smothered by some flabby moving horror. The suckers felt like hot rings pulling at my skin. It was only two seconds, I suppose, from then to the attack of my deliverer, but it seemed like a century of nausea.

"My friend came up between me and the reef. He pounced, pulled, bit down, and the thing was over—for everyone but me. At the sudden relaxation of the [arms], I let out a great breath, sank, and drew in the next under water. It took the united help of both boys to get me, coughing, heaving and pretending to join in their delighted laughter, back to the reef. I had to submit there to a kind of war dance round me, in which the dead beast was slung whizzing past my head from one to the other. I had a chance to observe then that it was not by any stretch of fancy a giant, but just plain average. That took the bulge out of my budding self-esteem. I left hurriedly for the cover of the jetty, and was sick."

Ten ECONOMIC

In the winter of 1899 there was a plague of common octopuses (*Octopus vulgaris*) off the north coast of France. Walter Garstang, who wrote a report on the plague, quotes a newspaper correspondent from Quettehou on the Cherbourg Peninsula who said that the shore was littered with octopuses, and in one morning he counted 68 in 200 yards. Some of them spanned over six feet.

Another correspondent on the coast of Finistère said it was "almost impossible to turn over a stone on the beach without finding one or more of the pests." After a storm at sea thousands were thrown on shore, and at some places their putrefying bodies threatened the inhabitants' health. Hundreds of cartloads were taken away and sold as manure.

The effect of this plague on the fisheries was disastrous. In addition to damaging fishing nets, the octopuses devoured crabs, lobsters, oysters [1] and shellfish generally in such quantities that the fishermen's livelihood was ruined. Many of them laid up their boats in despair and sought other work.

During the same year many common octopuses were seen off the south coast of England. Prior to 1899 they had been so scarce that the Marine Biological Station at Plymouth had difficulty in obtaining them, despite offers to the fishermen of ten shillings (a dollar and a half) for each live octopus—and that was good money in the 1890s. But from May 1899 more octopuses were brought to the Laboratory than it could use.

It was not, however, until 1900 that the full force of the octopus plague was felt in south coast waters. Writing in that year Garstang says "until the last two years the entrance of an octopus into

[1] One octopus ate 18 oysters during one tide.

a fisherman's pots was a most exceptional occurrence." Between
October 15 and 20, 1900, a crab and lobster fisherman of Plymouth
set 180 baited pots. He caught only 3 live crabs and 15 live lobsters. Forty-four crabs and 41 lobsters were killed by octopuses,
their mangled remains being left in the pots. Sixty-four octopuses
were caught when the pots were raised.

Fortunately the overall damage throughout the south coast fisheries was not on this scale, but it was serious enough to affect the
livelihood of many, chiefly in Devon and Cornwall. Although oyster beds were attacked, the chief damage was to the crab and lobster fisheries. The Board of Trade Returns show that during the six
summer months (April to September) of 1900, 69,000 fewer lobsters and 281,000 fewer crabs were taken on the South Coast than
during the same period in the previous year—a diminution of 18
per cent for lobsters and 32 per cent for crabs. The loss was even
greater if compared with the 1898 figures, particularly for lobsters.

Not all areas were equally affected. Plymouth appears to have
been particularly hard hit. Early in September the offshore waters
appeared to be infested with large bands of marauding octopuses
preying on the crabs. Caught between the insatiable cephalopods
and the inhospitable shores, the crabs chose the beaches. On September 8 over 100 large crabs, measuring five to seven inches in
breadth, were picked up between the tide marks on the eastern
side of Plymouth harbor. During the next few days crabs measuring four to six inches were exceptionally abundant on the shore
below the Hoe, and boys were capturing dozens at a time.

The local water bailiff told Garstang that between September 8
and the end of October at least 600 crabs and lobsters were picked
up, and added: "The occurrence was most unusual, and no one re-
members such a thing before."

Since 1900 there have been several other "plague years" in the
English Channel, with consequent losses to the shell-fisheries, although none has equaled that disastrous year. In 1922 the French
coast was affected, and in December of that year hundreds of dead
octopuses were washed ashore at Brighton after a storm.

In 1950 and 1951 octopuses were unusually abundant, and
caused damage to the fisheries, especially in France. (W. J. Rees.)
J. Z. Young was in the Cherbourg area in September 1950 and
writes thus of what he saw one day at Omonville:

"There is a little harbor there and the jetty runs out among the rocks. Looking down among these we could see a great number of *Octopus* moving about in the water at high tide. For instance, at one moment we counted no less than 25 in sight, even though the sea was rough and vision was limited to a few yards. Of course I cannot say whether they would be equally abundant away from the jetty, perhaps they had come in for food. They were certainly very hungry and attacked pieces of dead octopus as soon as lowered into the water; in fact the boys were fishing for them in this way and once the dead octopus had been seized the live ones would hang on to it and could be drawn out of the water on to the jetty. In this way one could pull them out one after the other almost as fast as the bait could be lowered into the water." (Quoted by Rees and Lumby.)

A side-effect of these plague years is that the lesser octopus (*Eledone cirrhosa*) becomes temporarily scarcer than usual in the Channel. Presumably many are eaten by their larger relative, and most of the others are driven to more northerly and hospitable waters.

What is the cause of these plague years? Garstang thought they were the result of several warm years in succession, but weather statistics do not bear out this theory. It is a widely held belief that sea temperatures affect the movements of octopuses but W. J. Rees and J. R. Lumby, in their study of these plague years, found little evidence to support this theory. Lumby tells me: "The only relation for which we can find any evidence at all is that the two 'plagues' occurring round about 1900 and 1950 were associated with warm winters." And in their paper the authors say:

"The inference is, rather, that the initial increase in numbers springs in the first instance from immigration of greater numbers of adults into inshore waters, and perhaps even into the Channel. Thereafter, since spawning is likely to be on an increased scale (in consequence of the greater numbers of adults present) and if the rate of survival in the larvae is not unduly diminished by particularly unfavourable conditions, the plague may be intensified by these means in subsequent years."

The initial immigration is probably due to a shortage of food on the south side of the Channel.

The English Channel is not, of course, the only area where plague years of octopuses occur. In 1936 common argonauts (*Ar-*

gonauta argo) and blanket octopuses (*Tremoctopus violaceus*), appeared in huge numbers for a few days only in the Northern Adriatic Sea. Normally these octopuses are extremely rare in this area. In 1955 only one blanket octopus was taken, but for a few days in 1936 they appeared in tens of thousands. In 1956 more octopuses were seen off the South Australian coast than ever before. They infested lobster pots, and sometimes as many as six octopuses were found in one pot.

Igor Akimushkin tells me that in August 1951 shoals of the common Japanese squid (*Ommastrephes sloanii pacificus*) appeared in Aniva Bay in the south of Sakhalin in such large numbers that as much as five tons were caught in one net. In August 1953 Akimushkin observed similar shoals on the coast of Iturup in the Kuril Islands. All the squids were females ready to spawn. Akimushkin believes they approach the coasts to deposit their eggs among the seaweed.

Scottish waters are sometimes invaded by large numbers of the squid *Ommastrephes sagittatus*. According to the Annual Reports of the Fishery Board for Scotland, these squids appeared in enormous numbers off Northern Scotland in 1930 and 1931. By July 1931 they had spread south, and were infesting the upper water layers on all the principal drift-net fishing grounds as far as Peterhead. The fishermen claimed that the squids caused considerable damage to the herring.

During the last week of February 1937 these squids invaded the east coast from Montrose to Dunbar, thousands being washed ashore either dying or dead. An observer told the Scottish zoologist, A. C. Stephen (1937), that there was "about a cartload" on one beach alone. At Portobello over 1,000 were counted on a stretch of the shore in a week, 668 being counted in a little over two miles in one day. Why such large numbers should be stranded when there was no storm to drive them in is not known. "The species is one which usually lives in the open sea and does not inhabit our inshore waters. On coming into the estuaries of the Forth and Tay the animals would meet water of lower salinity than occurs in the open North Sea or the waters to the north of Scotland, and it is possible that they may have been slowly poisoned."

Whatever the cause of the strandings, these squids caused virtually no damage to the fisheries, although sometimes squids steal bait and foul fishing lines. The large and ferocious Humboldt Current squids (*Ommastrephes gigas*) cause considerable damage to the coastal tuna fisheries off Peru and Chile. They attack hooked 50- and 60-pound yellowfin tunas and eat all but the heads.

Cuttlefish (*Sepia*) occasionally cause damage to fisheries. They attack fish caught in drift-nets, and eat or damage them so badly that the haul is ruined.

On a few occasions large numbers of common cuttlefish (*Sepia officinalis*) have been washed up on the coasts of Britain. Stephen (1944) says that in 1922 and 1923 cuttlebones were washed ashore on the Scottish coasts "in vast numbers." In Shetland the bones were described as "forming a white band along the tide-marks." In 1923 large numbers of cuttlefish were washed ashore in the Faröes.

During Christmas 1950, cuttlefish and cuttlebones were washed ashore on the east coast of England, especially in the Lowestoft area. On one strip of a Lowestoft beach 17 yards long there were 81 cuttlefish, in various stages of decomposition. According to a report in *The Times* for December 27, 1950, the especially cold sea temperature during that month was believed to be the cause of the fatalities.

But the total damage suffered by the fishermen of the world from the depredations of cephalopods weighs little in the balance against their economic value. Octopuses and squids are part of the sea fisheries of most maritime nations. In the fish markets of most of these countries they are regularly on sale, both fresh and dried. Willard Price says that in Japan he saw an octopus spanning about five feet, sun-dried and stretched on sticks, selling for the equivalent of about two dollars, which is more than most Japanese laborers earn in a day. In the Orient these dried octopuses are made into soup.

L. R. Brightwell has sent me this description of what he witnessed in Italy:

"In 1951 I spent a month in Italy studying the beast in Naples Aquarium, and often going out with the local octopus fishermen. It is almost the signature tune of Elba, they even have street corner stalls selling hot octopus—served whole on a fork. In the Mediterranean it seldom seems to reach any size—doesn't get a chance to grow. At Elba, on Saints' days, half the island goes octopus fishing—with a twig and a bent pin, and hermit [crab] bait."

Cephalopods are occasionally eaten in England. To those unacquainted with the gastronomic rarities of the Soho district of London, it will probably be a surprise to learn that cephalopods—fresh, dried and tinned—can be bought there. Most, if not all, of the supplies come from abroad. I have seen a box of fresh squids on a fishmonger's slab selling at 25 cents a pound. One shop advertises "Dried Chinese Squib"! Dried octopuses from Spain, looking like bunches of old tarred rope, sell at $1.15. I have a tin—Good Morning Brand—of "Cuttle Fish In Its Ink" with olive oil, salt and spices added. It came from Portugal and was bought in Soho.

Cephalopods are rarely eaten in North America save by those of Oriental and Mediterranean extraction. Yet there has been a squid fishery at Monterey Bay in California, the headquarters of this fishery in North America, dating from about the middle of the 19th century. Fishing is for the common Pacific squid (*Loligo opalescens*), which measures about a foot overall.

The squids are used in various ways. They are sold fresh in most of the important fish markets of California, Oregon, Washington and New York City. On the west coast they are eaten chiefly by those of Chinese and Japanese extraction, and in the east by Italian and Spanish. The squids are also frozen for storage. In 1945 nearly 8,000 tons were thus preserved.

The canning of squids, begun in California in 1920, has increased greatly since then. The United Nations Relief and Rehabilitation Administration ordered large quantities for export to Mediterranean countries and the Philippines. In 1946 some 30 million tins of squid were thus exported.

The most important method of preserving squid is sun-drying, and in California they are thus preserved for shipment to the Orient. The squids are split open, and after scraping they are spread flat on the ground and dried. They are turned frequently, and when thoroughly dry are packed by hand in barrels and boxes, and shipped to market. At Monterey several acres are sometimes covered with drying squids.

By far the largest annual catch for any country is that of Japan. It consists mainly of the common Japanese squid, which measures about two feet overall. In 1952 some 600,000 tons of this species were caught. This was about one-fifth of the total marine production of Japan for that year—shell-fish and seaweed included. Some of the catch is canned, and of the rest the dried mantle is eaten, oil is extracted from the viscera, and the remainder is used as a protein supplement in chicken food. Several Japanese laboratories work on the utilization of this squid. Among other uses it has been found to produce a good adhesive for wood! (M. Yamada and Y. Obata.)

The following table, the first ever to be published I believe, has been compiled from various sources. Most of the information has been supplied to me directly from the countries concerned or from their representatives in Britain. Annual catches fluctuate considerably, and for some countries no up-to-date figures are available. Generally, I have given the best catches in recent years.

WORLD CATCH OF CEPHALOPODS

Country			Year	Catch in tons (round figs.)	Remarks
Argentine	...	...	... 1954	150	
Brazil	...	...	... 1955	20	
Ceylon	...	...	... 1953	2,800	
China	...	...	... 1955	80,000	All cuttlefish, which comprise one of the four main branches of the Chinese fisheries. Squids and octopuses are also caught but the annual catch is unknown.
Cuba	...	...	... 1955	60	
Cyprus	...	...	... 1946	20	
Denmark	...	...	... 1949	950	Exceptionally good year. Mainly common British squid (*Loligo forbesii*).
Formosa	...	...	... 1953	2,700	The catch fluctuates greatly. In 1944 it was under 40 tons and in 1954 about 1,700 tons.
Greece	...	...	... 1955	2,000	
Hawaii	...	...	... 1949	10	
Hong Kong	...	...	... 1956	1,200	
Iceland	...	...	... 1955	440	Squid. The catch fluctuates greatly. In 1953 it was 7 tons.
India	...	...	... 1952	3,400	Does not include catch from mechanized vessels.
Italy	...	...	... 1953	22,000	
Japan	...	...	... 1952	646,000	Nearly all common Japanese squid. Catch represents about 1/5th of the total marine production for that year.

Country			Year	Catch in tons (round figs.)	Remarks
Mauritius ...	...	...	1950	300	
Newfoundland	...	...	1953	4,500	Short-finned squid (*Illex il-lecebrosus*). Nearly all used as bait.
Philippines	...	...	1957	150	Squid. In 1952 the catch was only 16 tons.
Portugal	...	...	1954	3,200	
Scotland	...	...	1955	400	Mostly the common British squid. In 1950 the catch was only 22 tons, but since 1953 there has been a demand for them on the Continent as food.
Singapore ...	...	...	1954	75	Figures for Malaya as a whole are not available.
South Korea	...	...	1948	8,000	
Spain	...	...	1952	4,700	
Sweden	...	...	1949	200	As for Denmark.
Tunisia	...	...	1952	750	140 tons of cuttlebone were exported.
United States of America ...	...	...	1953	6,500	Nearly all squid. Many more are caught but are thrown overboard as not worth landing.

These figures give some idea of the known annual cephalopod catch for the countries concerned. Allowing for the fact that generally I have taken bumper years, the table shows that the *known* annual world catch is in the region of three-quarters of a million tons—the great majority of which comes from Japan.

I have stressed the word "known" for two reasons. Even in the countries where figures are available the actual total is sometimes greater, as not all catches are reported officially. And, more important, I have no figures for some areas whose seas are known to be rich in cephalopods and where they are regularly eaten, as, for example, in the South Seas. Allowing for such factors, it is probably true to say that the annual catch of cephalopods throughout the world today is in the region of one million tons, or about one pound for every man, woman and child on earth.

To my knowledge there has never been a suggestion that cephalopods, unlike some other sea animals, are in any danger from over-fishing. In fact the cephalopod population could probably stand several times the present amount of fishing. The smaller squids in particular occur in immense numbers in various areas and seasons. A ship once sailed for two hours through a sea of dead squids covering the surface as far as the look-out could see (see page 10).

The problem of an adequate world food supply has never been so acute as it is now. Millions are still under-nourished, yet it has been conservatively estimated that, two World Wars notwithstanding, the population at the end of this century will be twice what it was at the beginning. Every possible food supply must therefore be considered.

The Japanese have shown what can be done to make cephalopods an integral part of the food supply of a nation. Judging from the figures in the table, Japan accounts for over 80 per cent of the known world catch. Such a figure is, of course, out of all proportion to Japan's share of the world cephalopod population. Is it too much to say that if other countries in whose seas cephalopods abound, studied, caught [1] and used them as extensively as the Japanese, a virtually new food supply would become available to the world?

Cephalopods are certainly appetizing to Western palates when properly prepared, cooked and served. Once the ingrained aversion to trying unknown food is overcome, cephalopods could become part of the standard sea harvest of countries where now they are seldom eaten.

Several scientific analyses have been made of the food value of cephalopods. In the U.S. Department of Agriculture's publication, *Composition of Foods Used in Far Eastern Countries* (1952), Woot-Tsuen Wu Leung, R. K. Pecot and B. K. Watt list the main constituents, excluding water, of the edible portion of squids (species?) per 100 grams as follows:

	Food Energy Cal.	Protein Gm.	Fat Gm.	Ash Gm.	Calcium Mg.	Phosphorus Mg.	Iron Mg.
Raw ...	78	16.4	0.9	1.0	12	119	0.5
Dried ...	305	62.3	4.3	6.9	46	471	2.0

Katsuji Yoshimura and Sakan Nara fed white rats with the common Japanese squid and found that it was absorbed as effectively

[1] In 25 years the Japanese doubled their annual catch. In 1925 this was about 250,000 tons. (Egerton Charles Grey.) Mexico does not appear in the table on page 165, yet I am told that an octopus-fishery has been started there, and as many as two tons have been landed in a day at one port.

as other animal protein. The food value of this squid when seasoned and canned has been analyzed by Eiichi Tanikawa and his co-workers. The proportion of the squid used is 28.8 per cent of the weight of the whole animal. The values, excluding water, are as follows:

Food Energy	Crude Protein	Fat	Carbohydrates
117 Cal./100 g.	17.3%	1.83%	7.11%

Many pages, in half a dozen languages, have been written on the gastronomic aspects of cephalopods. There are numerous references to them in classical accounts. In Greek and Roman banquets cephalopods were as common as salmon is at ours today. The gourmands of classical times thought cephalopods were the finest "fish" in the sea. It was a custom of the Greeks to send cephalopods as presents on the fifth day after the birth of a child.

In some countries today they are eaten instead of fish during Lent. At Washington cocktail parties Japanese dried squid is sometimes served as an *hors d'œuvre*, although few of the guests suspect the nature of the tasty morsels.

What do cephalopods taste like? Opinions vary. Those who try them for the first time, especially if they know what they are eating, are often repelled. And if prepared by a chef unversed in cephalopodan fare, the mere sight of squid or octopus on the carver's dish is enough to turn the initiate's stomach.

Henry Lee has a description of an "octopus-lunch" given by Sir John Cordy Burrows at Brighton in 1874. He says: "I shall never forget the utter loathing, ludicrously mingled with determination to conquer or conceal that feeling, which was depicted on the countenances of some of the guests."

It was the first octopus ever prepared by the cook, and the creature was placed on the table in all its revolting ugliness. "Its skin, which in the process of boiling had become lividly purple, and had not been removed, was in places offensively broken and abraded; and its arms, shrivelled and shrunk, sprawled helplessly on the dish, and, somehow, looked, as they proved to be, as tough and ropy as so many thongs of hunting-whips." The lunch, at least as far as the main dish was concerned, was a dismal failure.

But Lee adds that he has eaten octopus, cuttlefish and squid and that when they are well cooked they are "very palatable." He found the common squid (*Loligo*) the most tasty. In Italy chopped squids, fried in olive oil, are a common dish. But Thor Heyerdahl says that on the *Kon-Tiki* squids came last on the menu. To him they tasted "like a mixture of lobster and india-rubber."

Octopus meat has been called "a sort of marine tripe" and the flavor compared with skate or the white part of a scallop. G. E. and Nettie MacGinitie say: "Both octopuses and squids are very good food. We like them better than oysters and as well as most clams. They are very clean animals, but, because of prejudices, Americans make less use of them for food than do other peoples. However, along the coast of Southern California the mudflat octopus (*Octopus bimaculoides*) is regularly sought for food."

J. Charles Davis, 2nd, found octopus "delicious eating." In Mediterranean countries tinned octopus is sometimes sold as "lobster," and it is said that few save connoisseurs can tell the difference. Willard Price found the suction cups as crunchy as nuts, but did not share the Japanese enthusiasm for the eyes, which they consider a great delicacy. J. Malcolm Morris says that raw octopus is included in Japanese *hors d'œuvres,* and is the tastiest part of the dish. One night, when his wife was pregnant, she said: "I suddenly have the strangest craving for a piece of raw octopus."

There are numerous recipes for preparing octopus for the table. Some of them border on the fantastic to those better acquainted with American than Mediterranean and Occidental cook-books, many of whose readers would not find it too difficult to obey the injunction "first catch your octopus."

For anyone who intends to eat octopus—boiled, baked or fried —there is one infallible rule for all save the smallest specimens: pound it until its muscular tissues are beaten to a pulp. The result of not pounding the flesh sufficiently before cooking is well-illustrated by an experience of Paul Bartsch (1917). He chewed a single arm for the best part of an afternoon, and in the end had to stop because his jaws "aching from over-exertion, refused to operate more."

Preparing octopuses for the kitchen by thoroughly beating them with a mallet is a sight so often seen on the Côte d'Azur that, according to Gilbert Doukan, "the Provençals say of a husband who, being much in love with his wife, beats her thoroughly: *'La ba-*

cello como un pourpre'—'He beats her like an octopus.'" I am told that in Honolulu the islanders have been known to pound their octopuses all night in old washing machines kept on the beach for this purpose!

The gourmands of ancient Rome baked octopuses in a big pie, cutting up the arms and filling the head with spices. So careful were the cooks in preparing the dish that they used bamboo instead of knives, which were supposed to taint the flesh.

In Spain and Portugal cephalopods are a national dish. John Langdon-Davies, who found them delightful fare, gives a number of exotic recipes. He particularly recommends stuffed octopus with chocolate flavoring; *calamares fritos,* or rings from the body fried in batter; and baby octopus stewed with young potatoes in a dish which includes oil, garlic cloves, laurel leaves, seasoning and white wine. Langdon-Davies says that *calamares fritos* and stuffed octopuses can be bought in Barcelona delicatessen stores and heated up at home.

In Portugal octopuses and cuttlefish are cooked in their own ink, and canned for export. On the island of Ischia in the Mediterranean, and elsewhere in this region, baby octopuses are sliced, fried and served in soup. Sometimes an Ischian will put a fried baby octopus between two large chunks of bread to make an outsize sandwich. (Dorothea and Stuart E. Jones.) A Japanese delicacy is toasted octopus cooked in oil over a charcoal brazier. The Fisheries Inspector on Tonga tells me that dried octopus is cooked with coco-nut milk and taro (*Caladium*) leaves in an earth oven. In China a special delicacy is the cuttlefish's dried nidamental glands —the glands which secrete the covering for the eggs.

Jane and Barney Crile found that eating an octopus "involves tasks as strenuous as the 12 labors of Hercules," but they include finding, slaying, cleaning and preparing among these activities. Their recipe is as follows:

"When the octopus is tenderized, drop it in boiling water. Instantly the bruised, limp tentacles snap into coils like watch springs and the body leaps out of the water. The brown melanic pigment turns brick-red and the water becomes a deep mahogany. Add a stick of celery and plenty of salt and pepper, for the broth is going to be as good as the octopus itself. After 20 minutes strip off the soft red skin and the suction cups with a cloth, braise the naked octopus in butter with a squeeze of lemon, and add a dash of Worcestershire sauce. Octopus, when prepared this way, has the delicate flavor of lobster and the consistency of scallops. Cut the octopus into sections, put a toothpick in each section, and serve as a *hors d'œuvre* with a steaming cup of octopus broth.

"Save the biggest octopus for dessert. When the fire has burned low, and the moonlight filters through the olive trees, the time has come for the most delicious dish of all. The octopus has been boiled and its swollen tentacles studded with suction cups are coiled beneath it in red Medusan curls. Put it on a silver platter, douse it with strong brandy, and serve it surrounded with blue fire as a feast fit for Poseidon—a glorious conflagration of *Octopus au Diable.*"

Guy Gilpatric gives another recipe which he calls *Octopus à la Niçoise.* For this the octopus is cut into small pieces, none over an inch long, the suction cups being discarded. The pieces are put in a dry frying-pan over a slow fire for half an hour, which draws off most of the water. They are then cooked for two or three hours in a tomato sauce with plenty of onions and garlic, and well flavored with thyme, leeks, parsley and bay leaves. When the chopped octopus is very tender, a tumbler of white wine is added and the dish is ready to serve. Gilpatric says: "As nearly as I can describe the taste, it is a cross between lobster and baked clams." He adds that cuttlefish and squids can be cooked in the same way, but that most people prefer to fry them. "A fried cuttlefish tastes something like soft shell crab, but vastly better." Incidentally, cuttlefish stewed in milk is said to be excellent.

In many countries cephalopods are used for bait. According to Aristotle, fishermen roast them before use because fish are attracted by the smell.

The short-finned squid is used extensively by North American fishermen in the Atlantic. It has been estimated that half the total catch of cod taken on the Newfoundland Banks is caught with squid bait. *The Encyclopaedia of Canada* (1940) says that when the squids are not available for bait "the success of the cod fishery is seriously impaired." The cod are reported to be in the best condition after eating squids.

The squids are sometimes caught in vast numbers. According to N. J. Berrill, 16,000 bushels of squid were caught in one night off

Bailey Island, Maine. Peter Lund Simmonds says that during violent gales hundreds of tons of squid are often thrown up and stranded on the flat Newfoundland beaches. Surplus squids are occasionally fed to the pigs. In other countries cephalopods are used to manure the land.

In the Hawaiian Islands the ink sack from octopuses is used as bait for fish. The sack is roasted in the leaves of the lily palm (*Cordyline fruticosa*), ground into a paste, and then various flavorings are added. Joyce Allan mentions among the more common ones brandy, kerosene, tobacco juice and Perry Davis Painkiller! The resulting mixture is said to make very good bait, especially for small inshore fish. Vernon Brock tells me that the ink sack is also used by itself, either roasted or sun-dried.

In addition to using cephalopods either as food or for getting food, man has, through the ages, used these molluscs in other and sometimes unexpected ways. In the English-speaking world the most familiar use is as a beak-sharpener for cage-birds—the well-known cuttlebone or seabiscuit. The part used is the internal shell. When the cuttlefish dies and its body disintegrates, this shell floats and is frequently washed ashore. When eaten by cage-birds the bone provides them with lime and salts.

H. C. Russell of Van Lessen, Richardson & Co., London, has kindly given me the following details on the commercial aspects of cuttlebone. In a letter dated September 10, 1954, he says:

"Cuttle Bone can be found on the shores of the Mediterranean; that found in the region of Portugal is most popular, but there is also an Indian variety and it can be seen at certain seasons in the year around the English coast; the writer has seen it on the beach at Hove and Brighton in early summer. The bone is collected by local fishermen and peasants and then sold to local merchants who pack it, usually in sea-weed, and ship it to all parts of the world.[1] The trade in this country, owing to the increase in the cage-bird population, has increased of latter years, consequently the price is much higher and very often supplies are unobtainable."

But canary-owners and cage-bird fanciers are not the only people who have utilized cuttlebone through the centuries. Roman

[1] One hundred and seventy tons were exported from Sfax, Tunisia, in 1954.

ladies used it, burned and pulverized, as a cosmetic. In more recent times carmine was added to this preparation to form a kind
of rouge. Cuttlebone has been used as poultry grit and as a soil
fertilizer. It has provided a primitive dentifrice, and a correspondent in Funchal, Madeira, informs me that it is still used for this
purpose among the poor on the island. Cuttlebone has also been
used in medicine, especially as an anticid. An official of the Chinese Academy of Sciences in Peking tells me, in a letter dated
April 28, 1956, that cuttlebone "is used in Chinese medicine as a
remedy for purulent otorrhea, pain around the umbilicus and pain
and swelling of the pudendal region."

According to R. N. Chopra, S. Ghosh and A. T. Dutt, writing in
the *Indian Journal of Medical Research* in 1938, cuttlebone [1] is
widely used in India as a home-made remedy for earache. It is
prepared in three main ways: as a paste mixed with the juice of
thorn apples (*Datura*), as a powder to dust into the ear, and as a
medicated oil made by boiling fine scrapings of cuttlebone in sesame (*Sesamum indicum*) oil. Cuttlebone is also used in the treatment of skin diseases, being applied locally with lime juice or
rose water.

Jewelers have used pulverized cuttlebone for making casts and
as a polishing powder. The bone itself has been used as "blotting-
paper" and as an ink eraser. Its honeycombed structure has provided a ready-made pincushion. Finely ground and mixed with
gum-sandarach—cypress tree gum—it makes the finest pounce.
This powder, when dusted on parchment, diminishes its typical
greasiness, and thus makes it possible to write on it with pen and
ink. The "pouncebox" can still be found on Georgian inkstands—
a reminder that for centuries pounce was used as blotting-paper
is today.

The most unusual use for cuttlebone is surely that mentioned
by Gilpatric. He says: "I read about a police inspector in Lille who
had been pinched for counterfeiting 10-franc pieces. The coins
were perfect and their perfection was due to the moulds he used.
These moulds, it seemed, were made of pulverized cuttlebone."

Cephalopods have literally left their mark on man's culture, for

---

[1] It is called *Samudra phena* (sea foam) because it is believed to be the dried
foam of sea water. It is almost certainly the shell of *Sepia*. A chemical analysis of
the shell is given.

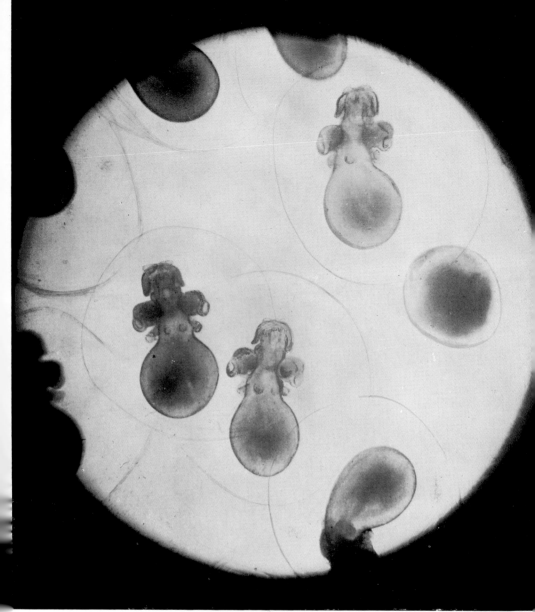

Ronald F. Le Sueur

EMBRYOS OF THE COMMON BRITISH SQUID

The tiny young, less than a pin-head in size, are swimming round their egg capsules with a graceful gliding motion. The egg sack is not yet absorbed. The outlines of the egg capsules have been drawn in as they are almost invisible in the original photograph.

About 70× natural size

Plate 33

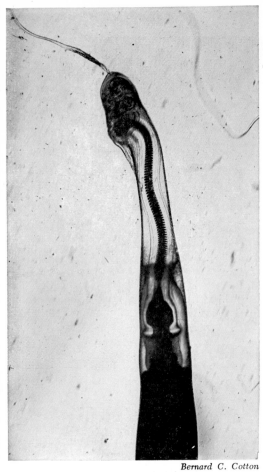

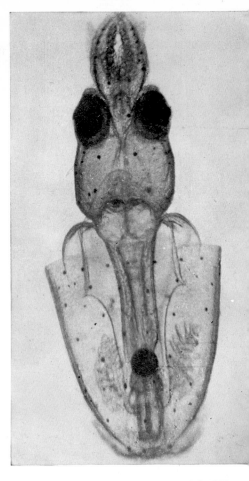

Bernard C. Cotton

A. TOP HALF OF THE SPERMATO-
PHORE OF THE COMMON SOUTH
AUSTRALIAN SQUID (*SEPIOTEU-
THIS AUSTRALIS*)

About 30× natural size

B. LARVA OF PACIFIC COAST
SQUID

Arms, eyes, gills, ink sack and chromatophores can be distinguished.
About 60× natural size

C. LARVA OF MUDFLAT OCTOPUS

About 10× natural size

B and C by permission from *Natural History of
Marine Animals*, G. E. and Nettie MacGinitie
(McGraw-Hill Book Co.)

Plate 34

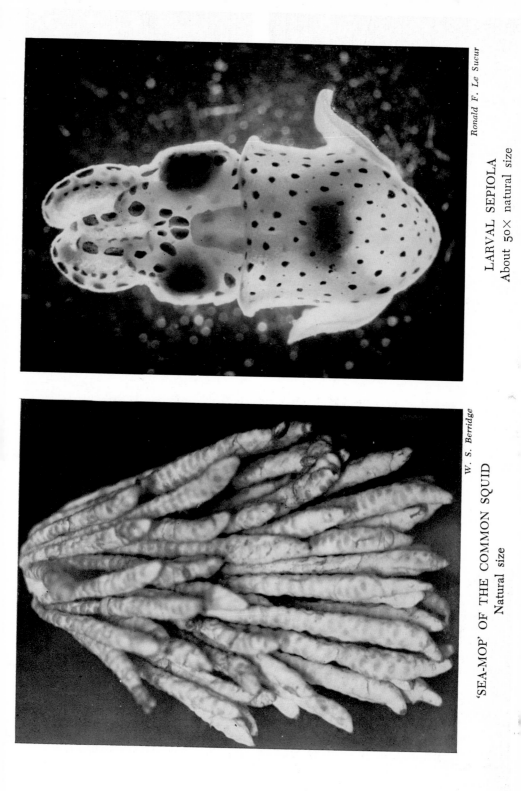

Ronald F. Le Sueur

LARVAL SEPIOLA
About 50× natural size

W. S. Berridge

'SEA-MOP' OF THE COMMON SQUID
Natural size

Plate 35

From *Fishing in Many Waters* (Cambridge)　　　　　　　　　　　　　　　*James Hornell*

SUN-DRYING OCTOPUSES IN MAURITIUS

Plate 36

POT-FISHING FOR OCTOPUSES IN HONG KONG HARBOR

T. C. Lau

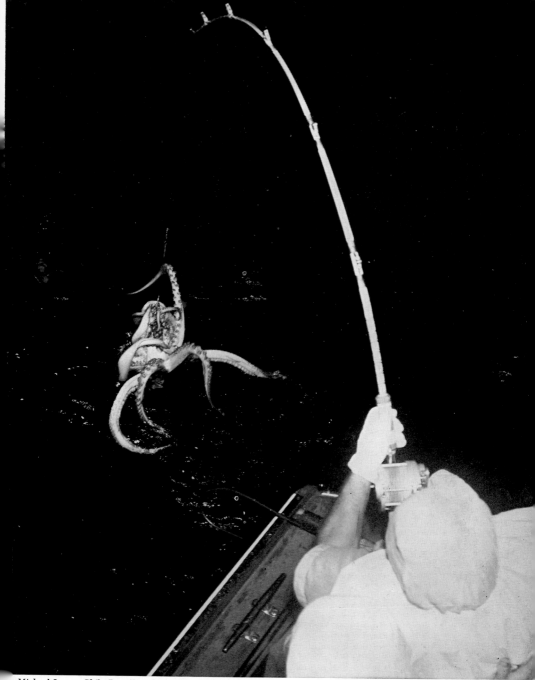

Michael Lerner Chile-Peru Expedition, The American Museum of Natural History   David D. Duncan

FISHING FOR THE BIG-GAME AMONG CEPHALOPODS—THE HUMBOLDT CURRENT SQUIDS

These squids weigh up to 300 pounds and measure 12 ft. overall. This is a small specimen, but the anglers have protected themselves against its blast of ink by wearing pillow-cases over head and shoulders

Plate 37

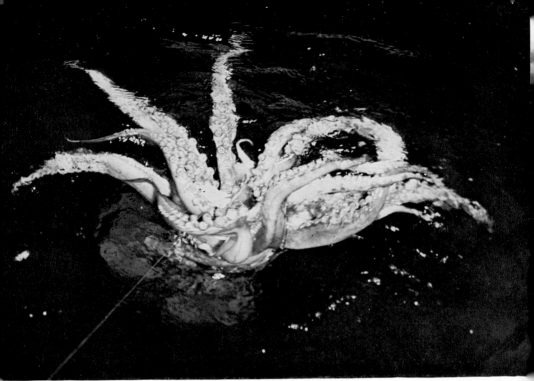

Michael Lerner Chile-Peru Expedition, The American Museum of Natural History   *David D. Duncan*

Plate 38   HOOKED—AND GAFFED

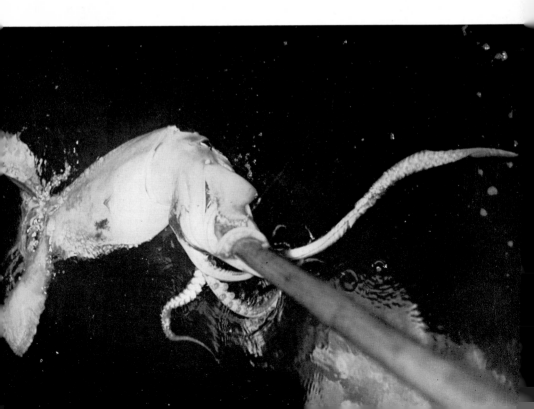

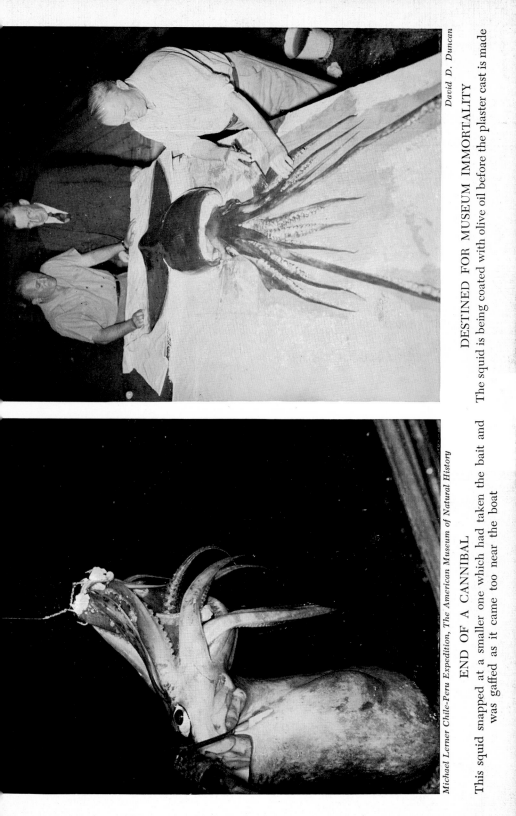

David D. Duncan

DESTINED FOR MUSEUM IMMORTALITY

The squid is being coated with olive oil before the plaster cast is made

Michael Lerner Chile-Peru Expedition, The American Museum of Natural History

END OF A CANNIBAL

This squid snapped at a smaller one which had taken the bait and was gaffed as it came too near the boat

Plate 39

Paul Bartsch (1931)

AN OCTOPUS USED AS A LIVING GRAPNEL

When a ship with a valuable cargo of porcelain bowls was sunk in the Japanese Inland Sea, ingenious fishermen retrieved them in the manner shown (see p. 175). The octopus on the left is entering a pot set by a fisherman

Plate 40

the writer and artist have used prepared cephalopod ink to record their creations on paper and canvas. The name of the coloring thus used is sepia, which is the scientific name for cuttlefish. Incidentally, "Sepia" is the telegraphic address of a well-known British firm of artists' colormen. The drawings which Georges Cuvier used to illustrate his work on the anatomy of the Mollusca, published in 1817, were made with the ink he collected while dissecting cephalopods. Several pages of the *Kon-Tiki* log-book were written with the ink from a small squid that came aboard one night, and was found dead in a pool of its ink in the morning. It was like Indian ink.

It is a surprising fact that the ink sack from fossil cephalopods sometimes yield serviceable ink. William Buckland, the Victorian geologist, once gave some fossil ink to Sir Francis Chantrey who remarked that it was of unusually good quality, and with it he made a drawing of the specimen from which it was taken. When this drawing was shown to a painter he said it was tinted with sepia of excellent quality and asked what colorman had prepared it. Lee, who refers to this incident, says: "I have also seen a cake of fossil sepia prepared by Messrs. Newman for Professor Dick, of Cambridge, about the year 1850, which rubs as smoothly, and is as rich in color, as that manufactured from the ink of recent cuttlefishes." Think of it—writing with ink from animals dead for millions of years!

Before the 19th century natural sepia was used much more extensively in Europe than it is today, when substitutes are available. Its chief disadvantage is that it is not permanent. It was found, for example, that drawings made with sepia in the early part of the 19th century had distinctly faded by 1889. Another drawback is that natural sepia is unsuitable for grinding in oils.

However, at least one large London firm of artists' colormen still uses cuttlefish ink for its sepia. Max Doerner says: "Sepia, a pigment from the ink bag of the cuttlefish, is not entirely but still reasonably lightproof, and is soluble in ammonia. Sepia is very good as a water color, but not in other techniques. Colored sepia 'beautified' with madder-lake [red pigment], sienna, etc., is permanent." The most highly prized sepia comes from Mediterranean cuttlefish.

Sepia has also been used in medicine, especially in homeopathy.

It is listed in the *British Pharmaceutical Codex* (1934), and *Stedman's Medical Dictionary* (1950) says "a tincture prepared from dried and powdered sepia" is used in such conditions as dyspepsia, chronic nasal catarrh, and "facial neuralgia in pregnant women." The dosage ranges from the 6th to the 30th potencies. Sepia, mixed with formalin and distilled water, has been used in the treatment of malaria. (S. Livierato *et al.*) Incidentally, prepared oil from the common Japanese squid has been proved to have an antibiotic effect. (Yukio Tomiyasu *et al.*)

The beautiful shells of the pearly nautilus (*Nautilus*) have been used for a variety of purposes. George Tryon, writing in 1879, records that in parts of the South Seas the shells are an important article of exchange with natives, who make armlets and ornaments from them. He saw a string made from very small shells which had the brilliance "of the most highly burnished silver." Nautilus shells have also been used as elegant drinking cups, flower vases, spoons, to inlay food bowls, and for making buttons.

Strange as it may sound, the eyes of cephalopods have been used as ornaments. The crystalline lens is hard and solid, and is divided into two sections. When separated they reflect the light with a pearl-like luster and play of colors. Gilpatric says that they resemble opals or moonstones. The lenses have been sold to credulous travelers as pearls.

Cephalopods are an indirect source of another aid to feminine allure: the sperm whale's ambergris which is used as a fixative in the best perfumes. The latest theory is that the ambergris is directly formed by faeces impacted round the horny beaks of squids, on which it feeds. A British authority on the sperm whale, Robert Clarke, says "it may be possible to produce ambergris in the laboratory by incubating whale faeces in suitable conditions."

Fossil cephalopods, like many other fossils, are of value to petroleum geologists. The steps by which a potential oil trap, and eventually an oil accumulation, is located are complex and highly technical, but sometimes cephalopods are among the best fossils available for determining the ages of the rocks encountered. And that can be fundamental to "striking oil." In the same way fossil cephalopods are useful in the search for coal deposits.

Live octopuses have at times been put to strange uses. About the year 1800 a vessel with a cargo of valuable porcelain bowls was wrecked in the Japanese Inland Sea. For 100 years the wreck and its precious cargo lay at the bottom. Then local fishermen decided to retrieve the treasure. They knew from experience that octopuses are easily caught in sunken pots. So the fishermen experimented by tying a cord firmly round an octopus and lowering it in the vicinity of the wreck. It worked. The octopus crawled into a bowl and clung fast to it while the fisherman pulled up the cord. One of the most unusual salvage operations of all time was under way!

H. M. Smith, who recounts this, avers that he was originally told the story by a professor in the Imperial University, but he was later able to verify it for himself. He saw several pieces of the retrieved pottery and he says that they were very beautiful and seemed little the worse for their 100 years' sojourn on the sea bottom. (Quoted by Bartsch.)

There is a European parallel to this strange Oriental use of octopuses. During the First World War a number of warships were based on Crete, and coal which fell overboard while the ships were re-fueling accumulated on the sea floor. The Cretans decided to try to retrieve this unexpected treasure. Not being mechanically minded, and having no dredgers, they followed their Oriental brethren and chose the octopus as their submarine coal-heaver.

By means of a water-glass they found the exact position of the coal-dump and then lowered a tethered octopus, the larger the better. Disliking the whole proceeding the octopus, as soon as it touched bottom, seized the first solid object within reach—i.e. the lump of coal—and held on. And like the Japanese octopus in the porcelain, it retained its grip when drawn up. Thus the Cretans got good Allied coal for their fires.

There are two authorities for this almost incredible story. J. D. Lawson, Fellow of Pembroke College, Cambridge, told it to William Radcliffe who recounted it in his erudite volume *Fishing from the Earliest Times*, published in 1921. Then in 1924 Sir Arthur Shipley, F.R.S., published his book on travels in the Aegean and elsewhere, and told the same story. Incidentally, Radcliffe says that in the East the octopus has been used in a similar manner for catching fish "for many centuries" but I have not been able to verify this.

Since the 1930s another use has been found for cephalopods, and this may prove to be the most valuable of all (see also page 86). Physiologists and medical research workers have been studying the action of the nervous system in animals for many years. Information thus gained can be applied to man, for the chemistry and physiology of nerve conduction is generally the same whether in a worm or a human being. And the differences, such as in the actual structure of the nerve-fibers, can also be used to give information on man's neural processes.

Neural studies, however, suffered from a severe handicap—the nature of the material available. The difficulty was this: in man and in most mammals a nerve-fiber is only 1/1,000th in. or so in diameter (it may be a million times longer than it is thick) and that leaves very little space to work in. But in the 1930s J. Z. Young [1] published a series of papers in which he described the relatively huge nerve-fibers found in the common squids (*Loligo*), and pointed out their great potential value to physiologists. A squid's giant nerve-fibers are about one-twentieth-inch thick, which increases fifty-fold the width of the physiologist's basic material.

It became possible to insert tiny electrodes into the living nerve-fibers of squids and obtain electrical measurements hitherto impossible with other animal material. This information has helped considerably in discovering how nerves work—including human nerves. And that is an essential step in learning how to care for them in sickness and in health.

[1] Leonard W. Williams had first noted the giant size of the squid's nerve cells and fibers in 1909. He says: "The very size of the nerve processes has prevented their discovery, since it is well-nigh impossible to believe that such a large structure can be a nerve-fiber." Perhaps nobody really did believe it, for it was not until Young, nearly a quarter of a century later, redescribed them with more precision and detail, that it was realized that in the nerve-fibers of the squid lay invaluable material for physiological and medical research. Most of this work is done at the marine laboratories at Woods Hole, Plymouth and Naples.

Eleven DANGER

"Although we have handled several thousand octopuses we have never been bitten by one, in spite of having tried to provoke them to bite." (G. E. and Nettie MacGinitie.)

"Four cases of octopus bites in human beings are reported herein." (S. Stillman Berry and Bruce W. Halstead.)

"In my opinion the chance of a diver being attacked by an octopus is as remote as the possibility of a hunter in the woods being attacked by a rabbit." (Max Gene Nohl, President of the American Diving Equipment Co. in a letter to me.)

"A large octopus is the most dangerous animal encountered by divers." (R. J. Daniel.)

"A farmer in a cornfield is in more danger of being attacked by a pumpkin than a swimmer is of being attacked by an octopus." (Stephen Riggs Williams, quoted by Bergen Evans.)

These quotations are typical of the remarkably contradictory statements which abound on the danger to man from cephalopods. After a careful study of the evidence I think the truth is that the vast majority of cephalopods which are normally encountered are generally harmless, but that some of these have occasionally killed people. Moreover, I believe that there are rare giant cephalopods which have sunk small boats.

It is easy to understand why cephalopods, and particularly octopuses, have been credited with grossly exaggerated lethal powers. Their strange repulsive appearance, and the fictional stories of their attacks, have built up in the popular mind a picture of the "devil fish" which no amount of accurate description is ever likely to cut down to authentic size. Probably the most famous of these accounts is Victor Hugo's fearsome description in *The Toilers of the Sea* of Gilliatt's fight to the death with an octopus in a cave. Henry Lee (1875) devotes a chapter to separating fact from fiction in this classic narrative. Because of the lurid atmosphere which has been engendered, quite harmless encounters between octopuses and humans are often written up as unprovoked and deadly attacks.

But when all allowances have been made for misinterpretation, exaggerated newspaper accounts, and fictional episodes masquerading as fact, there are enough authentic accounts on record to prove that cephalopods can be dangerous to man. I believe many attacks have begun accidentally—either by the cephalopod mistaking a human leg or arm for something else, or through an instinctive reaction to seize moving objects that come within reach of an arm. But once battle is joined the cause matters nothing, and a man may quickly find himself fighting for his life.

The Victorian naturalist, Frank Buckland, says: "When fishing for whiting at Folkestone, a great 'man-sucker' (as the octopus is there called by the fishermen) came floating past the boat, and I put my hand and arm into the water in his way. In an instant the long arms were coiled round my hand, quick as the end of a driving-whip twists round a gig shaft." Some accidental "attacks" during the breeding season are apparently due to octopuses mistaking a part of human anatomy for another octopus, as a sexually excited toad will seize a finger placed near it. Squids will very occasionally attack a rowing boat, possibly thinking it is an outsize fish.

Even a small octopus has surprising strength and tenacity. J. Stevenson-Hamilton tells me that while bathing in shallow water in the South of France he was seized by an octopus. Its grip was so strong that he had to exert considerable force to break it, and when he had stripped off one arm another took its place. When he was finally free of the octopus and examined it he found it spanned about 18 in.

A man may weigh twenty times as much as an octopus but he is at a serious disadvantage in water, and the octopus is very much at home. A consideration of the physics of the matter makes clear the extent of the octopus's advantage in any under-sea battle with a man. Providing he doesn't struggle, the body of a man weighing 200 pounds can be held below the surface by a pull of about ten pounds. But a medium-sized octopus with a span of six to eight feet can exert a holding force several times greater than this, so that if such an octopus, securely anchored to rocks with several arms, seized a strong heavy man under water, the sheer physical odds would be very much against him. Even if he were struggling violently there would still be an ample margin in favor of the octopus. The arms can grasp their prey so firmly that they will often remain in position after they have been torn from the octopus's living flesh.

What does it feel like to be gripped by an octopus? Joseph Sinel thought the skin felt like "damp kid leather," and others have described the feel of the suckers as a "creepy sensation." Lee, who handled scores of octopuses, never quite, I think, overcame a slight feeling of repulsion. "To have the long, cold, damp arms of an octopus writhing and twining about one's wrist and hand, and fastening its hundreds of sucking cups all over them, gives a singularly uncomfortable sensation."

In view of the widespread skepticism about their danger I have endeavored to find authentic examples of attacks by octopuses. I have deliberately omitted a number of old attacks, such as the oft-told story of the attack on a diver off Melbourne on November 4, 1879. (See John Gibson.) I have concentrated on finding comparatively recent accounts which can be more easily checked. Had I persevered longer I should no doubt have found more, but I have sufficient to prove that octopuses are sometimes dangerous to man.

Several people answered my letters in the Press asking for authentic accounts of dangerous encounters with cephalopods.

D. H. Norrie told me that in 1940 he was in Poverty Bay, New Zealand, where a large rock shelf is uncovered at low water. One day he and several Maori friends were wading up to their armpits in one of the channels which traverse the shelf, searching for "sea eggs" (echinoderms) and lobsters in the crevices.

"One friend suddenly began shrieking and trying to free himself from something that was holding him fast. We moved over to help him and found him to be struggling with a young octopus. By peeling the tentacles off his bare body we managed to free him, and were only too pleased to leave the animal to its own devices! Where the suckers had been on my friend's body, were left round reddish patches where the blood had been sucked to the surface. Although the animal would have measured no more than 36 in. across the tentacles, the boy would have been unable to free himself unaided, and would have drowned when the tide came in. In this case, I do not think it to be an attack by the octopus, as I think its reactions were mainly defensive."

The same explanation cannot be given of the account sent to me by John C. Rau. During the First World War he was one of a party of boys, in charge of a parson, who were tramping along a stretch of the Victorian coast, near Cape Otway, Australia. Rau says that although it happened so long ago the incident is still quite vivid in his memory.

"We were proceeding along the sea edge at the base of cliffs and bluffs, a jumble of rocks, some stratified and shelving. I was about six or seven paces behind the parson, who was leading, when I heard him shout and looked toward him. He was standing on a shelf of rock about three feet above the water and about a foot from the edge. An octopus had left the water and attacked him. Its tentacles were in rapid motion, at least one around each leg and one at his waist and arm. I judged them to be about four feet long and as thick as a man's arm at the base. The body of the octopus was well out of the water and almost at the edge of the rock shelf.

"The parson was jabbing at the octopus with the butt of his fishing rod, and leaning back against the drag of the creature which seemed to be well anchored by other tentacles going down into the water. I did a very stupid thing. I was carrying a .22 rifle and took a pot shot at the octopus and fortunately missed both it and the parson. After jabbing at the creature for perhaps 20 seconds, during which it squirted its black discharge over the rock and the legs of the parson, he was free and it went back into the sea taking with it the bottom section of the parson's fishing rod. It released this almost immediately and it was recovered by means of the line.

"I often wonder what would have been the fate of one of us boys had we been alone and attacked in this way. The youngest of us was about 12 years of age. I was 15 or 16 at the time.

"There is one curious thing that has always puzzled me. It was high summer at the time and early in the afternoon, tide commencing to flow and the sea calm. At that time of the year the rocks in that region were made so hot by the sun that they were almost unbearable to naked feet, yet that creature did not seem to be affected by the heat of the rock surface over which it attacked." (The octopodan disregard of pain when excited is dealt with on p. 92.)

I have had correspondence with an eye-witness of another attack which might well have been fatal if help had not been at hand. In January 1920 Mrs. C. Tattersall Dodd, the wife of one of the masters of Tonbridge School, in England, was bathing in a secluded bay on the Mediterranean coast of France near San Tropez. When the water was just above her knees an octopus darted from under a rock and fastened an arm round her foot, holding it immovable. Then several more arms shot out and gripped her leg. Mrs. Dodd was then held so securely that she was helpless. Fortunately her brother-in-law and his wife—Mrs. H. M. Lawson Dodd—were on the shore and the victim's cries quickly brought them to her aid. (Sam Dunton records a similar incident from Florida where a comparatively small octopus held a youth immovable in shallow water.)

Mrs. Lawson Dodd tells me:

"I happened to have a pointed stick and remembering Victor Hugo I stuck the point into the octopus's eye and it let go. Later my husband and I went back with a couple of sticks, hooked the creature out and beat it up to the shore where we killed it. Spread out it measured five feet four inches from tip to tip of the tentacles. It was about the weight of a rabbit. When it was dead I stuck my finger into one of the little round cups on a tentacle and the suction was quite incredible." Mrs. Dodd adds: "Still more incredible were the stories manufactured by the press, enlarging from paper to paper, until it was two lovely young Americans being dragged to a watery grave by an octopus with tentacles forty feet long!"

Here was an octopus, weighing only a few pounds and with arms not more than 30 in. long, which attacked without provocation and, had help not been near, might well have held its victim until she collapsed and drowned. Guy Gilpatric says: "I have heard of people wading at low tide being seized and held helpless for hours until the tide rose over them, and I know from almost daily tussles with him that even in his medium development the octopus is far stronger than a man." And Sir Grenville Temple records that a soldier was drowned while bathing off Southern Tunisia when he was seized by an octopus in water "scarcely four feet in depth."

No more dangerous than a pumpkin?

Sir Arthur Grimble records another encounter with an octopus in shallow water which could have had fatal results. He was wading on the lip of the reef at Ocean Island in the Gilbert Archipelago, South Pacific, when he saw a native trying to beach his canoe. The native stood on the reef, knee-deep in water, to drag the canoe over the edge. But as Grimble watched, the native became rooted to the spot. The canoe washed away from him and, with legs braced, he appeared to be tugging desperately to free himself from invisible hands.

Then Grimble caught a glimpse of the tapered tip of an arm curled round the native's right wrist. He had chosen to land the canoe on top of an octopus' lair. Grimble ran to his aid, but before he reached him the native gave one desperate last tug and broke away. But as the suckers were wrenched free they left a bloody bangle encircling his wrist where the skin had stripped off in one piece. When the mechanism of cephalopod suckers is borne in mind the injury to the native's wrist is understandable (see page 21).

Thor Heyerdahl had a similar experience to Grimble's native

near Raroia Reef in the South Pacific where the *Kon-Tiki* ran aground. He was wading towards an island when he suddenly felt his ankle gripped on each side and held tight. He jerked his foot as hard as he could and the octopus, which measured barely three feet, followed it without letting go.

"It must have been the bandage on my foot which attracted it. I dragged myself in jerks towards the beach with the disgusting carcase hanging on to my foot. Only when I reached the edge of the dry sand did it let go and retreat slowly through the shallow water, with arms outstretched and eyes directed shoreward, as though ready for a new attack if I wanted one. When I threw a few lumps of coral at it it darted away."

William Wyatt Gill describes another way in which an octopus can be dangerous to a man in water. When he was in the South Seas one of his native servants went out in a canoe with his son. Leaving the boy in charge of the canoe the native dived overboard to try to catch an octopus. He was gone a long time, and the son wondered what was happening. At last the father broke surface, and his son at once saw that his face was blanketed by an octopus, and he could not breathe. The boy immediately grasped his father's mass of woolly hair with one hand, and with the other stripped the octopus off his face and whisked the animal into the canoe.

"But for this timely aid the old man must have been suffocated, as was actually the case many years ago with a man who foolishly went alone. . . . It has been disputed in Europe whether the octopus ever attacks human beings. No native of Polynesia doubts the fact. A fisherman rarely goes alone in quest of octopi; he has usually a trusty friend in the canoe to take care of it." In his book Gill recounts several other instances of attacks which came to his attention during the twenty-odd years he spent in the South Seas.

Several divers claim to have had dangerous encounters with octopuses. During the Second World War, however, neither the British Admiralty nor the U.S. Navy Department thought the danger warranted any instructions being issued to frogmen about them. Bruce S. Wright, who was in charge of the Sea Reconnaissance Unit of Combined Operations Command for the last two and a half years of the war, tells me:

"I undertook a study of all marine fauna that were potentially

dangerous to man. Shark attacks were easy to find, and a few bar-
racuda attacks, but I did not find one case of a fatality due to an
octopus. However in the Pacific where large specimens are known
some of the American frogmen just did not return from missions,
and it was known that their loss was not due to enemy action. Of
course it is not known whether or not an octopus was responsible,
but crawling around coral reefs in the dark is as good a way to
meet one as I know."

Whatever the truth may be about frogmen, there seems no
doubt that divers sometimes meet large octopuses, although I
think the danger has been overemphasized. I once had a conver-
sation with an experienced deep sea diver who had operated
throughout the world. He said that although he had met octopuses he had never been in danger from one. Moreover, he said
that he had never met a fellow diver who had been attacked.

Despite this diver's experience I think it is true that occasionally divers have battles with large octopuses. It must be remembered that these outsize animals live well below the surface
where, of course, divers operate. It is expecting too much of human nature to imagine that the accounts of battles are told without any adornment, but the basic facts are dramatic enough.

John D. Craig, a deep sea diver and Hollywood camera technician, was diving off San Benito Island, Lower California, and
found a deep rocky hole about 40 ft. in diameter. He clambered
down for some 20 ft., and then stood on a shelf of rock. Peering
downwards he saw two large octopuses which appeared to swarm
over the entire bottom of the hole.

Craig's first impulse was to get out as fast as he could, but he remembered the advice of the local Japanese divers. "Don't move
when an octopus takes hold of you. It will get excited and attack
if you struggle. But if you remain perfectly still the chances are it
will merely touch you here and there with a tentacle [arm] to satisfy its curiosity and will then move away." Craig adds that this
warning saved him dozens of times.

With considerable self-restraint Craig remained motionless
while the larger of the two octopuses, now aware of his presence,
extended an arm and began feeling his leg. After a short while the
octopus appeared to lose interest and withdrew its arm. Craig
thought now was the time to go. He unhooked his lead shoes, in-

flated his diving suit and started for the surface. But he made his move too soon; the octopus hadn't done with him yet. As he rose from the rocky shelf a long arm shot upwards and twined round his ankle. Luckily the octopus was resting only in loose gravel and was not anchored by its other arms to its rocky fastness. It was this fortunate circumstance which probably saved Craig's life.

As he shot to the surface the octopus was jerked off the bottom and in the few seconds it took Craig to reach the surface it had swarmed all over him. His attendants immediately attacked the octopus with axes and hacked off several arms. Craig preserved one of these. It measured 8 ft. 2 in.—so this octopus must have spanned some 18 ft.

Victor Berge, a Swedish pearl diver of many years' experience, had a battle with an octopus when he was 19 which taught him a healthy respect for the creatures for the rest of his diving life. In the Macassar Strait, between Borneo and Celebes, he descended to about 120 ft. As he was stooping to pick up a shell he felt a light touch on his left arm. Instinctively he drew his razor-sharp knife from his belt and slashed. The blow severed two arms of a giant octopus which was just about to pinion Berge's arms. Immediately two more arms snaked out and gripped his ankles, nearly jerking him to the ground.

Each time he bent to cut his ankles free the octopus wrenched so violently that his head banged against the heavy helmet. He hit a rock so hard that the breath was knocked from his body, and he nearly lost consciousness. He decided to give the diver's S O S— four pulls on the rope, signaling: "Pull till the line breaks."

He stretched up his hand to give the signal but couldn't make it. Just at that moment the octopus gave a sudden pull which dragged him a dozen feet and all but sent him sprawling. Only ten minutes or so had gone by since the octopus first gripped him, but he had received such a battering that he knew he would lose consciousness any moment—and that would be the end.

"I knew I was going. Just before a wave of unconsciousness swept over me I threw up my arms, caught both lines, and gave four frantic pulls. There was an instant when I had the sensation of being pulled in two. Then I knew nothing."

On the deck of the lugger from which Berge was operating was his Polynesian friend Ro. He could see nothing of the struggle on the sea floor, but he sensed that something was wrong. The moment he got the signal he pulled, but nothing budged. Another man joined him but still the rope would not give. A third man pulled on the rope, but all their strength failed to free Berge from the Herculean power that held him.

Obviously something more than man-power was wanted if help were to come in time. Ro noticed that the lugger was rising and falling on the swell and that gave him the idea that saved Berge's life. Just as the lugger was at the bottom of a surge Ro made several turns with the rope round a stout stanchion. The ocean swell picked her up, and the terrific force on the two taut lines jerked Berge towards the surface.

But the octopus had not released its victim. As Berge regained consciousness he saw that the arms were still fast to his ankles, and that the octopus, although free of its anchorage, was struggling to prevent his escape. He was hanging helpless about six or seven feet below the surface, the center of a macabre tug-o'-war. The two men were trying to haul him up, the octopus was trying to drag him back. But Ro could now see Berge, and he slipped into the water and fastened a rope round his body. As the men hauled on this Ro went down again and cut the arms from Berge's ankles.

"There was not much life left in me as they hauled me aboard. Round my boots were traces of the [arms], now glued to them. My face, neck and shoulders were all bloody from the blows against the helmet and the breastplate; my arms and legs were covered with scratches from the coral reefs. My friends thought I would die, but after an hour I recovered and screamed and cried like a hysterical woman."

At least two other divers have had somewhat similar experiences. One was a Japanese diver who was seized by a large octopus near South Goulburn Island, off Arnhem Land, Australia. (George Herbert Sunter.) And Virgil Burford was an eye-witness of a tug-o'-war between a diver and his crew and a large octopus in Alaskan waters that lasted for three hours.

Henry J. Bruce, a Royal Naval diver, had a weird—as well as dangerous—experience with an octopus while searching the sea floor, some 40 ft. down off Gibraltar. A practice torpedo had been lost and Bruce went down to find it. He found plenty of other things—"the usual old pots, pans, and bits of scrap-iron"—but no sign of the torpedo.

As Bruce looked around he saw a suit of overalls lying in a shapeless heap on the bottom. Hardly thinking what he was doing he grasped one of the sleeves. He got the shock of his diver's life. The suit began to move. It reared up and swayed before him like a grotesque ballet-dancer. Bruce says: "I was literally paralyzed with fear."

Then something happened which—again literally—jerked him out of his stupor. He felt something wrap itself round his right ankle and give it a vicious tug. Bruce then knew the explanation of the *danse macabre*. A large octopus had made its home in the overalls and he had disturbed it.

He dropped on his left knee, drew his heavy knife and jabbed at the arm holding his right ankle. The octopus reacted violently. The suit of overalls was whirled away, and for the first time Bruce saw his enemy. He had a momentary vision of a shadowy body behind a mass of waving arms then everything was blotted out as the octopus discharged its ink.

Bruce managed to move in close to its body and stabbed it repeatedly with all his strength. For a few moments the octopus fought back, and shook Bruce as a terrier shakes a rat. Then it weakened and he was able to tear himself free, and was hauled up.

Are there authentic accounts of octopuses deliberately attacking man? Gilpatric thinks there are and cites several experiences of his own and his fellow gogglers as evidence.

One day while fishing under water Gilpatric speared an octopus spanning eight feet. He missed the vital spot and the octopus looked so threatening that Gilpatric let go his spear and swam quickly away. Just before he surfaced he looked back. "From the under-side of the big fellow, thrashing around with the spear stuck in him, there came another octopus, about a yard across. He rocketed straight for me, grabbed my arm at the biceps and pinned it to my side with tentacles stuck across my back and chest." Gilpatric killed it with his knife. This octopus was being eaten by the one he had speared. Why then did it act as it did?

Death by drowning is not the only danger from octopuses, although it is by far the most common hazard of their admittedly infrequent battles with humans. Although the well-known species rarely bite when handled, they do sometimes, and pain and very rarely death may result. Such effects appear to be due to the poisonous secretion which the octopus uses to kill its prey (see page 28). Bruce W. Halstead and S. Stillman Berry have dealt with this aspect of the octopodan danger. Halstead is a Doctor of Medicine, and a specialist in medical zoology. The writers deal specifically with six case histories and refer to several other accounts. Halstead says that marine zoologists who have worked in the tropical Pacific have reported occasional instances of natives being bitten by small octopuses.

Mrs. Giles W. Mead was bitten by an octopus spanning only six or seven inches, which she was holding on the palm of her hand. She said it felt "like a mild bee sting." There was moderate bleeding from the tiny clean-cut wound but no other after-effects.

But Fred Herms, Jr., an attendant at the Steinhart Aquarium in San Francisco, had more serious symptoms after being bitten by an octopus with a 12-in. span. Herms took the octopus from one of the stock tanks, and as he did so it bit him near the middle of the back of his right hand. He received two small wounds, the size of pinheads, which bled excessively for 20 minutes. There was a tingling sensation and the pain, which was comparable to a bee sting but more intense, continued for about an hour.

Herms' hand began to swell immediately. For the next three days there was a clear serous discharge but no sign of secondary infection. The swelling gradually subsided over a period of ten days, during which the area of the wound was painful to touch.

Donald A. Simpson, of the same aquarium, was also bitten by an octopus of about the same size. Simpson placed it on the back of his left hand and while it was being photographed he felt a sharp scratch. His symptoms were similar to those of Herms', and although not so severe, the swelling did not finally subside until a month later. Writing some three weeks after being bitten Simpson said: "My hand is still swollen; it is red and inflamed; it still feels sore and itches like a chronic mosquito bite." He adds that there was a colored ring round the area of the actual bite.

Perhaps the most interesting case history that Berry and Halstead report is that of Harvey Bullis. He was walking along the exposed sand flats on the ocean side of Biscayne Key, Florida, when he saw a small cockle (*Laevicardium*) in a tide-pool.

"It readily opened when I twisted the valves, breaking the hinge, and a small octopus emerged and crawled up the index finger of my left hand. The shell was perhaps 1½ in. in length, and the octopus about one inch from arm-tip to arm-tip.

"Its small size and interesting movements of locomotion held me quite fascinated while it made its way to the knuckle of my middle finger. There it attached itself by expanding its arms and suckers and clamping down with amazing pressure. At this same instant I felt a sharp pain, comparable I imagine, to being stuck with a hot pin, in the skin over the knuckle. Although the pain was not excruciating, it so startled me that I briskly brushed the octopus off with my other hand, tearing off a few of its arms in the process.

"Although the animal was thus removed the pain persisted for several minutes. Within a minute or two a small red dot appeared where the bite occurred. I noticed no blood or evident breaking of the skin, although this must have occurred if only microscopically. . . . The pain of the bite quite disappeared within an hour or two and the red dot had turned bluish. I had almost forgotten the incident when, some five or six days later, an annoying itching sensation developed at the point of the bite, while the dot had turned reddish again. This itching sensation continued for about a month and finally disappeared. The red mark persisted for almost a year although I felt no further irritation from it."

Berry and Halstead say that the relatively extensive effects from the bite of such a tiny octopus appear to be without parallel. The animal would presumably have grown much larger and its bite accordingly more severe. "Indeed, should such species as the gigantic octopods of the west American and Japanese coasts prove to possess venomous properties at all proportionate to their formidable size, the danger to a diver from entanglement with one of them may be of a different character and potentially much more serious than even the imaginative writers of popular sea yarns have conceived."

The authors thus summarize the case histories reviewed in their papers:

"Symptoms consisted of a sharp pain upon contact (described as similar to a bee sting), tingling, throbbing, redness, swelling, and in one case abnormally profuse bleeding. Symptoms seem to vary considerably, depending upon the size and possibly the species of octopus, the size of the wound, and doubtless the amount of venom injected. Octopus bites are of the puncture wound variety and with the smaller animals commonly handled are relatively minor in nature. The venom is secreted by the anterior and posterior salivary glands."

Some octopuses appear to be "quicker on the bite" than the species dealt with by Halstead and Berry. K. Virabhadra Rao tells me the fishermen in the Madras area of India say that all the octopuses "are capable of biting viciously when handled carelessly and the wounds they make are severe and do not easily heal, probably because of some poison."

James Hornell (1917), writing of the same area, reports that the fishermen fear a small octopus known as the "poisonous kanavai." He does not give the species. The fishermen claim that this octopus is very active, and if not thrown overboard at once, it will try to fasten on a leg or foot and bite through the skin. The pain is like the sting of a scorpion and if untreated the leg swells and the victim feels giddy. The effects may last for months.

On September 18, 1954,[1] Kirke Dyson-Holland, a 21-year-old seaman and member of the Arafura Skindivers' Club, went spearfishing off East Point, near Darwin, Australia. With him was John Baylis, another member of the club. As they were coming ashore for a rest Baylis saw a blue octopus, spanning about six inches, swimming near him. Both men had handled such octopuses before without any ill effects.

Baylis caught the octopus and let it crawl over his arms and shoulders. He then threw it to Dyson-Holland and it lodged on his shoulder. It crawled over his back, stopping for a short while high up near his spine. Then it dropped into the water and the men came ashore without it.

Almost as soon as they landed Dyson-Holland complained that his mouth was very dry and he was having difficulty in swallowing. He made no complaint of being bitten, although Baylis noticed that there was a small puncture wound with a trickle of blood on his back, where the octopus had paused before dropping off.

---

[1] The date given in the medical report by Flecker and Cotton is wrong.

Dyson-Holland's condition quickly deteriorated. He vomited, swayed about as he tried to walk, then collapsed into a sitting position and became rapidly weaker. He was carried to a car and taken to Darwin Hospital, four miles away. Baylis heard him say: "It was the little octopus. It was the little octopus."

On the way to the hospital Dyson-Holland was only semi-conscious and on arrival he was blue and had stopped breathing, although his heart was still beating. He was given emergency treatment, including injection of adrenalin, and was placed in an iron lung. But a quarter of an hour after being admitted to the hospital, and less than two hours after being bitten, he was dead.

An autopsy was performed. The mark on his back where he had been bitten had faded and could not be found. No organic disease was found, but it was known that Dyson-Holland suffered mildly from asthma. H. Flecker and Bernard C. Cotton, who reported this case in *The Medical Journal of Australia* for August 27, 1955, say: "Although his symptoms are not typical of allergic response, the possibility of some hypersensitivity reaction exists." (See also Hugh Mabbet.)

The octopus involved in this fatality—the only proved case of a human being dying after a bite from a cephalopod—was not kept, and its identification is not certain. It was alleged to be *Octopus rugosus*, but Grace Pickford, who is an authority on the genus, tells me this name is not valid and has been used indiscriminately for a variety of specimens belonging to other species.

What is the best thing to do if an octopus attacks, deliberately or not? Benjamin Franklin is supposed to have said that a few drops of vinegar sprinkled on the back of the animal persuades it to release its hold immediately. Lee, who quotes this remark, says that no doubt the application of a red-hot poker would have the same result. But as octopuses have been known to walk through beach fires, even this drastic treatment might not be effective! The best general rule to remember is that if an octopus is grasped firmly round its "neck"—the junction between head and mantle— it will instantly release its hold, as this action suffocates it.

Jabbing at the eyes with a stick sometimes makes an octopus let go. If a knife is handy, strong downward jabs *between* the eyes sever the main nerve-center and kill the octopus instantly. Fishermen sometimes use their teeth for this purpose, turning the arms back over the head and biting hard into the brain. They also kill octopuses by "turning the cap."

I have heard that some divers equip themselves with a "Nitric Gun": a plunger pistol loaded with glass-encased cartridges of nitric acid. When in danger of an attack the diver "fires" one of these cartridges. As the acid-impregnated water enters the octopus's gills it either fatally injures it or drives it away.

Although a good deal has been written about the danger of tangling with octopuses, a few people have made it a profitable pastime. When Roy Campbell was a boy in South Africa he and four friends used to stage octopus fights. They caught the octopuses along a rocky shore-line near Durban, put them in a basket and then went to the seaside swimming pools at the nearby holiday resorts. An octopus would be slipped into the pool while they were swimming, and one of them would give an agitated shout: "Hey, people, look out! There's a big animal in the water there. It sucks all the blood out of your veins." Pretending to panic they clambered out, thus encouraging the other swimmers to quit the pool. Soon they had a ready-made audience for the "show."

In the pool there was virtually nothing to fear from a small octopus, but the boys stage-managed it so well that it looked as if there were mortal danger. Leaving one of their companions on the side to point out where it was, the other four intrepid octopus-killers dived in. Struggling through the octopus's defensive cloud, they drove it to the shallow end and then one of them let it grip him. The sight of the boy with the loathsome creature's arms swarming over him, his mock terror and heart-rending cries for help ("It's strangling me and sucking all my blood!"), and the pretended helplessness of his companions to rescue him from a ghastly death, ensured that not a spectator moved away.

Then the boys really piled on the bogus horrors. Pretending to pluck up courage they seized the arms and tugged them off their companion's quivering flesh. The suckers tore loose with a squelching smack, and reddish (harmless) blisters were marked on the boy's skin. Then one of the boys surreptitiously emptied a bottle of red ink—previously secreted under his swimsuit—and they rolled about in the shallows in a welter of "bloody" foam.

The finale of the macabre display was in true Grand Guignol

tradition. The victim grasped his tormentor and, to the accompaniment of a sickening plop, "turned its cap."

After the demise of the villain the hat was passed round and, if the offerings were satisfactory, the show was repeated. Campbell says:

"We had such a success with this act that it made no difference whether the visitors knew it was staged from the beginning or not. They would clamor for the show as soon as they saw us coming with our baskets; and then they would want one encore after another, till our octopuses were finished. Some days we had 15 dollars or so in the kitty. The clowns and jugglers came to hate us at all the resorts."

Such was the youth of one of our modern lyric poets.

Some skindivers who operate in Puget Sound, Washington, have also tangled with octopuses for amusement. The divers, who call themselves the Puget Sound Mudsharks, equip themselves with rubber diving suits and aqualungs, and descend some 80 ft. to the bottom of the Sound. Some very large octopuses live here: I have seen a photograph of one (*Octopus hongkongensis?*) reputed to weigh 125 pounds.

The divers usually descend in pairs, wrestle an octopus from its lair and bring it to the beach alive. The animals are then usually freed. "Octopus wrestling" has become so popular that in 1957 a contest was held between skindiving clubs. Formal rules were drawn up and divers from Washington, Oregon and Canada competed. Fourteen octopuses were landed during this event.

Bill Barada, who filmed divers in action, thus describes how one octopus was captured.

"Ted Rothlisburger spotted an octopus in the rocks and called the whole group over to watch the catch. While we hovered motionless over the hole, Ted demonstrated that it is almost impossible to pull an octopus out of his lair without help. He reached into the hole and grabbed the creature and pulled with all his might without success. The octopus stretched like a giant rubber band until it slipped from his grip and snapped back into its den. Ted had no trouble freeing himself as the octopus made no attempt to hold him. Probably it was too surprised and frightened, only thinking of escape from attack.

"Then Ted put a special bait into and around the hole. I am not at liberty to tell the bait used. I then witnessed the most weird performance I have seen in all my years underwater. While we hung suspended above the lair, the tentacles began to emerge. They came wiggling out around the entrance like so many giant snakes. Gradually, more and more of their length cautiously emerged, feeling carefully all around the area. Even with several divers in the water with me the sight sent chills creeping up my spine.

"When the body crawled clear of the den, Ted made a quick grab at the head and jerked the entire animal clear of the rocks. From then on it was only a question of wrestling him until he became exhausted. This one was subdued quickly as it was termed a 'baby' of only ten feet."

Gene Daniels has also written of the exploits of the Puget Sound Mudsharks, illustrating his account with his own photographs. In one battle he witnessed the octopus jerked the mouthpiece of the aqualung from a diver's mouth. When this octopus was finally landed it spanned 15 ft. 8 in.

Cuttlefish and squids are more apt to bite than octopuses. Gilpatric says that he never met anyone who had been bitten by an octopus but in his experience a cuttlefish will readily take a bite at a finger. The British zoologist, J. L. Cloudsley-Thompson, tells me that he has been bitten by sepiolas (*Sepiola*) which he has caught in a shrimping net. Although only two inches overall they "can produce quite a sharp prick." The bite from a common squid (*Loligo*) has been likened to "a cut from a pair of scissors."

When Thor Heyerdahl and his companions were making preliminary enquiries for their epic crossing of the Pacific on their raft *Kon-Tiki*, they were warned by the officials of the National Geographic Society and the Peruvian marine experts that the most dangerous sea creatures they would encounter were the large squids of the Humboldt Current.

"We were reminded that they lay floating in the darkness with phosphorescent eyes, and that their arms were long enough to feel about in every small corner of the raft, if they did not care to come right on board. We did not at all like the prospect of feeling cold arms round our necks, dragging us out of our sleeping bags at night, and we provided ourselves with saber-like machete knives, one for each of us, in case we should wake to the embrace of groping tentacles."

Had the worst happened, and giant squids (*Architeuthis*) had attacked, the world would probably never have heard of the *Kon-Tiki*. Fortunately they had visits from only the smaller species. But although no large squid molested them they were nearby. "We saw the shine of phosphorescent eyes drifting on the surface on dark nights, and on one occasion we saw the sea boil and bubble as something like a big wheel came up and rotated in the air, while some of our dolphins [the fish, *Coryphaena*] tried to escape by hurling themselves desperately through space."

The best account I know of the rapacious behavior of the Humboldt Current squids (*Ommastrephes gigas*) is that of David D. Duncan. This has already been referred to in describing the experiences of the Michael Lerner Expedition while fishing for large squids off the coast of Peru. When the Peruvian member of the crew knew that they intended to fish for the *jibia* he was nervous; and he was a brave man. They had seen him dive into shark-infested waters and put the gaff into a harpooned manta ray, but he was frankly afraid to tackle the squids, saying to Duncan: "These are not fish, or animal, but demon."

The tiniest scrap of food thrown overboard was the signal for a rush by hordes of squid. So many of them tried to take the bait that the only difficulty was to get it to the depths where the real giants lived. As it was, the largest "giant" they caught was only a nine-foot 100-pounder—a mere pygmy compared to a real kraken (see page 212). Subsequent fishermen, however, have caught Humboldt Current squids measuring about 12 ft. overall and weighing some 300 pounds.

Often the extra-tough wire leader was bitten clean through by a horny beak. When a squid was securely hooked it at once became the target for a horde of its cannibalistic brethren. A man who fell overboard in such waters would not last half a minute. Bill Ackerman, in his account of the expedition, says a flailing tentacle that lashed one of the crew's arms "left it gouged and bleeding from elbow to wrist."

There are two records which show how formidable large squids can be in actual combat with man.

On April 18, 1921, the Cunard liner *Caronia* (the first) ran into a gale when two days out of Queenstown during an east-west crossing of the Atlantic. After she had shipped a particularly heavy sea over the forecastle, the carpenter went to see if any damage had been done—and found a large squid wedged between two winches. The carpenter went too close and the squid shot out its tentacles and grappled with him. The newspaper reports vary [1] —they were based on eye-witness accounts when the ship landed —but *The Times* (April 26, 1921) said that the carpenter struck back with an iron bar, and after a violent struggle killed the squid and freed himself. According to *The New York Times* (April 25, 1921), members of the crew and some of the passengers helped in the fight which lasted ten minutes.

The squid, which weighed 40 pounds and measured some 12 ft. overall, was put in the ship's cold-storage room. It was intended for the Liverpool Museum when the *Caronia* returned to England. The Museum authorities inform me, however, that they have no record of it there now. But the Cunard Steam-Ship Company at Liverpool have confirmed that the incident occurred, and it was reported at the time in various newspapers on both sides of the Atlantic. Mr. E. B. Diggle, son of the captain of the *Caronia*, informs me that some photographs were taken but he cannot trace them now. He says: "I remember the incident very well indeed."

The other encounter, one of the most macabre cephalopod stories I know, occurred during a horrifying experience in the Second World War. When the troopship *Britannia* was in the Central Atlantic, 1,400 miles west of Freetown, she was attacked and sunk on March 25, 1941, by the German raider *Santa Cruz*. Lieutenant R. E. G. Cox, as he then was, and eleven other men, clung to a raft "no bigger than a hearthrug." The men took it in turns to sit on the raft, while the others clung to it with only their head and shoulders above water.

One night a large squid threw its tentacles round a sailor, broke his hold on the raft and pulled him under. He was not seen again. Shortly afterwards Cox was attacked. He tells me:

[1] One said that the squid attacked the carpenter with its cuttlebone!

"A tentacle quickly twisted around my leg and caused terrible pain. It removed itself almost immediately afterwards but left me in agony. This pain I think was caused by the suckers in the tentacle for later the next day I noticed that where it had gripped me large ulcers had formed, and after I was rescued I remember the constant treatment which was given me for these ulcers which seemed to eat right into the flesh and were red and raw. I still have these marks to this day" (1956). Cloudsley-Thompson, who examined Cox's leg some two years after the attack, tells me that the circular scars were the size of a quarter dollar.

Cox lived to tell the tale because after five days in the water a Spanish ship found the raft—and three survivors, Cox and two naval officers. The story was reported in the *News Chronicle* for October 21, 1941, and the *Illustrated London News* for November 1, 1941.

Twelve KRAKEN

Stories of a giant many-armed sea creature occur in the ancient literature of several maritime nations. The earliest European reference, perhaps the earliest in the world, is in Homer's *Odyssey*, written at least 700 years before the birth of Christ. Describing Odysseus' encounter with Scylla, the inhabitant of the sea cavern, Homer says she was a terrifying sight and

> Round her a dozen of feet she is always waving suspended
> Six long sinuous necks outstretching before her and each one
> Beareth a head terrific with teeth in a threefold order,
> Many and thickly arrayed. . . .

Part of the monster's body hid in the cave and several

> . . . heads she extendeth
> Hunting for fish at the foot of the rock and peering
> around it. . . .
> [Free translation quoted by Willy Ley.]

Here are definite, if exaggerated, references to a cephalopod. The lair in the cavern, the ugly appearance, the nervous play of the arms, the numerous suckers which are certainly "many and thickly arrayed," and the watchful appearance with arms at the ready, point unmistakably to a large octopus.

The many-headed Hydra which Hercules fought may also have been a cephalopod. In the representation of this battle in several of the Roman terra-cotta statues in the Campagna and Vatican Museums, Hydra is clearly a large octopus, although the number of arms varies somewhat from those on the living animal.

Pliny also tells of a "polyp" which raided the fishponds of Carteia, now known as Rocadillo, in Spain. Dogs were set on it which it "now scourged with the ends of its tentacles and now struck with its longer arms, which it used as clubs; and with difficulty they succeeded in despatching it with a number of three-pronged harpoons." When the "polyp" was examined afterwards it was found to have arms "knotted like clubs, 30 ft. long, with suckers or cups." Despite obviously mythical elements in the story, its foundation seems to have been an adventure with a large cephalopod.

These Greek legends are the earliest references to a many-armed sea beast and they almost certainly refer to a large octopus. This, however, is not the true kraken, although such legends can hardly be omitted from an historical survey of the subject.

The first definite references to the kraken are contained in Norwegian literature. In fact the name is derived from the Norwegian dialect word *krake*, the *n* denoting the definite article.

The earliest identifiable reference appears to be by Olaus Magnus who, in a history of the northern nations published in 1555, refers to "monstrous fish on the Coasts or Sea of Norway" and says: "Their Forms are horrible, their Heads square, all set with prickles, and they have sharp and long horns round about, like a Tree rooted up by the Roots [1] . . . one of these Sea-Monsters will drown easily many great ships provided with many strong Mariners." Magnus also refers to the beast's huge eyes and the unusual size of the head compared with the rest of the body. Apart from obvious exaggerations the "monstrous fish" is clearly a huge cephalopod.

Magnus was the last archbishop of the Swedish Roman Catholic Church, and was for years Archbishop of Upsala. He was an assiduous but uncritical collector of other men's tales. His account of the kraken seems to have come from men who had seen it—and had been badly frightened.

Two hundred years after Magnus another ecclesiastic, the Protestant Bishop Erik Pontoppidan, wrote at length about the kraken in his *Natural History of Norway*, the English edition of which was published in 1755. In fact he has been falsely accused of inventing the monster. He recounts various tales which, while containing gross exaggeration, obviously refer to giant cephalopods.

[1] One of the meanings of *krake* is "a stunted tree." Quotations from English edition (1658).

He reports the stranding of a kraken, a well-known occurrence with large cephalopods, which bears evidence of coming from an eye-witness.

"In the year 1680, a Krake (perhaps a young and foolish one) came into the water that runs between the rocks and cliffs in the parish of Alstahoug, though the general custom of that creature is to keep always several leagues from land, and therefore of course they must die there. It happened that its extended long arms, or antennae, which this creature seems to use like the snail, in turning about, caught hold of some trees standing near the water, which might easily have been torn up by the roots; but beside this, as it was found afterwards, he entangled himself in some openings or clefts in the rock, and therein stuck so fast, and hung so unfortunately, that he could not work himself out, but perished and putrefied on the spot. The carcass, which was a long while decaying, and filled a great part of that narrow channel, made it almost impassable by its intolerable stench."

Pontoppidan summarizes his account of the kraken in these words:

"We learn from all this that the Polype or Starfish have amongst their various species some that are much larger than others; and, according to all appearance, amongst the very largest inhabitants of the ocean. If the axiom be true that greatness or littleness makes no change in the species, then this Krake must be of the Polypus kind, notwithstanding its enormous size."

In 1735 Carl von Linnaeus published the first edition of his *Systema Naturae*, the pioneer work which introduced system into the nomenclature of the animal world. In this work he included the kraken, and gave it the specific name *Sepia microcosmos*. But he omitted it from subsequent editions.

The scene now shifts to the France of the early 19th century where Pierre Denys de Montfort played the kraken story for all it was worth—and a lot more. Denys de Montfort worked in the Museum of Natural History in Paris, and wrote a book on systematic conchology. But the book which made him notorious was his *Histoire Naturelle générale et particulière des Mollusques*, published in six volumes between 1802 and 1805.

In this work Denys de Montfort shamelessly mixed science with fantasy. He invented a *Poulpe colossal* and said that it wrapped its

tentacles round the masts of a vessel and was on the point of dragging it to the bottom when the crew saved themselves by cutting
off its immense arms with cutlasses and hatchets. Not content with
that, which may, as will be seen later, have had *some* foundation
in fact, he then asserted that a horde of giant cephalopods sank
ten men-o'-war in one night!

In view of the wild stories which always seem to have accompanied accounts of the kraken, it is hardly surprising that scientists did not take it seriously. As has happened before in science,
the pendulum swung too far the other way. Rather than be taken
in by a vulgar fraud, most scientists closed their minds even to the
possibility that the legendary kraken could have any basis in fact.

Then in the middle of the 19th century Japetus Steenstrup in
Denmark and Pieter Harting in Holland studied old records of
captures and strandings of giant cephalopods, and re-examined
some of their remains, preserved and long forgotten, in museums.
Their studies showed that there was evidence of the occasional
capture or stranding of large cephalopods from the middle of the
16th century to contemporary times.[1] Moreover, the "spirit vaults
and bottle departments" of great museums had long preserved
physical evidence of the kraken's existence. In the basement of the
British Museum of Natural History in London there was, at this
time, a tall glass jar containing one of the arms of a giant cephalopod of unknown origin. This arm was 9 ft. long and 11 in. in circumference at the base, and bore some 300 suckers. (W. Saville
Kent.)

Despite the foregoing evidence, the scientific world was still
skeptical of the kraken. Then in 1861 something happened which,
to say the least, required a lot of explaining away—a French war-
ship engaged a kraken off the Canary Islands. The ship was the
steam despatch boat *Alecton* commanded by Lieutenant Frédéric-
Marie Bouyer. Although this incident is often referred to, it is sel-

[1] Unknown to Steenstrup and Harting at the time, there was in the library of
the Royal Dublin Society a collection of rare tracts and other documents giving
detailed evidence, including a drawing, of a huge cephalopod that was stranded in
Dingle Bay in the south-west of Ireland in October 1673. Parts of the animal were
put on show in Dublin and a handbill was printed advertising the "Wonderful
Fish or Beast." A broadsheet was also printed in London about it. The beast's body
was the "size of a horse," one of the tentacles was 11 ft. (the end was apparently
missing), the jaws were like an eagle's but broader, and each of its eyes was as
large as "a pewter dish." (A. G. More, 1875b.)

dom recounted in the lieutenant's own words. I have, therefore, had his report of the encounter, which he made to the Minister of Marine, and other relevant documents, translated by T. L. Edwards. Bouyer's report reads:

"Sainte Croix de Ténériffe. *Alecton* 2 Dec. 1861.

". . . My voyage was marked by a peculiar incident. On the 30th November, 40 leagues N.E. of Ténériffe, at two o'clock in the afternoon, I came upon a monstrous creature which I recognized as the 'Giant Octopus,' the disputed existence of which seems to have been relegated to the realms of fable.

"Finding myself in the presence of one of those strange creatures which the Ocean brings forth at times from its depths as if to challenge science, I resolved to study it more closely and to try to catch it.

"Unfortunately a heavy swell, as soon as it caught us on the beam, set up violent rolling in the *Alecton* and hindered maneuvers, while the animal itself, while almost always at the surface, moved about with a kind of intelligence and seemed to try to avoid the ship.

"After several encounters, which had only enabled us to hit it with some ten shots, I succeeded in drawing alongside of it closely enough to throw a harpoon as well as a noose at it. We were making ready to add other lines, when a violent movement on the part of the animal made the harpoon give way; the part of the tail [fin] round which the rope was coiled broke off, and we only succeeded in bringing aboard a fragment weighing about 20 kilograms [about 44 pounds].

"We had seen the monster closely enough to make an exact colored drawing of it.[1] It is the giant horned type. But the shape of the tail seems to make it a variety not described. It appears to measure 15–18 feet [2] as far as the head, shaped like a parrot's bill, surrounded by eight arms five to six feet long. [The two tentacles are mentioned later in the report.] Its appearance is frightful, its

[1] I am told by the Academy of Sciences that they no longer have this drawing in their possession, but A. E. Verrill says that it is copied in Plate 59 in Vol. I of George W. Tryon's *Manual of Conchology*. This figure is very different from the more sensational drawings which subsequent writers have used to illustrate the incident, e.g., John Gibson in *Monsters of the Sea*, published in 1887.

[2] *Pieds*, the old term for feet, indicating some vagueness.

color brick-red, and this creature sketched, this colossal and slimy embryo, presents a repulsive and terrible figure.

"Officers and men asked me to have a boat brought and to go to tie up the animal again, and to bring it alongside. They would perhaps have succeeded, but I feared that in this hand to hand combat the monster might fling out its long tentacles armed with suckers on the side of the boat, make it capsize and perhaps strangle some of the sailors in its fearful lashes charged with electric effluvia. ['*Ses fouets redoutables chargés d'effluves électriques.*']

"I did not think it my duty to endanger the life of my men to satisfy a feeling of curiosity, though this curiosity was based upon science, and, in spite of the heat which accompanies such a chase, I had to abandon the mutilated animal. . . ."

This report was read to the Zoology Section of the Academy of Sciences in Paris. Additional information about the incident was given in a letter from Sabin Berthelot, the French Consul in the Canary Islands, who spoke to Bouyer and some of his officers when the *Alecton* anchored there. They estimated the weight of the beast at more than 2,000 kilograms, or about two tons. It had enormous eyes, which were flush with its head. Its mouth was like a parrot's beak and it could open it to almost half a meter, or about 1½ ft.

The "battle" lasted over three hours, during which the kraken was hit by several harpoons, but they failed to hold. Berthelot was shown the only part of the animal which the crew were able to get aboard and says: "I have myself questioned old Canary Island fishermen, who have assured me that they have seen several times, out at sea, great reddish Calmars [squids] two meters [6½ ft.] and more in length, which they did not dare to capture."

It is said that this remarkable incident prompted Jules Verne to include in his *Twenty Thousand Leagues Under the Sea* the famous battle between the submarine *Nautilus* and a kraken. This has been made into a fantastic sequence in Walt Disney's film of Verne's novel—complete with two-ton rubber kraken which it took 24 men to operate with electronics, compressed air, hydraulics and remote controls! (See Plate 46.)

The documentary evidence of strandings, the parts of cephalopods preserved in museum basements, the occasional sightings,

and now the *Alecton's* evidence presented to the French Academy
of Sciences—all these together made it difficult to doubt that there
was a definite basis in fact for the legend of the kraken. But in the
1860s it was still possible for the skeptics to fall back on the well-
tried scientific maxim "No body, no animal." It was, of course,
true that up to that time no scientist had examined and described
a kraken in reasonably complete condition, but in the next few
years the seas provided all the evidence that even the most hard-
ened skeptic could require. In fact the 1870s supplied more bodies
—and therefore irrefutable evidence—than any decade since.

On October 26, 1873, two fishermen, Theophilus Piccot and
Daniel Squires, and Piccot's twelve-year-old son Tom, were fishing
for herring off Portugal Cove, Newfoundland. They saw a large
object floating on the surface and, thinking it was a piece of wreckage, rowed over to it. One of the men struck it with a boat-hook.
Instantly the supposedly dead mass reared up, and the fishermen
saw what they had attacked—a kraken.

With its huge eyes flashing, the animal lunged towards them
and struck the gunwale with its horny beak. A long thin tentacle
shot out and instantly coiled round the boat. A shorter but thicker
arm followed, and held it fast. The body of the kraken sank beneath the surface, and began to drag the boat with it. (H. J.
Squires tells me that the boat would be 15–20 ft. long and 4–5 ft.
across at the widest part.)

The fishermen were almost paralyzed with fear. Water was
pouring into the boat as it settled in the water and they thought
it was only a matter of seconds before they would all drown. But
if the men were resigned to die young Tom Piccot was not. He
picked up a small tomahawk from the bottom of the boat and
smashed at the arm and tentacle. He severed them just in time.
The boat righted itself but the kraken was still alongside. It discharged pints of ink which darkened the water all round them. But
it did not renew the fight. The beast's huge bulk seemed to "slide
off" and disappear. The last the men saw of it were the huge fins
at the end of its body which, they said, measured six or seven feet.

Fearing pursuit, the fishermen rowed for the shore with all their
strength. Tom Piccot, the boy-hero to whom the men owed their
lives, clutched the arm and tentacle and brought them ashore as
his battle trophies. The arm he threw on the ground where it was

Gustave Doré

THE MOST FAMOUS OCTOPUS FIGHT IN FICTION
Gilliatt, the hero of Victor Hugo's *Toilers of the Sea,* in combat with the 'devil fish' in a
Channel Island sea cave

Plate 41

Plate 42   AN UNDER-SEA ENCOUNTER BETWEEN A SKINDIVER
AND A LARGE COMMON OCTOPUS

Bernard Gorsky

ARMED AND IN OPEN WATER THE SKINDIVER
HAS LITTLE TO FEAR

Plate 43

Bernard Gorsky

KRAKEN
This giant squid was stranded at Ranheim, Norway, in October 1954. Its overall length was nearly 30 ft., but specimens have been captured which were nearly twice this length.

Plate 44

Moses Harvey

THE BEST KNOWN PHOTOGRAPH OF A GIANT SQUID

The head, arms and tentacles of the first giant squid to be scientifically examined, draped over the Rev. Moses Harvey's sponge-bath in St. John's Newfoundland, in November 1873

Plate 45

A HOLLYWOOD KRAKEN

It was used in Walt Disney's film adaptation of Jules Verne's *Twenty Thousand Leagues Under the Sea*. The model weighed two tons and it took 24 men to operate it with electronics, compressed air, hydraulics and remote controls. The beak is wrong, as in all cephalopods the lower mandible is the longer and closes over the upper

Plate 46

THE IMPRINTS OF THE TOOTH-RIMMED SUCKERS OF A GIANT SQUID ON THE SKIN OF A SPERM WHALE

Similar imprints have been found which were about three inches across. Slightly smaller than natural size

From *The Depths of the Ocean, John Murray and Johan Hjort* (Macmillan)

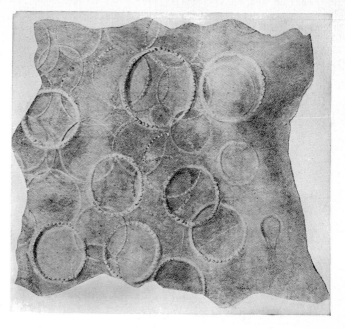

Plate 47

A BATTLE BETWEEN A SPERM WHALE AND A GIANT SQUID

Notice the cloud of ink being ejected by the squid. The illustration is from a painting in the Hall of Ocean Life in the American Museum of Natural History

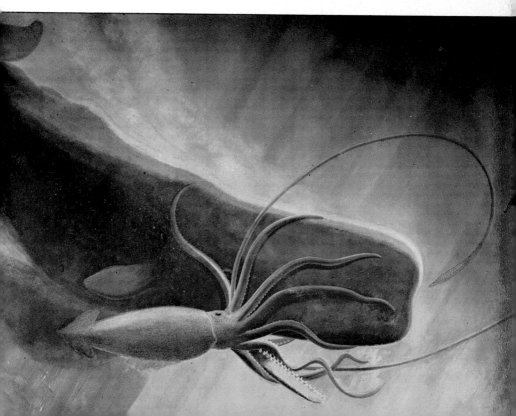

AN OLD PRINT OF A GIANT (MYTHICAL) OCTOPUS ATTACK

Plate 48

soon eaten by dogs. The long thin tentacle, however, he carefully preserved.

The local clergyman at Portugal Cove heard of the affair and suggested to Tom that he should take the long tentacle to the Rev. Moses Harvey who lived in nearby St. John's, and was a keen naturalist with a special interest in kraken lore. Remember that even at this time, 1873, although marine zoologists were greatly interested in the stories of sightings, encounters with krakens and their occasional strandings, conclusive evidence was still missing. Harvey's enthusiasm when he saw young Tom's prize knew no bounds. He listened eagerly to his story and paid him handsomely for the tentacle. This was 19 ft. long but was only part of the total length. It was 3½ in. in circumference, and was "exceedingly tough and strong."

The thrill that Harvey felt at that moment, the thrill of the true naturalist when he feels he is about to solve a long-debated mystery of natural history, can still be felt in this passage, published in 1899:

"I was now the possessor of one of the rarest curiosities in the whole animal kingdom—the veritable [tentacle] of the hitherto mythical devil fish, about whose existence naturalists had been disputing for centuries. I knew that I held in my hand the key of the great mystery, and that a new chapter would now be added to Natural History."

Harvey hastened to interrogate the men to see what details they could add to the boy's story.

"I found the two fishermen but partially recovered from the terror of the scene through which they had passed. They still shuddered as they spoke of it. What most impressed them was the huge green eyes gleaming with indescribable fury, and the parrot-like beak that suddenly leaped from a cavity in the middle of the head, as if eager to rend them."

Harvey now knew beyond doubt that krakens existed, although the all-important *body* was still missing.

In November, less than a month after the Portugal Cove encounter, four fishermen were hauling in a large herring-net in nearby Logy Bay. The net was unusually heavy, and as it neared the surface they were startled by its behavior. It was moving violently and they were afraid their catch might either burst the net or carry it away. It took the strength of all four men to raise the net, and when it broke surface they almost let it go. They had caught a kraken!

The net was a mass of writhing arms, and in the center were two large gleaming eyes. The two tentacles shot out through a rent in the net, reaching for the boat. They quivered for a moment in the air, seeking their prey, but the distance was too great and they shot back again.

The fishermen were so alarmed they were tempted to cut the net free rather than risk battle with such a foe. But one of the men drew his sharp fish-splitting knife and, waiting his chance, plunged it in behind the kraken's eyes and rapidly severed the head from the rest of the body. One of the fishermen told Harvey afterwards that he had had such a bad half-hour that no amount of money would induce him to take part in capturing another of the beasts.

The moment Harvey heard of the capture he went to Logy Bay. A quarter of a century later he wrote:

"I remember to this day how I stood on the shore of Logy Bay, gazing on the dead giant and 'rolling as a sweet morsel under my tongue' the thought of how I would astonish the savants, and confound the naturalists, and startle the world at large. I resolved that only the interests of science should be considered. I speedily completed a bargain with the fishermen, whom I astonished by offering 10 dols. to deliver the beast carefully at my house.

"They evidently thought me 'cracked' to be paying away so much money for a nasty brute that nearly cost them their lives before they could get it into their boat, and almost carried off their herring-net. To allay their curiosity and make them more careful, I hinted that I wanted it as *a present for the Queen!* Next day, to my great satisfaction, a cart arrived at my door almost filled with the hideous, corpse-like creature, which I speedily stowed away in an outbuilding, in a huge vat filled with the strongest brine."

News of the strange inhabitant of the clergyman's outhouse soon spread and "a stream of daily visitors came to gaze in shuddering horror at the dead giant." But Harvey carried out his resolve that the interests of science should come first. He carefully measured his specimen and found that the tentacles were 24 ft. long, and the total length of the animal was 32 ft. The head, arms and tentacles were draped over Harvey's large sponge-bath and photographed. It has since become the most famous squid photograph in the world (see Plate 45). This, together with several other photographs taken at the same time, were sent to the Governor of Newfoundland and were despatched by him to Lord Kimberley at the Colonial Office. They are now in the British Museum of Natural History in London.

This specimen proved beyond doubt that krakens exist, that they are giant squids, and that they are the largest invertebrates on earth. Now, ironically enough, further evidence accumulated rapidly throughout that marvelous decade, teuthologically speaking, the 1870s. And it was Newfoundland waters that provided nearly all the specimens. It may be significant that the coast of Newfoundland and that of Norway, where the name kraken originated, are alike in being indented with deep fjords. The Newfoundland whalemen and fishermen of the Grand Banks have long been familiar with the "big squids," and asserted their existence many years before scientists admitted them to the zoological lists. The fishermen, incidentally, used to cut them up for bait, feed them to dogs or use them for manure!

The large number of giant squids seen floating at the surface or found stranded during the 1870s suggests that some unfavorable change occurred in their living conditions. Before and after this decade the sight or stranding of one of these squids was a rare event, but during these ten years dozens were found floating on the surface of the waters off Newfoundland.

The peak period appears to have been October 1875. Verrill says Captain J. W. Collins told him that numbers of giant squids were then found floating at the surface on the Grand Banks. Most of them were dead and had been mutilated by birds and fishes. A few were just alive but were entirely disabled. Collins thought that between 50 and 60 were taken by fishing vessels and used as bait for cod. Three giant squids were taken in an afternoon by one ship. Collins' own ship, the schooner *Howard,* secured five, the largest having a body (mantle) 15 ft. long and arms as thick at the base as a man's thigh. Another ship captured a squid that was not quite dead which had tentacles 36 ft. long. Verrill says that Collins' statements were confirmed by other fishermen, some of whom said that "big squids" were also common at this time at the Flemish Cap, a bank northeast of the Grand Banks.

One of the largest specimens on record was stranded on November 2, 1878. Three fishermen were out in a boat off Tickle Bay, Newfoundland, when they saw a huge squid near the shore. Harvey (1879) thus describes what followed:

"They rowed towards it, and, to their horror, found themselves close to a huge fish, having large glassy eyes, which was making desperate efforts to escape, and churning the water into foam by the motion of its immense arms and tail. It was aground and the tide was ebbing. From the funnel at the back of its head it was ejecting large volumes of water,[1] this being its method of moving backward, the force of the stream, by the reaction of the surrounding medium, driving it in the required direction. At times the water from the siphon was black as ink.

"Finding the monster partially disabled, the fishermen plucked up courage and ventured near enough to throw the grapnel of their boat, the sharp flukes of which, having barbed points, sunk into the soft body. To the grapnel they had attached a stout rope which they had carried ashore and tied to a tree, so as to prevent the fish from going out with the tide. It was a happy thought, for the devil fish found himself effectually moored to the shore. His struggles were terrific as he flung his ten arms about in dying agony. The fishermen took care to keep a respectful distance from the long tentacles, which ever and anon darted out like great tongues from the central mass. At length it became exhausted, and as the water receded it expired."

Unfortunately the fishermen cut up their find for dog's meat, but Harvey believed this squid was about 55 ft. long.

Although a keen amateur naturalist, Harvey was not the man to conduct the minute examination and description of the wealth of material on giant squids which was now available. He wisely got in touch with Addison Emery Verrill, Professor of Zoology at Yale University, whose special interest was the Mollusca, the phylum which includes the squids.

It would have been difficult to pick a better man to make the utmost of the zoological treasure-trove which the Newfoundland seas had provided. Verrill was a more painstaking scientist with a

[1] Another stranded giant squid "ploughed up a trench or furrow about 30 ft. long and of considerable depth by the stream of water that it ejected with great force from its siphon." (Quoted by Verrill.)

remarkable capacity for work. When his enthusiasm was thoroughly roused he worked almost nonstop for days. Meals were forgotten, sleep merely an indulgence to be satisfied with a cat-nap or two every 24 hours. Verrill had an iron constitution which virtually never knew illness or fatigue from early manhood till his death at 87. At 85 he set off on a two-year expedition to the South Seas and brought home nearly a thousand lots of marine invertebrates. And his memory was such that he could recall the name and distinguishing characteristics of almost every one of the 900-odd new species which he had added to the zoological lists. (Wesley R. Coe.)

Such was the man to whom Harvey sent his specimen and plied with valuable information. Verrill subsequently returned the compliment when, after an exhaustive examination of this first real kraken to be thoroughly studied by a professional zoologist, he named it *Architeuthis harveyi*. His description, together with a mass of other material on the giant squids, was published in a paper of 81 pages and 14 plates in December 1879 in the *Transactions of the Connecticut Academy of Arts and Sciences*. Verrill published several articles before this on Harvey's specimen, but this is the definitive paper. It is the classic treatise which finally brought the story of the kraken from the realm of folk-lore to that of science. In December 1881 Verrill published an appendix of 51 pages giving further details of giant and other squids which had become available since the main paper was published.

Giant squids are found in most of the world's seas, but very little is known about them. Verrill put all the Newfoundland specimens into two species: *Architeuthis harveyi* and *Architeuthis princeps*. But Georg Pfeffer, in his review of Verrill's work on the Newfoundland specimens, says that there was insufficient knowledge for a final determination of species. Various opinions have been expressed on the total number of species in the genus *Architeuthis*. Twelve species have been named, but it is doubtful if all these are valid. W. J. Rees (1949) says: "There is much uncertainty as to how many species of *Architeuthis* there are. This is understandable when it is realized that what we know is based on various fragments and incomplete specimens obtained mainly from strandings."

While the history-making Newfoundland squids were being

found in the surface waters or stranded on the shore, there occurred in British waters one of the most remarkable running fights with a kraken ever recorded. In April 1875 three fishermen were at sea near Boffin Island off the Connemara coast of Ireland. They were in a curragh, a large type of coracle constructed from tarred canvas over wooden ribs.

Having shot their lines the men waited. After a while their attention was caught by a flock of gulls hovering round a large shapeless mass floating on the surface. They thought it might be some wreckage so they paddled over to investigate. As they drew near they were astonished to see that the object was a giant squid, lying perfectly still, basking on the surface.

Squid bait is highly prized by Irish fishermen, but it is generally available only in small amounts. These fishermen could not bear to see *hundredweights* of it just lying there going to waste. But what could they do? A squid of such dimensions was a dangerous opponent and the men's only weapon was a knife. A bold frontal attack was out of the question, so the men decided on guerrilla tactics. Paddling slowly they got within reach of an outstretched arm, seized it and in a moment cut it off.

The squid exploded into action. Its arms thrashed around, its funnel shot out great jets of water, and amid a cloud of spray it made out to sea. The men gave chase, paddling with all their strength. But it is impossible to row fast in a curragh [1] and it was nearly a mile before they caught up with the squid. Keeping behind it they attacked one arm at a time, slashing with the knife while taking care to avoid being struck by the other flailing arms. Thus the running battle of attrition continued for two hours, and by this time the curragh was five miles out in the open Atlantic.

The quarry was now sufficiently subdued for the fight to be carried to close quarters. Although the stumps of the arms slashed about violently they did no damage. The sea was darkened for yards around by the clouds of ink which the squid ejected.

The men now hacked at the beast's "neck" and cut off its head. The great body then sank quickly. But the rest of the squid was stowed aboard and when, after the long pull back, they reached Boffin Island their bizarre cargo created a sensation.

[1] The fastest speed I know is seven miles per hour over a measured mile.

No one on the island was more interested than the local police sergeant, Thomas O'Connor, and it is to him that the scientific world is indebted for details of the capture. But for his care the whole prize might soon have been converted into bait.

"Of the portions of the mollusc taken ashore two of the great arms are intact, and measure 8 ft. each in length and 15 in. round the base. The two tentacles attain a length of 30 ft. The mandibles are about 4 in. across, hooked, just like the beak of an enormous parrot, with a very curious tongue. The head, devoid of all appendages, weighed about 6 stone, and the eyes were about 15 in. in diameter. Doubtless this account may sound exaggerated, but I hold such portions of the fish as are fully sufficient to establish its enormous size, and verify the dimensions above given."

He forwarded parts of the squid to the Museum of the Royal Dublin Society. These were described by A. G. More (1875a and c) who accepted O'Connor's figures.

Although no subsequent period has equaled the decade 1870–80 in numbers of stranded giant squids, they have been reported periodically ever since. Rees (1950) published a summary of ten records of large squids stranded or caught in British waters between 1673 and 1937. Six of the records refer to this century—including a giant squid that was retrieved from the stomach of a sperm whale in 1914 at the Belmullet Whaling Station in County Mayo, Ireland.

How big do giant squids grow? As far as I know, the longest giant squid which has been authentically measured is one that was found on the beach at Lyall Bay, New Zealand. It was measured by T. W. Kirk (1888), who found it was 57 ft. overall, of which the tentacles measured 49 ft. 3 in., and the body (mantle) 5 ft. 7 in. Because of the exceptional length of the tentacles this species was named *Architeuthis longimanus*. Other species of *Architeuthis* have been measured which had bodies about twice the length of the New Zealand specimen, but the tentacles were shorter.

R. K. Dell, Conchologist of the Dominion Museum, New Zealand, comments:

"The more I have searched the literature on giant squids the less I have come to believe is authentic. I suspect that most of the weights are guesses and that many of the measurements were done with an elastic rule. I have resolved to take little account of any giant squid that has not been measured by a scientist. I suspect that squids do grow larger than those that have come to scientific notice but it seems better to be conservative in such matters. I haven't seen any reasonable account of a squid with a body longer than about 12 ft."

Judging by what is known of other giant squids, a specimen of *A. harveyi* or *A. princeps* with a body (mantle) length of 12 ft. would measure about 60 ft. overall—tip of fins to tip of tentacles.

There is evidence, however, that there are squids which are longer than this. R. J. Daniel once measured a squid which had been found in the stomach of a sperm whale. The tentacles were 21 ft. long, and the largest sucker was an inch in diameter. But when the whale was examined sucker marks were found on its head which were 3½ in. across. It is admittedly dangerous to place too much weight on such arguments, but if increase in sucker size is proportionate to increase in total length, then a 3½-in. sucker must belong to a squid some 70 ft. long.

The British seaman and travel writer, Frank T. Bullen, once examined a fragment of a squid which had been vomited by a dying sperm whale. It proved to be "a tentacle or arm as thick as a stout man's body, and with six or seven sucking-discs on it. These were about as large as a saucer, and on their inner edge were thickly set with hooks or claws all round the rim, sharp as needles, and almost the shape and size of a tiger's." If Bullen's account is accepted, this indicates that the squid did not belong to the genus *Architeuthis*, as the dentition of their sucker rims is different, the teeth being very small.

An arm "thick as a stout man's body," suckers "as large as a saucer," their rims set with "tiger's claws"—such phrases are too indefinite to be used for calculating the measurements of giant squids, but they do suggest caution in accepting even 70 ft. as the extreme size of living krakens. And Nancy Frost (1934) refers to a claim made by Captain A. Kean to have found a giant squid at Flowers Cove, Newfoundland, which measured 72 ft. overall.

Not much is known about the weight of giant squids, and there are no reliable figures at all for the tonnage of the largest specimens. A 34½-ft. squid weighed 405 pounds (see page 215). A specimen with a body some five feet long which was captured at Trinity Bay, Newfoundland, in December 1933, was stated in the

Press report to weigh 570 pounds. (Frost.) Verrill says that one cut up by Newfoundland fishermen filled a 75-gallon tub, and he estimated that it originally weighed nearly 1,000 pounds. Unfortunately its measurements are not given. A. S. Packard quotes a letter from a correspondent in which details are given of a giant squid which was found floating on the surface off Newfoundland in October 1871. It was taken aboard a schooner and its weight was estimated to be 2,000 pounds.

The Norwegian marine zoologist, Erling Sivertsen, tells me that the 30-ft. squid stranded at Ranheim, Norway, in October 1954 was estimated to weigh between 200 and 300 kilograms, or 440 to 660 pounds (see Plate 45). He adds "a real big one, a 60-footer, may certainly have a weight much more than 1,000 kilograms [2,205 pounds]." The giant squid encountered by the *Alecton*—a 60-footer?—was estimated to weigh "more than 2,000 kilograms," or about two tons. This is twice the weight of a heavy cart-horse.

The foregoing accounts, and some that are to follow, may give the impression that giant squids are vigorous, powerful and ferocious animals. Yet a study of their structure does not support such a picture. G. C. Robson (1933) says that the locking apparatus of the funnel mechanism is comparatively weak, and the fins are small in relation to the total size of the animal. Moreover, these squids lack the giant nerve-fibers which aid rapid movement and are found in the fast-swimming species. Gilbert L. Voss says that he agrees with Robson that giant squids "are in all probability very poor or weak swimmers and not at all adapted for catching active prey. . . . They probably live, as Robson suggests, along the continental slope or beyond in depths of 100 fathoms or over where they feed on small, inactive animals." But it should be remembered that when provoked even sluggish animals can fight back, and when they are the size and weight of giant squids they can be formidable.

Voss tells me that he does not overlook the possibility that there may exist other giant squids so far unknown to science. The fragments Bullen reported may have belonged to such a squid. The Humboldt Current squid (*Ommastrephes gigas*) is known to reach 12 ft. overall and to weigh 300 pounds. Suppose there exist gigantic species of squid of the dimensions indicated by Bullen, and with the characteristics of these vigorous and ferocious ommastrephids? Such an animal might well be capable of some of the extraordinary feats recorded in this chapter.

What are the enemies of giant squids? It is possible that large sharks sometimes attack them, but their only proven foe, apart from man, is the sperm whale, or cachalot (*Physeter catodon*).[1] This is the largest of the toothed whales and the males, which grow to about twice the length of the females, sometimes measure 60 ft. and weigh over 50 tons. The old-time whalers claimed to have caught some cachalots measuring 85 ft.

The sperm whale's enormous head is about a third of its total length. The upper jaw is virtually toothless, only a few vestigial teeth occurring in some specimens. The lower jaw, 10 to 12 feet long but slight in comparison with the huge head, is armed with about 50 teeth, the number varying with different whales. These cone-shaped teeth weigh about two pounds and measure up to eight inches, a third of which protrudes above the gum. The points of the teeth fit into sockets in the strong fibrous tissue of the palate.

Moby Dick was a sperm whale and his character was in keeping with what is known of the breed. When roused it can be a terrible foe. Ships have been sunk when charged by enraged sperm whales —they can charge at 20 miles per hour. The most famous sinking occurred on November 20, 1820, when the 238-ton whaleship *Essex* was twice rammed by a huge sperm whale which inflicted such damage that she sank. This was the tragedy—most of the crew never reached land—that prompted Herman Melville to end his novel with the whale sinking the ship. (A. B. C. Whipple, and Clifford W. Ashley.)

Such is the foe of the giant squid, and the titanic struggles that take place between the two must be among the most awesome in Nature. The bodies of sperm whales bear some evidence of what occurs when kraken meets leviathan. The heads of these whales are nearly always scarred by the sucker-rings of giant squids. Sometimes the wounds are an inch deep in the blubber, and the head bears huge sores where the tooth-rimmed suckers have gouged and torn the skin. Often the rounded imprint of the suck-

[1] Giant squids are by no means the only fare of sperm whales. They eat smaller cephalopods and occasionally fish as well. Robert Clarke, who has examined the stomach contents of many of these whales, found that the average size of the squids eaten measured only some 3½ ft. from fin to arms—which is much less than the length of the real giants.

ers is branded into the flesh. The struggle sometimes continues inside the whale, for occasionally squids are swallowed alive, and sucker marks have been seen on the walls of the whale's stomach.

When a sperm whale is dying it often vomits the contents of its stomach. Sometimes this includes parts of giant squids which digestion has hardly touched. Squid beaks are often found in the intestines of sperm whales. When the Prince of Monaco's expedition was off the Azores in 1895 the headless body of a cephalopod was recovered from a sperm whale and proved to be an unknown genus. The squid had a scale-like skin, and was named *Lepidoteuthis grimaldii* by Louis Joubin. Grimaldi is the family name of the reigning house of Monaco. A new species of giant squid (*Architeuthis physeteris*) was also discovered in the stomach of a sperm whale on another of the Prince's expeditions. This was described by Joubin in 1899.

Surprising as it sounds, sperm whales sometimes swallow giant squids whole, although I know of no record of a 50- or 60-footer being thus devoured intact.

Rees and Maul say that a sperm whale which was harpooned off São Lourenço, Madeira, on June 12, 1952, vomited a squid which still showed signs of life! The squid was 34 ft. overall and weighed about 330 pounds. Clarke was at a whaling station on Fayal Island in the Azores on July 4, 1955, when a 47-ft. sperm whale was brought in. In its stomach was an intact giant squid measuring 34 ft. 5 in. and weighing 405 pounds.

A few men have witnessed fights between sperm whales and giant squids.[1] No doubt some of the old whalers, when the main quarry was the sperm, saw such fights on rare occasions, but as far as I can discover very few have left records of what they saw.

Bullen, to whom we are indebted for the best-known description of one of these Homeric duels, says "the indifference and apathy manifested by whalers generally to everything except commercial matters is wonderful." Bullen asked a mate of 40 years' experience if he had ever seen giant squids "alive and kicking." The mate replied: "Wall, I guess so; but I don't take any stock in fish, 'cept for provisions er ile [oil]—en thet's a fact."

Sivertsen also says that fights between giant squids and sperm

[1] Georges Blond has an imaginative description of an under-sea fight between a whale and a squid in his book *The Great Whale Game*.

whales have been observed by whalers. Norwegian whalers told
him of one such battle they witnessed in which the squid's arms
and tentacles surrounded the whale's head so tightly that it appeared unable to open its mouth. The whale then dived and when
it resurfaced "it was chewing happily on the smashed squid."

Bullen's account of a whale's fight with a squid is a classic. He
was on the whaleship *Cachalot*—the date would be about 1875—
and one night near Car Nicobar in the Indian Ocean he was detailed to take another man's watch. He was not at all pleased.

"I remember being so tired and sleepy that I knew not how to
keep awake. I did not imagine that anything would happen to
make me prize that night's experience for the rest of my life, or I
should have taken matters with a far better grace.

"At about 11 P.M. I was leaning over the lee rail, gazing steadily
at the bright surface of the sea, where the intense radiance of the
tropical moon made a broad path like a pavement of burnished
silver. Eyes that saw not, mind only confusedly conscious of my
surroundings, were mine; but suddenly I started to my feet with
an exclamation, and stared with all my might at the strangest sight
I ever saw. There was a violent commotion in the sea right where
the moon's rays were concentrated, so great that, remembering
our position, I was at first inclined to alarm all hands; for I had often heard of volcanic islands suddenly lifting their heads from the
depths below, or disappearing in a moment, and, with Sumatra's
chain of active volcanoes so near, I felt doubtful indeed of what
was now happening.

"Getting the night-glasses out of the cabin scuttle, where they
were always hung in readiness, I focused them on the troubled
spot, perfectly satisfied by a short examination that neither vol-
cano nor earthquake had anything to do with what was going on;
yet so vast were the forces engaged that I might well have been
excused for my first supposition. A very large sperm whale was
locked in deadly conflict with a cuttlefish, or squid, almost as large
as himself, whose interminable tentacles seemed to enlace the
whole of his great body. The head of the whale especially seemed
a perfect net-work of writhing arms—naturally, I suppose, for it
appeared as if the whale had the tail part of the mollusc in his
jaws, and, in a business-like, methodical way, was sawing
through it.

"By the side of the black columnar head of the whale appeared the head of the great squid, as awful an object as one could well imagine even in a fevered dream. Judging as carefully as possible, I estimated it to be at least as large as one of our pipes, which contained three hundred and fifty gallons; but it may have been, and probably was, a good deal larger. The eyes were very remarkable from their size and blackness, which, contrasted with the livid whiteness of the head, made their appearance all the more striking. They were, at least, a foot in diameter, and, seen under such conditions, looked decidedly eery and hobgoblin-like.

"All around the combatants were numerous sharks, like jackals round a lion, ready to share the feast, and apparently assisting in the destruction of the huge cephalopod. So the titanic struggle went on, in perfect silence as far as we were concerned, because, even had there been any noise, our distance from the scene of conflict would not have permitted us to hear it.

"Thinking that such a sight ought not to be missed by the captain, I overcame my dread of him sufficiently to call him, and tell him of what was taking place. He met my remarks with such a furious burst of anger at my daring to disturb him for such a cause, that I fled precipitately on deck again, having the remainder of the vision to myself, for none of the others cared sufficiently for such things to lose five minutes' sleep in witnessing them. The conflict ceased, the sea resumed its placid calm, and nothing remained to tell of the fight but a strong odor of fish, as of a bank of seaweed left by the tide in the blazing sun. Eight bells struck, and I went below to a troubled sleep, wherein all the awful monsters that an over-excited brain could conjure up pursued me through the gloomy caves of ocean, or mocked my pigmy efforts to escape."

Bullen thought that the squid had been dragged to the surface by the whale. Paul Bartsch (1917) thinks that the whale's victim may have been a giant octopus rather than a squid because of the geographical location, but the illustration of the incident in Bullen's book clearly shows a squid.

On January 10, 1877, five men appeared before a magistrate at Liverpool to testify to something they had witnessed while on a voyage some 18 months previously. This was their affidavit:

"We, the undersigned officers and crew of the barque *Pauline* (of London), of Liverpool, in the county of Lancaster, in the United Kingdom of Great Britain and Ireland, do solemnly and sincerely declare that, on July 8, 1875, in lat. 5°13′S., long. 35°W., we observed three large sperm whales, and one of them was gripped round the body with two turns of what appeared to be a huge serpent. The head and tail appeared to have a length beyond the coils of about 30 ft., and its girth 8 ft. or 9 ft. The serpent whirled its victim round and round for about 15 minutes, and then suddenly dragged the whale to the bottom, head first.

"Geo. Drevar, Master, Horatio Thompson, John Henderson Landells, Owen Baker, and William Lewarn."

Some of the men said that they also saw a similar serpent "shooting itself along the surface" a few days later.

The *Pauline* had been on a voyage from South Shields to Zanzibar with a cargo of coals for *H.M.S. London,* the guardship of the Zanzibar station. When they arrived the crew were obviously full of the amazing sight they had seen. One of the men who was impressed with the story was the Rev. E. L. Penny, Chaplain to the *London.* He sent to the *Illustrated London News* a letter and a drawing of the incident, which he drew from the descriptions given by the captain and crew. These were published in the issue for November 20, 1875. He says that Captain Drevar was a particularly able and observant man, and that there were no discrepancies in the accounts of the incident given by the various witnesses.

Lee (1884), who recounts the incident, received the following letter from Drevar:

"You may rely upon my report as strictly true, and in no way exaggerated. I called the second officer out of his bed to witness the conflict, and he remarked at the time that had the occurrence been further off he would have concluded that it was a swordfish and a thrasher [shark] fighting a whale, which he thought he saw on his first voyage to sea. Several shipmasters told me that they had seen the same conflict near the locality that I saw it, but had not been close enough to see the coils; they thought it was two separate fish fighting the whale, but were satisfied that it might have been the head and tail portion of a huge serpent about the whale."

I agree with Lee's comment: "It is impossible to doubt for a moment the genuineness of the statement made by Captain Drevar and his crew, or their honest desire to describe faithfully that which they believed they had seen."

But what was it they really saw fighting the sperm whale? For honest observers can be mistaken in the nature of what they think they see, as has been proved many times in natural history. It may have been a sea serpent. I believe that these animals exist, and have given my reasons for doing so in two papers. (Lane, 1941 and 1949.) Rupert T. Gould has dealt with the theory that the giant squid may be the explanation of reported sightings of the sea serpent. It may be for some, but Gould shows, I think conclusively, that the giant squid cannot possibly account for all such sightings.

On the other hand it may have been a squid of gigantic proportions. It is difficult to believe that sea serpents, if they exist, dine off 50-ton whales. And no one has claimed, as far as I know, to have found the remains of a sea serpent in a sperm whale's stomach—but the remains of giant squids are often found there. It is also known that the giant squid clasps its enemy with its arms and tentacles.

The "head and tail" of the *Pauline* report *might* have been the tail-fins (head) and an arm (tail) of an outsize giant squid—say a 70-footer—although if the girth of the enveloping coils were really "eight feet or nine feet" this theory must obviously be abandoned. With the two monstrous animals "whirling" about in the water amid the inevitable cloud of spray exact observations would be difficult. Whereas the observers would undoubtedly have heard of the sea serpent, they might well have been ignorant of the giant squid. They were not whalers, and this was 1875, only half-way through the decade when the existence of the giant squid was finally admitted.

Whatever Drevar and his men saw it was without doubt one of the most remarkable natural history observations ever made at sea.

I began this chapter by pointing out that references to a giant many-armed sea creature occur in the ancient literature of several maritime nations. I have shown, I hope, that the belief was founded on fact. But in addition to the stories of the kraken's existence there was another equally widespread belief—that this animal was dangerous not only to man but also to the ships he sailed in. How far was this belief based on fact?

It must be remembered that the giant squid is one of the largest animals in the sea and it carries formidable armament. In the tentacles it possesses a pair of living tongs which may measure 40 ft. or more, armed at their tips with clubbed heads each carrying a hundred or so suckers rimmed with sharp tiny teeth. The eight arms, each measuring up to 12 ft., also bear suckers, so that altogether the squid carries over a thousand living vacuum cups. The hard bony beak can exert great pressure. Squids weighing less than a hundred pounds have severed tough steel wire leaders.

The giant squid which, after being provoked, attacked Tom Piccot's boat was large but was not, apparently, of maximum size. Yet only the courage of a boy, and the happy chance that a tomahawk was handy, prevented the squid from sinking the boat and destroying the crew. Again, the squid which was imprisoned in a herring-net put up such a struggle against four men for half an hour that they nearly cut their valuable net adrift rather than continue the fight.

In view of such well-attested accounts there can be no question that under provocation giant squids can be dangerous to small craft. (And sometimes, apparently, without provocation. Katsuya Tago says "an enormous squid, 20 ft. long, jumped into a fishing boat near Kinkazan [Japan].") But some of the old-time stories about the kraken allege that not only small boats but sailing ships have been endangered by these "devil fish." Is there any foundation for this belief? Today, the vast majority of ocean-going vessels are too large to be in danger from marine animals. But before the present century, in the days of wooden sailing ships, such attacks were a real, though fortunately rare, hazard of the sea. Sinkings from attacks by sperm whales have already been mentioned. In these old records are there any reliable accounts of ships being endangered by giant squids? Robson (1925) says: "The early naturalists' and voyagers' journals are full of incredible tales about the feats of these creatures. Well-attested stories seem to limit their ferocity and aggressiveness to occasional attacks on small fishing boats."

Readers will judge the following stories for themselves, but I think they should be recounted in this history of the kraken. It must again be emphasized that unknown species of giant squid may be involved in these incidents.

Denys de Montfort, who admittedly was not a trustworthy naturalist, recounts the story of Capt. Jean Magnus Dens of Dunkirk. While crossing the Atlantic his ship was becalmed, and the crew started to scrape and paint her.

"The men were standing on stages suspended near the water's edge, scraping with iron scrapers, when suddenly a huge cuttlefish [squid] appeared and, throwing one of his arms about two of the men, tore the unfortunates, with their stage, from the side of the vessel and dragged them into the water. At the same time it threw another arm about a man who was just mounting the main rigging; but here its arm became entangled with the shrouds and ratlines, and it was unable to disentangle itself. The man, who was being severely squeezed, cried out for help, and the crew immediately ran to his assistance. Several threw harpoons into the body of the beast, which was now rising along the ship's side; others with axes cut in pieces the arm which held the man to the rigging and took the unfortunate down on deck.

"This done, the cuttle sank down, but the captain payed out on the lines which were fast to the harpoons, in the hope that presently he would be able to drag the beast up again and recover the two men who had been dragged down. In fact, at first he was able to drag the animal toward the surface; but presently the huge beast again sank down, and they were obliged to pay out line after line, till at last, having but a little left, they were forced to hold on; and now four of the harpoons drew out, while the fifth line broke, and thus all hope of saving the unfortunates or killing the monster was lost."

Bartsch quotes this story with apparent approval and Lee (1875) says: "I believe the old sea-captain's narrative of the incident to be true."

Denys de Montfort also tells of a sailing ship which was alleged to have been attacked off the West African coast.

"She had just taken in her cargo of slaves, ivory, and gold dust, and the men were heaving up the anchor, when suddenly a monstrous cuttlefish appeared on top of the water and slung its arms about two of the masts. The tips of the arms reached to the mastheads, and the weight of the cuttle dragged the ship over, so that she lay on her beam-ends and was near being capsized. The crew seized axes and knives, and cut away at the arms of the monster; but, despairing of escape, called upon their patron saint, St. Thomas, to help them. Their prayers seemed to give them renewed courage, for they persevered, and finally succeeded in cutting off the arms, when the animal sank and the vessel righted.

"Now, when the vessel returned to St. Malo the crew, grateful for their deliverance from so hideous a danger, marched in procession to the chapel of their patron saint, where they offered a solemn thanksgiving, and afterwards had a painting made representing the conflict with the cuttle, and which was hung in the chapel."

I have been unable to obtain confirmation from St. Malo about the painting, but it may well have been destroyed in the 150 years or so since Denys de Montfort says that he heard the story. A correspondent of Frank Buckland's spent the best part of a day in St. Malo unsuccessfully trying to find the picture. He adds, however, that "there appears to be such a story as Montfort speaks of known to the Malosiens."

If these were the only references to attacks on ships by giant squids they would hardly be worth quoting. But there are others which are much better authenticated, and if these are accepted then the other accounts may be regarded less skeptically.

In *Naturen* (published by the Bergen Museum in Norway) for December 1946 there appeared one of the most remarkable reports about cephalopods that I have read. It was by Commander Arne Groenningsaeter of the Royal Norwegian Navy. In correspondence he has kindly given me further details which did not appear in his original report. I have included some of these in what follows.

When Groenningsaeter was Executive Officer of the 15,000-ton tanker *Brunswick,* she was attacked on three occasions during the years 1930–33 by giant squids, each time between Hawaii and Samoa in the South Pacific. Each attack occurred during the day in good light. On each occasion Groenningsaeter was on the bridge, about 50 ft. above sea-level, and was able to see clearly what happened. He estimated that the length of the squids as they moved through the water was 30 ft. or more. As the tentacles would then be partly retracted the squids' overall length was probably about 60 ft.

When the first attack occurred Groenningsaeter thought the animal was a sea serpent because "it left behind a thick trail of ink during its run up, and this trail seemed to be one with the animal in the fresh trade wind sea. Its speed was so great that this inky water stayed behind and, with the choppy and rippled sea, it was difficult to distinguish, looking like a long snake. Only the fact that I was standing so high up on the steady bridge of a 15,000-tonner made it possible for me to see the whole maneuver. If it had been observed from a sailing ship's poop at about 15 ft. it could easily have been mistaken for a sea serpent."

Each attack followed the same pattern. The squid surfaced abaft the ship on the port side and rapidly overhauled her. Groenningsaeter tells me that the *Brunswick's* speed was 12 knots, so the squid's speed was probably more than 20 miles per hour. The squid swam parallel to the ship until it nearly reached the bow, then turned in to attack, hitting the ship a third of her length from the stern. Gorenningsaeter says: "It certainly gave us a very determined thud as it hit us full speed."

As the squid slid alongside giant tentacles, "equivalent to an 8 to 10 in. pipeline," reared up, apparently trying to reach the main deck, but as the squid had struck the ship just ahead of the aft superstructure they could not stretch far enough. (It is possible that the writhing of the arms and tentacles was because the squid was wounded.) The squid could get no hold on the ship's smooth plates and slid to the stern, where it was churned to death by the propeller.

Groenningsaeter believes that the squids attacked because they mistook the ship for a sperm whale. He points out that in each attack the squid struck the ship at a point—a third of her length from the stern—which, in a sperm whale, would be equivalent to a position just behind the "hump." "It was the fact that the squid was *overtaking* the ship which made this method of attack unusual. Otherwise I do not think that a collision between a ship and a marine animal was worth while reporting."

It is, of course, generally believed that it is the sperm whale which attacks squids, but if Groenningsaeter's explanation of the

attacks on the *Brunswick* is accepted, it would appear that sometimes it is the squid which attacks. Igor Akimushkin tells me that
when he was on the Kuril Islands in the Northwest Pacific he in-
vestigated the stomach contents of some 700 sperm whales, but in
none of them did he find any remains of very large squids. But the
bodies of many of these whales bore fresh traces of struggles with
such squids. Were these marks left by the squids "that got away,"
or were they received by the whales after attacks by squids on
the Groenningsaeter pattern? A squid would, of course, stand virtually no chance of killing an adult cachalot.

The most detailed account of an alleged sinking of a ship by a
kraken is that which appeared in *The Times* for July 4, 1874.
Whether the report is authentic or not I do not know, but it
should, I think, be included in this history of the kraken. The
story was published at the bottom of the column devoted to shipping news. I give it exactly as it appeared.

"A SUCCESSOR TO THE SEA SERPENT.—The following strange story
has been communicated to the Indian papers:—'We had left Co-
lombo in the steamer Strathowen, had rounded Galle, and were
well in the bay, with our course laid for Madras, steaming over a
calm and tranquil sea. About an hour before sunset on the 10th of
May we saw on our starboard beam and about two miles off a
small schooner lying becalmed. There was nothing in her appearance or position to excite remark, but as we came up with her I
lazily examined her with my binocular, and then noticed between
us, but nearer her, a long, low, swelling lying on the sea, which
from its colour and shape I took to be a bank of seaweed. As I
watched, the mass, hitherto at rest on the quiet sea, was set in
motion. It struck the schooner, which visibly reeled, and then
righted. Immediately afterwards the masts swayed sideways, and
with my glass I could clearly discern the enormous mass and the
hull of the schooner coalescing—I can think of no other term.
Judging from their exclamations, the other gazers must have witnessed the same appearance. Almost immediately after the collision and coalescence the schooner's masts swayed towards us,
lower and lower; the vessel was on her beam-ends, lay there a few
seconds, and disappeared, the masts righting as she sank, and the
main exhibiting a reversed ensign struggling towards its peak. A
cry of horror rose from the lookers-on, and, as if by instinct, our

ship's head was at once turned towards the scene, which was now marked by the forms of those battling for life—the sole survivors of the pretty little schooner which only 20 minutes before floated bravely on the smooth sea. As soon as the poor fellows were able to tell their story they astounded us with the assertion that their vessel had been submerged by a gigantic cuttlefish or calamary, the animal which, in a smaller form, attracts so much attention in the Brighton Aquarium as the octopus. Each narrator had his version of the story, but in the main all the narratives tallied so remarkably as to leave no doubt of the fact. As soon as he was at leisure, I prevailed on the skipper to give me his written account of the disaster, and I have now much pleasure in sending you a copy of his narrative:—"I was lately the skipper of the Pearl schooner, 150 tons, as tight a little craft as ever sailed the seas, with a crew of six men. We were bound from the Mauritius for Rangoon in ballast to return with paddy, and had put in at Galle for water. Three days out we fell becalmed in the bay (lat. 8 50 N., long. 84 5 E.). [This is about 600 miles from Car Nicobar where Bullen saw the fight between a giant squid and a sperm whale, see p. 216.] On the 10th of May, about 5 p.m.,—eight bells I know had gone,—we sighted a two-masted screw on our port quarter, about five or six miles off; very soon after, as we lay motionless, a great mass rose slowly out of the sea about half a mile off on our larboard side, and remained spread out, as it were, and stationary; it looked like the back of a huge whale, but it sloped less, and was of a brownish colour; even at that distance it seemed much longer than our craft, and it seemed to be basking in the sun. 'What's that?' I sung out to the mate. 'Blest if I knows; barring its size, colour, and shape, it might be a whale,' replied Tom Scott; 'and it ain't the sea sarpent,' said one of the crew, 'for he's too round for that ere crittur.' I went into the cabin for my rifle, and as I was preparing to fire, Bill Darling, a Newfoundlander, came on deck, and, looking at the monster, exclaimed, putting up his hand, 'Have a care, master; that ere is a squid, and will capsize us if you hurt him.' Smiling at the idea, I let fly and hit him, and with that he shook; there was a great ripple all round him, and he began to move. 'Out with all your axes and knives,' shouted Bill, 'and cut at any part of him that comes aboard; look alive, and Lord help us!' Not aware of the danger, and never having seen or heard of such a monster, I gave no orders, and it was no use touching the helm or ropes to get out of the way. By this time three of the crew, Bill included, had found axes, and one a rusty cutlass, and all were looking over the ship's side at the advancing monster. We could now see a huge oblong mass moving by jerks just under the surface of the water, and an enormous train following; the oblong body was at least half the size of our vessel in length and just as thick; the wake or train might have been 100 feet long. In the time that I have taken to write this the brute struck us, and the ship quivered under the thud; in another moment, monstrous arms like trees seized the vessel and she heeled over; in another second the monster was aboard, squeezed in between the two masts, Bill screaming 'Slash for your lives;' but all our slashing was of no avail, for the brute, holding on by his arms, slipped his vast body overboard, and pulled the vessel down with him on her beam-ends; we were thrown into the water at once, and just as I went over I caught sight of one of the crew, either Bill or Tom Fielding, squashed up between the masts and one of those awful arms; for a few seconds our ship lay on her beam-ends, then filled and went down; another of the crew must have been sucked down, for you only picked up five; the rest you know. I can't tell who ran up the ensign.—JAMES FLOYD, late master, schooner Pearl." '—*Homeward Mail.* [This means the story was sent to London by a homeward-bound mail vessel.]"

I have tried hard but unsuccessfully to find confirmation of this incident in Britain—from Lloyd's, the National Maritime Museum, the General Register of Shipping and Seamen, shipping lines and other likely sources. The reliability of the account must, therefore, be judged by internal evidence alone.

The opening of *The Times'* report indicates that the story was well-known in India. Where did it come from? Men and ships are named, date and time are given, the position is pin-pointed to minutes of latitude and longitude, and circumstantial accounts of the incident are recorded from both the onlooker's and the victim's points of view. If it were all fiction—and there seems no alternative to a complete hoax if the story is untrue—how did the hoaxer persuade newspapers to publish the baseless story? Evidently the Editor of *The Times* was satisfied it was not a hoax.

I sent a copy of *The Times'* report to Commander Groenningsaeter, the only man I know who has witnessed such an incident, and he replied that the "method of attack" on the *Pearl* seemed to be identical to that on his own ship. He suggests that the *Pearl* may "have had a very low stability being in ballast and with sails up. Its ballast may have shifted."

Groenningsaeter's suggestion may explain why the squid, although so much lighter than the *Pearl* and without having a solid object to give it purchase, was able to capsize it. These two facts, the great disparity in weight and lack of support, are probably the strongest arguments against the authenticity of the report.

The Times' account shows evidence of being written by eyewitnesses. The appearance of the animal as it lay on the surface; the jerky movement as the squid propelled itself by jets from its funnel; the trailing arms ("the wake or train"); and the use of the word coalescing ("I can think of no other term") when the squid swarmed over the schooner—that is just the word to describe such an action—all these are exactly right, and indicate that the reports came from people who were describing what they actually saw.

To me, however, the most convincing evidence of authenticity is the casual remark that the man who warned the master of the *Pearl* not to molest the squid was a Newfoundlander. As the preceding pages have shown, at the time of this incident the one place in the world where men were most likely to know about large squids, and their ferocity if attacked, was Newfoundland.

Information traveled much more slowly then than now, and it is unlikely that Moses Harvey's accounts of two squids, which had been written only some six months before, would be common knowledge in India at the time of the alleged sinking of the *Pearl*. Moreover, at that time, May 1874, nobody knew that Newfoundland was to become famous during the next few years for its stranded giant squids. The most *reasonable* explanation seems to be that the account was a report of an actual incident, including the presence on the *Pearl* of a man from the one place where, at that time, giant squids and their behavior were reasonably well-known.

It was all so long ago that the truth may never be known, but it is at least possible that on that calm summer evening in the Bay of Bengal the schooner *Pearl* was sunk by a gigantic kraken.

Appendix I ANATOMICAL DIAGRAMS

These diagrams have been made by Miss Sabine Baur under the direction of Dr. Adolphe Portmann. They are intended to give only a general outline of the main anatomical details of the three genera: *Octopus, Loligo* and *Sepia.* No attempt has been made to indicate specific sexual characters. Technical works, especially Portmann's monograph on the Cephalopoda in Grassé's *Traité de Zoologie,* should be consulted for detailed descriptions and drawings.

In the Cephalopoda there is a difference between the physiological and morphological orientations of the body. In life—the physiological position—the long axis of the body is generally held in a horizontal plane, the head pointing forwards and the end of the body backwards. But the actual structure—the morphological position—is with the long axis of the body held in a vertical plane, the head pointing downwards (cephalopod = "head-footed") and the end of the body upwards.

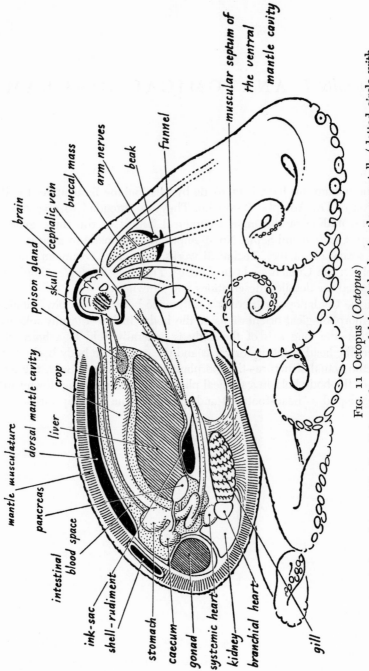

FIG. 11 Octopus (*Octopus*)

Schematic lateral view. The head shows the vertical lobe of the brain, the eye-stalk (dotted circle with diagonal lines) and the separation between the two bridges which connect the upper and lower parts of the brain (small circle). The "poison gland" is the posterior salivary gland.

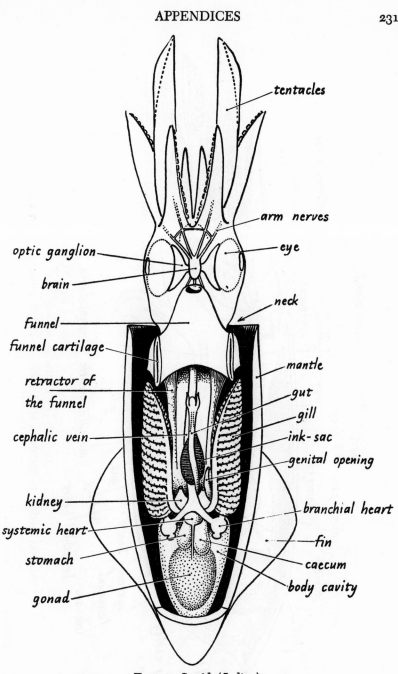

FIG. 12 Squid (*Loligo*)

Ventral view showing mantle opened. The head is shown as if transparent and the covering of the kidneys has been removed.

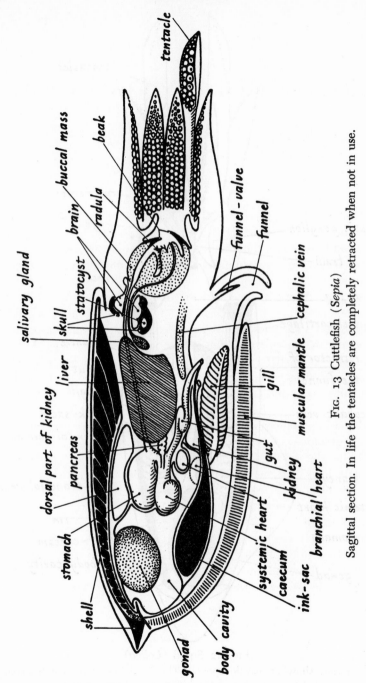

FIG. 13 Cuttlefish (*Sepia*)

Sagittal section. In life the tentacles are completely retracted when not in use.

Appendix II FAMILY TREE OF THE CEPHALOPODA

The class Cephalopoda was formerly divided into two subclasses—Tetrabranchiata (Ammonoidea and Nautiloidea) and Dibranchiata (the rest)—based on the number of gills the animals were presumed to have: four for the tetrabranchs and two for the dibranchs. This classification has been discarded by most systematists because gills do not leave their record in the rocks and it is, therefore, impossible to tell whether a fossil cephalopod had two, four or any number of gills. The class is now sub-divided on the basis of shell characters, since they are generally the only parts of the animal to become fossilized.

Some systematists sub-divide the Teuthoidea into two groups—Myopsida (eyes covered by a continuous membrane or open only by a minute pore) and Oegopsida (eyes not so covered). In this classification the families Loliginidae, Pickfordiateuthidae, Promachoteuthidae and Lepidoteuthidae comprise the Myopsida, all other families in the Teuthoidea comprising the Oegopsida.

While the terms Decapoda (ten-armed) and Octopoda (eight-armed) have become widely accepted, some systematists prefer Decembrachiata and Octobrachiata respectively for these orders. This is because Decapoda also applies to an order of crustaceans and has priority of usage.

Systematists are not agreed on all the details of the cephalopodan family tree. In this book a modified version of the system used by Voss (1956) has been adopted. A somewhat different system is given by Portmann in Grassé's *Traité de Zoologie*.

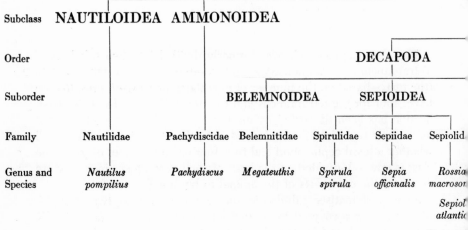

Class				CEPHA
Subclass	NAUTILOIDEA	AMMONOIDEA		
Order				DECAPODA
Suborder			BELEMNOIDEA	SEPIOIDEA
Family	Nautilidae	Pachydiscidae	Belemnitidae	Spirulidae Sepiidae Sepiolid
Genus and Species	*Nautilus pompilius*	*Pachydiscus*	*Megateuthis*	*Spirula spirula* *Sepia officinalis* *Rossia macroson*
				Sepiol atlantic
				Heteroteu dispar

NOTE: There is space to cite only a few families, genera and species.
I have chosen those which are referred to most frequently
in the text. The Ammonoidea and Belemnoidea are extinct.

PODA

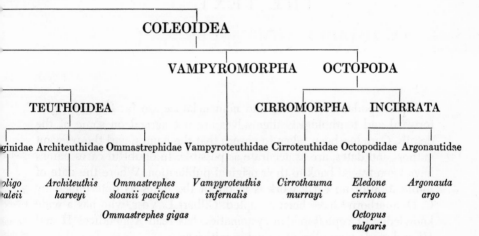

COLEOIDEA

VAMPYROMORPHA   OCTOPODA

TEUTHOIDEA   CIRROMORPHA   INCIRRATA

ginidae   Architeuthidae   Ommastrephidae   Vampyroteuthidae   Cirroteuthidae   Octopodidae   Argonautidae

oligo   *Architeuthis*   *Ommastrephes*   *Vampyroteuthis*   *Cirrothauma*   *Eledone*   *Argonauta*
aleii   *harveyi*   *sloanii pacificus*   *infernalis*   *murrayi*   *cirrhosa*   *argo*

         Ommastrephes gigas   *Octopus*
                                                  vulgaris

Appendix III SCIENTIFIC NAMES OF CEPHALOPODS MENTIONED IN THE TEXT

Cephalopodan systematics and nomenclature are far from straightforward and teuthologists themselves are not agreed on some of the details. Care has been taken to ensure that the names, and the relevant authors and dates, are as accurate as possible. In doubtful cases names have been traced back to their original publication. Where the date of publication of an early work is in doubt the dates as determined by C. D. Sherborn [1] have been accepted. Gilbert L. Voss, who has a wide knowledge of cephalopodan systematics, has read Appendices II and III and made a number of valuable criticisms.

It is necessary to add that because so much copying of names, authors and dates from secondary sources inevitably occurs, the nomenclature in otherwise authoritative works is sometimes wrong.

In Chapter I, I have followed Tom Iredale (1944) in saying that there are six species of *Nautilus*, although I know teuthologists are not agreed on the actual number, suggestions ranging from three to ten.

CLASS CEPHALOPODA

SUBCLASS NAUTILOIDEA

Family PLECTRONOCERATIDAE
Plectronoceras Ulrich & Foerste, 1933
P. cambria (Walcott, 1913)

Family ENDOCERATIDAE
Endoceras Hall, 1847

---

[1] *Index Animalium 1758–1800* (1902) Cambridge: University Press and *Index Animalium 1801–1850* (1922–1933) London: British Museum (Nat. Hist.).

Family NAUTILIDAE
    Nautilus Linnaeus, 1758
      N. pompilius Linnaeus, 1758
      N. macromphalus Sowerby, 1849

SUBCLASS AMMONOIDEA

Family ARIETITIDAE
    Cymbites Neumayr, 1878

Family PACHYDISCIDAE
    Pachydiscus Zittel, 1884

SUBCLASS COLEOIDEA
ORDER DECAPODA
SUBORDER BELEMNOIDEA

Family BELEMNITIDAE
    Belemnocamax Crick, 1910
    Megateuthis Bayle, 1878

SUBORDER SEPIOIDEA

Family SPIRULIDAE
    Spirula Lamarck, 1799
      S. spirula (Linnaeus, 1758)

Family SEPIIDAE
    Sepia Linnaeus, 1758
      S. officinalis Linnaeus, 1758
      S. orbignyana Férussac, *in* d'Orbigny, 1826
      S. latimanus Quoy & Gaimard, 1832
      S. elegans Blainville, 1827
    Solitosepia Iredale, 1926
      S. liliana Iredale, 1926
    Hemisepius Steenstrup, 1875
      H. typicus Steenstrup, 1875

Family SEPIOLIDAE
    Rossia Owen, 1835
      R. macrosoma (Delle Chiaje, [1830])
      R. australis Berry, 1918
    Heteroteuthis Gray, 1849
      H. dispar (Rüppell, [1844])

Sepiolina Naef, 1912
    S. nipponensis (Berry, 1911)
Sepiola Leach, 1817
    S. birostrata Sasaki, 1918
    S. atlantica d'Orbigny, [1840]
Inioteuthis Verrill, 1881
    I. bursa (Pfeffer, 1884)

SUBORDER TEUTHOIDEA

Family PICKFORDIATEUTHIDAE
    Pickfordiateuthis Voss, 1953
        P. pulchella Voss, 1953

Family LOLIGINIDAE
    Loligo Lamarck, 1798
        L. vulgaris Lamarck, 1798
        L. pealeii Lesueur, 1821
        L. forbesii Steenstrup, 1856
        L. opalescens Berry, 1911
    Alloteuthis Wulker, 1920
        A. media (Linnaeus, 1758)
        A. subulata (Lamarck, 1798)
    Sepioteuthis Blainville, 1824
        S. sepioidea (Blainville, 1823)
        S. australis Quoy & Gaimard, 1832
        S. lessoniana Lesson, 1830 (= *S. arctipinnis* Gould, 1852)
    Uroteuthis Rehder, 1945
        U. bartschi Rehder, 1945

Family LEPIDOTEUTHIDAE
    Lepidoteuthis Joubin, 1895
        L. grimaldii Joubin, 1895

Family LYCOTEUTHIDAE
    Lycoteuthis Pfeffer, 1900 (= *Thaumatolampas* Chun, 1903)
        L. diadema (Chun, 1900)
    Nematolampas Berry, 1913
        N. regalis Berry, 1913

Family ENOPLOTEUTHIDAE
    Abralia Gray, 1849
        A. veranyi (Rüppell, [1844])
    Abraliopsis Joubin, 1896
        A. morisii (Verany, 1839)
    Watasenia Ishikawa, 1914

W. scintillans (Berry, 1911),
Pyroteuthis Hoyle, 1904
Pterygioteuthis Fischer, 1895
P. giardi Fischer, 1895

Family ONYCHOTEUTHIDAE
    Onychoteuthis Lichtenstein, 1818
      O. banksii (Leach, 1817)

Family ARCHITEUTHIDAE
    Architeuthis Steenstrup, 1857
      A. harveyi (Kent, 1874)
      A. princeps Verrill, 1875
      A. longimanus Kirk, 1888
      A. physeteris Joubin, 1899

Family GONATIDAE
    Gonatus Gray, 1849
      G. magister Berry, 1913

Family HISTIOTEUTHIDAE
    Calliteuthis Verrill, 1880
    Histioteuthis d'Orbigny, 1840
      H. bonellii [1] (Férussac, 1835)

Family OMMASTREPHIDAE
    Illex Steenstrup, 1880
      I. illecebrosus (Lesueur, 1821)
    Ommastrephes d'Orbigny, 1825 (= *Ommatostrephes* Agassiz,
        1846; *Rhynchoteuthis* d'Orbigny, 1847; *Todarodes* [2]
        Steenstrup, 1880)
      O. sagittatus (Lamarck, 1798)
      O. sloanii pacificus [3] (Steenstrup, 1880)
      O. gigas d'Orbigny, [1835]
      O. pteropus Steenstrup, 1855
    Symplectoteuthis Pfeffer, 1900
      S. oualaniensis (Lesson, [1831])

Family CHIROTEUTHIDAE
    Chiroteuthis d'Orbigny, 1839 (= *Doratopsis* Rochebrune,
      1884)

[1] Published as *bonellii* by Férussac. The emendation to *bonelliana*, made by
d'Orbigny, is incorrect although often used.
[2] I have put this genus as a synonym although I know there is still some doubt
about its status.
[3] Voss thinks this should be *Todarodes pacificus*, see page 242.

C. *veranyi* (Férussac, 1835)
C. *imperator* Chun, 1908
C. *lacertosa* Verrill, 1881
Mastigoteuthis Verrill, 1881
M. *grimaldii* (Joubin, 1895)

Family CRANCHIIDAE
Cranchia Leach, 1817
C. *scabra* Leach, 1817
Taonius Steenstrup, 1881
T. *pavo* (Lesueur, 1821)
Belonella [1] Lane, 1957
B. *belone* (Chun, 1906)
Bathothauma Chun, 1906
B. *lyromma* Chun, 1906
Galiteuthis Joubin, 1898
Sandalops Chun, 1906
S. *pathopsis* Berry, 1920

ORDER VAMPYROMORPHA

Family VAMPYROTEUTHIDAE
Vampyroteuthis Chun, 1903
V. *infernalis* Chun, 1903

ORDER OCTOPODA
SUBORDER CIRROMORPHA

Family STAUROTEUTHIDAE
Grimpoteuthis Robson, 1932
Chunioteuthis Grimpe, 1916

Family CIRROTEUTHIDAE
Cirrothauma Chun, 1914
C. *murrayi* Chun, 1914
Cirroteuthis Eschricht, 1838

Family OPISTHOTEUTHIDAE
Opisthoteuthis Verrill, 1883

[1] *Toxeuma* Chun, 1906 (*Zool. Anz.* **31**: 86) is an invalid junior homonym of *Toxeuma* Walker, 1833 in Hymenoptera (a chalcid). I therefore propose the name *Belonella* to replace *Toxeuma* Chun. The type species, by monotypy, is T. *belone* Chun, 1906.

SUBORDER INCIRRATA

Family AMPHITRETIDAE
 Amphitretus Hoyle, 1885
  A. pelagicus Hoyle, 1885

Family VITRELEDONELLIDAE
 Vitreledonella Joubin, 1918
  V. richardi Joubin, 1918

Family OCTOPODIDAE
 Eledone Leach, 1817
  E. moschata (Lamarck, 1798)
  E. cirrhosa [1] (Lamarck, 1798)
 Octopus [2] Cuvier, [1797]
  O. vulgaris Cuvier, [1797] (? = *O. rugosus* (Bosc, 1792))
  O. arborescens (Hoyle, 1904)
  O. filamentosus Blainville, 1826
  O. apollyon (Berry, 1912)
  O. bimaculatus Verrill, 1883
  O. bimaculoides Pickford, 1949
  O. joubini Robson, 1929
  O. briareus Robson, 1929
  O. macropus Risso, 1826
  O. hongkongensis Hoyle, 1885
  O. hummelincki Adam, 1936
 Bathypolypus Grimpe, 1921
  B. arcticus (Prosch, 1849)
 Thaumeledone Robson, 1930
 Graneledone Joubin, 1918
  G. setebos Robson, 1932
 Scaeurgus Troschel, 1857 (= *Macrotritopus* Grimpe, 1922)

Family TREMOCTOPODIDAE
 Tremoctopus Delle Chiaje, 1830
  T. violaceus Delle Chiaje, 1830

Family OCYTHOIDAE
 Ocythoë Rafinesque, 1814
  O. tuberculata Rafinesque, 1814

---

[1] Fort (1941) removed this species to a new genus, *Acantheledone*.
[2] See Opinion 233 of the International Commission on Zoological Nomenclature.

Family ARGONAUTIDAE
Argonauta Linnaeus, 1758
A. argo Linnaeus, 1758
A. nodosus Solander, 1786

Note: Voss writes: "Since your first [British] edition was published, I have finished my monograph of the squids of the Philippines. In this I had to settle the systematics of the ommastrephids of the West Pacific. The species known as *sloani* belongs to the genus *Nototodarus* which occurs in various subspecies from New Zealand to the Philippines and eastward to Hawaii. It does not occur in Japan. The Japanese species, *pacificus* belongs to a different genus, *Todarodes*, of which there are two species, *pacificus* and *sagittatus* (the latter from Europe). Since the genus *Ommastrephes* applies to *bartrami*, its type, and *pteropus*, the name *Ommastrephes* cannot apply to the West Pacific species. I doubt if *Ommastrephes* is applicable to *gigas* either, but this species needs more study. But the Japanese species should certainly be given as *Todarodes pacificus*. Both Hoyle and Steenstrup used this name at one time or another but deserted it from a lack of knowledge of certain name changes in the literature."

Appendix IV COMMON AND SCIEN-TIFIC NAMES OF OTHER ANIMALS, PLANTS, ETC. MENTIONED IN THE TEXT

Well-known names such as horse, lion, palm tree, tobacco, which are referred to incidentally, have been omitted.

ANIMALS

Common Name	Scientific Name
Abalone (shellfish)	*Haliotis* Linnaeus, 1758
Albatross	*Diomedea* Linnaeus, 1758
Archer fish	*Toxotes* Cuvier & Cloquet, 1816
Barracuda	*Sphyraena* Schneider, 1801
Boa constrictor	*Boa constrictor* Linnaeus, 1758
Booby	Sulidae
Brittle star	*Ophiocoma echinata* (Lamarck, 1816)
Broadbill swordfish	*Xiphias gladius* Linnaeus, 1758
Canary	*Serinus* Brisson, 1760
Chameleon	*Chameleo* Bonnaterre, 1789
Clam (p. 27)	*Chione* Megerle, 1811
Clam, giant	*Tridacna* Bruguière, 1797
Clam, littleneck	*Protothaca jedoensis* (Lischke, 1874)
Cockle	*Laevicardium* Swainson, 1840
Cod	*Gadus callarias* Linnaeus, 1758
Coelacanth	*Latimeria* Smith, 1939
Conch (p. 139)	*Strombus* Linnaeus, 1758
Conch, five-fingered	*Pteroceras lambis* (Lamarck, 1799)
Cone shell	*Conus textile* Linnaeus, 1758
Copepod	Copepoda
Cowrie	*Cyprea* Linnaeus, 1758
Crab, common blue	*Callinectes sapidus* Rathbun, 1896

243

Common Name	Scientific Name
Crab, fiddler	Portunidae
Crab, hermit	Paguridea
Crab, shore	*Carcinus moenas* (Linnaeus, 1758)
Crayfish	*Astacus* Fabricius, 1775
Ctenophore	Ctenophora
Dogfish	*Scyliorhinus* Blainville, 1816
Dogfish, lesser spotted	*Scyliorhinus caniculus* (Linnaeus, 1758)
Dolphin	Delphinidae
Dolphin fish	*Coryphaena hippurus* Linnaeus, 1758
Eel	Anguillidae
Eel, common moray	*Gymnothorax mordax* (Ayres, [1859])
Eel, conger	*Conger* Schaeffer, 1760
Eel, giant moray	*Enchelynassa* Kaup, 1855
Eel, moray	Muraenidae
Euphausiid	Euphausiacea
Fish-like reptile	*Ichthyosaurus* [Koenig], 1818
Flying fish	Exocoetidae
Herring	*Clupea harengus* Linnaeus, 1758
Jellyfish (p. 9)	*Crambionella orsini* (Vanhöffen, 1888)
Jellyfish (p. 10)	*Cyanea* Peron & Lesueur, 1810
Jewfish	?*Stereolepis* Ayres, 1859
Lancet fish	*Alepisaurus ferox* Lowe, 1833
Limpet	*Patella* Linnaeus, 1758
Lizard	Lacertilia
Lobster	*Homarus* Weber, 1795
Lumpfish	*Cyclopterus lumpus* Linnaeus, 1758
Mackerel	*Scomber* Linnaeus, 1758
Manta ray	*Manta* Bancroft, 1829
Mussel, Californian	*Mytilus californianus* Conrad, 1837
Mussel, fan	*Pinna* Linnaeus, 1758
Oyster, common	*Ostrea* Linnaeus, 1758
Oyster, pearl	*Margaritifera* Schumacher, 1816
Penguin, emperor	*Aptenodytes forsteri* Gray, 1844
Penguin, king	*Aptenodytes patagonicus* Miller, 1778
Petrel, giant	*Macronectes giganteus* (Gmelin, 1788)
Plaice	*Pleuronectes platessa* Linnaeus, 1758
Porpoise	Phocaenidae
Prawn	Palaemonidae
Rock goby	*Gobius paganellus* Linnaeus, 1758
Sailfish	*Istiophorus* Lacépède, 1802
Salmon	*Salmo* Linnaeus, 1758
Scallop	*Pecten circularis aequisulcatus* (Carpenter, 1865)
Sea anemone	Anthozoa
Sea cucumber	Holothuroidea

Common Name	Scientific Name
Sea elephant	*Mirounga leonina* (Linnaeus, 1758)
Sea lion, Falkland Is. ..	*Otaria byronia* (Blainville, 1820)
Sea lion	Otariidae
Seal	Phocidae
Shrimp, common	*Crangon crangon* (Linnaeus, 1758)
Skate	*Raja* Linnaeus, 1758
Snail, common land ..	*Helix* Linnaeus, 1758
Snail, marine	*Tethys* Linnaeus, 1767
Spider, littoral	*Desis martensii* Koch, 1871
Sprat	*Clupea sprattus* Linnaeus, 1758
Starfish	Asteroidea
Starfish (p. 140)	*Patiria miniata* (Brandt, 1835)
Starling	*Sturnus vulgaris* Linnaeus, 1758
Thresher shark	*Alopias vulpes* (Gmelin, [1789])
Tuna	*Thunnus* South, 1845
Tuna, yellowfin	*Neothunnus macropterus* (Temminck & Schlegel, 1844)
Tunny (*see* Tuna)	
Turtle	Testudinata
Wahoo	*Acanthocybium solandri* Cuvier & Valenciennes, 1831
Whale, blue	*Balaenoptera musculus* (Linnaeus, 1758)
Whale, bottle-nosed ..	*Hyperoodon* Lacépède, 1804
Whale, pilot	*Globicephala melaena* Traill, 1809
Whale, sperm	*Physeter catodon* Linnaeus, 1758
Whale, toothed	Odontoceti
Wheel animalcule ..	Rotifera
Whiting	*Gadus merlangus* Linnaeus, 1758
Winkle	*Littorina* Férussac, 1822

PLANTS, ETC.

Common Name	Scientific Name
Arbutus	*Arbutus* Linnaeus (1707–1778)
Bay	*Laurus nobilis* Linnaeus
Cane sugar	*Saccharum officinarum* Linnaeus
Cassia	*Cassia* Linnaeus
Cedar	*Cedrus* Trew, 1757
Chrysanthemum	*Chrysanthemum morifolium* Ramatuelle, 1792
Eel grass (grass wrack) ..	*Zostera marina* Linnaeus
Fleabane	*Pulicaria* Gaertner, 1791
Garlic cloves	the bulbs of *Allium sativum* Linnaeus
Horse bean	*Vicia faba* Linnaeus
Laurel	*Laurus nobilis* Linnaeus

Common Name			*Scientific Name*
Leek	..	.. ..	*Allium porrum* Linnaeus
Lily palm ..	..	..	*Cordyline fruticosa* Chevalier, 1919
Mastic	..	.. ..	*Pistacia lentiscus* Linnaeus
Myrtle	..	.. ..	*Myrtus communis* Linnaeus
Pandanus tree	..	..	*Pandanus* Linnaeus
Parsley	..	.. ..	*Petroselinum crispum* Nyman, 1925
Patna rice ..	..	..	*Oryza sativa* Linnaeus
Pumpkin ..	..	..	*Cucurbita pepo* Linnaeus
Rattan	..	.. ..	*Calamus* Linnaeus
Rush	..	.. ..	*Juncus* Linnaeus
Sargassum	..	..	*Sargassum* Agardh, 1820
Sea lettuce	..	..	*Ulva* Linnaeus
Sesame plant	..	..	*Sesamum indicum* Linnaeus
Tamarisk ..	..	..	*Tamarix* Linnaeus
Tavo	..	..	*Caladium* Ventenant, 1800
Thorn apple	..	..	*Datura* Linnaeus
Thyme	..	..	*Thymus vulgaris* Linnaeus

Appendix V GLOSSARY

Most technical words and terms are explained on their first occurrence in the text, but readers may like to have this glossary in addition. Generally, only those words are defined which have special relevance to molluscs and cephalopods. Any words which are not explained can easily be traced in a reasonably comprehensive ordinary or technical dictionary.

Autophagy: Eating part of oneself.

Autotomy: Voluntary separation of part of the body; self-amputation.

Bathypelagic: Living in fairly deep waters but not on the sea-bed. "The pelagic animals which live below a depth of 150 to 200 meters form what is usually called the bathypelagic fauna." N. B. Marshall (1954).

Bioluminescence: Production of light by living organisms.

Buccal mass: In cephalopods, the rounded orifice containing the mouth and surrounded by tissue (the buccal membrane) at the base of the arms (see Plate 9).

Calcareous: Coated with or containing lime.

Cambrian rocks: Oldest rocks in which well-preserved fossils are found. About 500 million years old.

Carapace: Dorsal covering shield, as the shell on the back of a crab.

Cement body: Gland near the top of a spermatophore containing a glue-like fluid.

Chiroteuthid: Squid belonging to the family Chiroteuthidae.

Chitin: Horn-like material composing pen of squids. Also found in skeletal material of insects, crustaceans, etc.

Chromatophore: Tiny, transparent, elastic cell filled with pigment.

Cilia: Microscopic hair-like processes which beat rhythmically.

Ciliated: Bearing cilia.

Collar: In cephalopods, the free edge of the mantle in squids, etc., at the "neck."

Conchiolin: Horn-like material in some molluscan shells, as in *Spirula*.

Continental slope: An inclination of the ocean floor, near the continental land masses.

Coprolite: Fossilized dung.

Decapod: In cephalopods, those species possessing eight arms and two ten-tacles.

Dibranch: Possessing two gills; the name applied to all living cephalopods except *Nautilus*.

Distal: Away from the center of the body.

Doratopsis stage: Larval form of the chiroteuthids.

Dorsal: Back, or upper, surface. Opposite to ventral.

Dymantic response: Reaction to fear or disturbance characterized by changes in coloration and appearance.

Embryo: In cephalopods, the immature organism before it emerges from the egg.

Enoploteuthid: Squid belonging to the family Enoploteuthidae.

Enzyme: Chemical from living animal inducing or accelerating fermenta-tion, digestion and other biochemical processes. An "organic catalyst."

Epithelium: Tissue forming a covering, internal or external.

Exoskeleton: Hard, external, supporting or protective structures, character-istic of crustaceans, insects and other arthropods.

Funnel: In cephalopods, the tube on the ventral side of the body used to ex-pel water from the mantle cavity.

Ganglion (plural ganglia): Group of nerve cells forming a nerve center.

Gonad: Sex gland in which the sperm or eggs are formed.

Guanin (guanine): White insoluble compound formed by the breakdown of protein.

Hectocotylus (plural hectocotyli): Arm of cephalopods modified into a sex organ.

Histioteuthid: Squid belonging to the family Histioteuthidae.

Iridocyte (iridophore): Tiny cell containing reflector platelets of guanin.

Larva (plural larvae): Self-supporting immature form of an animal differing markedly from the adult in structure.

Lobe: A rounded or flap-like projection.

Luciferase: An enzyme found in some animals which induces oxidation of luciferine to produce luminescence.

Luciferine: A protein-like substance found in some animals which, in the presence of luciferase, becomes oxidized to produce luminescence.

Mantle: In molluscs, covering of skin and sometimes muscle, enclosing the visceral mass.

Mantle cavity: Space enclosed between the mantle and the visceral mass. More strictly: a space excavated from the visceral mass and covered by a reduplication, or fold, of the mantle. The phrase is also used to denote the entire cavity formed by the mantle in cephalopods "and thus contains the visceral mass, neck, part of the funnel, etc. Techni-cally speaking, it is the cavity, or space, between the surfaces of all of these various parts and the inner wall of the mantle." Gilbert L. Voss.

Median line: That which divides the body into two equal symmetrical parts

Mesozoic era: Rocks laid down between some 70 and 200 million years ago. The age of the dinosaurs.

Müller's organ: In cephalopods, glandular tissue in the funnel.

Needham's sack: Reservoir for the temporary storage of spermatophores before they are used in fertilization.

Nerve-fiber: Unit of conduction of the nervous system, including the nerve center, or axon, and covering, or sheath.

Nidamental gland: Organ which secretes covering for eggs.

Ommastrephid: Squid belonging to the family Ommastrephidae.

Oviduct: In cephalopods, tube which leads from the ovarian chamber to the ventral mantle cavity.

Oxidation: Chemical combination of oxygen with some other element or compound.

Papilla: Small pimple-like projection.

Pedicle: Small stalk-like structure.

Pelagic: Living—often drifting—in open water, especially on the surface and in middle depths of the sea.

Pen: Shell of squids.

Photophore: Luminous organ, generally very small.

Phylum: Major subdivision of the animal kingdom, as Mollusca, Arthropoda. There are some twenty phyla altogether. All vertebrates are included in the Chordata.

Planktologist: Specialist on plankton.

Plankton: Floating or drifting animals and plants, generally very small. Of great importance as food for fishes and whales.

Radula: Dental ribbon of minute horn-like teeth on the upper front surface of the tongue of most molluscs.

Regeneration: Replacement of a part of the body which has been lost or damaged.

Rhynchoteuthis stage: Larval form of the ommastrephids.

Sagittal section: Drawing or diagram of an animal as if it were cut in half along the longitudinal median line.

Schematic: Of the nature of a diagram or plan, as opposed to a drawing.

Sepioid: Cephalopod belonging to the suborder Sepioidea.

Septum (plural septa): Partition between cavities.

Sessile: Attached directly, opposite to stalked.

Siphon: *See* Funnel.

Siphuncle: In cephalopods, delicate hose-like extension from the visceral mass that runs through all the chambers of the shell in *Nautilus* and *Spirula*.

Spadix: In cephalopods, the cone-shaped organ in *Nautilus*, formed by four of the small inner tentacles, which acts in the same way as the hectocotylus in other cephalopods.

Spermatophore: Capsule, generally small, containing sperm cells.

Sperm duct: Tube leading from the gonad to the external male organ.

Spiral filament: Spring-like structure at the top of a spermatophore.

Statocyst: Organ of balance.

Symbiote (symbiont): Organism living in mutually beneficial partnership with another.

Tetrabranch: Possessing four gills, the name applied to *Nautilus,* all other living cephalopods being dibranchs.

Teuthologist: Specialist on cephalopods.

Veliger: Larval form of most molluscs. Does not occur in cephalopods.

Velum: In molluscs, the ciliated locomotor organ of the veliger.

Ventral: Under, or belly, surface. Opposite of dorsal.

Visceral mass: In cephalopods, the internal organs enclosed by the mantle: hearts, gills, stomach, etc.

Wall: Tissue lining an organ or body cavity.

Web: In cephalopods, membrane connecting the arms in many species.

Note: There are differences of opinion on the correct adjectives for cephalopod and octopus. Generally, I have used cephalopodan and octopodan with non-physical nouns (cephalopodan systematics, the octopodan temperament) and cephalopod and octopus with physical nouns (cephalopod blood, octopus ink).

BIBLIOGRAPHY

The abbreviations of the titles of scientific periodicals generally follow those approved by *The World List of Scientific Periodicals* (1952) London: Butterworth. A small proportion of the entries has not been seen personally.

CHAPTER I

CEPHALOPODS

ABBOTT, R. TUCKER (1954): *American seashells.* New York: Van Nostrand

ABEL, O. (1916): *Paläobiologie der Cephalopoden aus der Gruppe der Dibranchiaten.* Jena: Gustav Fischer

—— (1922): *Lebensbilder aus der Tierwelt der Vorzeit.* Jena: Gustav Fischer

ADAM, W. (1940): Les races de la seiche commune (*Sepia officinalis* Linné). *Bull. Soc. zool. Fr.* **65**: 125–131

—— (1952): Résultats scientifiques des expédition océanographique belge dans les eaux côtières africaines de l'Atlantique Sud. (1948–1949). Céphalopodes. *Résult. sci. Expéd. océan. belg. Eaux côt. afr.* (*1948–1949*). 3 3: 1–142

AGASSIZ, ALEXANDER (1865): *Illustrated catalogue of the Museum of Comparative Zoölogy, at Harvard College.* Cambridge, Mass.: Sever & Francis

AKIMUSHKIN, I. I. (1954): [New data on the geographical distribution of cephalopod molluscs in the Far Eastern Waters.] *Dokl. Akad. nauk S.S.S.R.* **94**: 1181–1184 [in Russian]

—— (1955): [*Atlas of the invertebrates of the far eastern seas of U.S.S.R.* (Cephalopoda: 198–202).] Moscow, Leningrad: Zoological Institute, Academy of Sciences U.S.S.R. [in Russian]

ALLAN, JOYCE (1950): *Australian shells.* Melbourne: Georgian House

APPELLÖF, A. (1893): Die Schalen von *Sepia, Spirula* und *Nautilus. K. svenska Vetensk-Akad. Handl.* 25 7: 1–105

ATZ, JAMES W. (1940): The timid octopus. *Bull. N.Y. zool. Soc.* **43** 2: 48–54

BARTSCH, PAUL (1917): Pirates of the deep—stories of the squid and octopus. *Rep. Smithson. Instn.* 1916: 347–375

—— (1931): The octopuses, squids and their kin. *Smithson. Sci. Ser.* **10**: 321–356. New York: published privately by the Smithsonian Institution Series, Inc.

BASSE, ÉLIANE, DELÉPINE, G. & ROGER, JEAN (1952): Classe des céphalopodes in Piveteau's *Traité de Paleontologie* **2**: 461–755. Paris: Masson

BENHAM, W. B. (1942): The octopodous Mollusca of New Zealand. 1. The midget octopus of the coastal waters. *Trans. roy. Soc. N.Z.* **72**: 226–236

—— (1943): The octopodous Mollusca of New Zealand. *Trans. roy. Soc. N.Z.* **73**: 53–57

—— (1943): The octopodous Mollusca of New Zealand. 3. The giant octopus, *Macroctopus maorum* (Hutton)—in youth, adolescence and maturity. *Trans. roy. Soc. N.Z.* **73**: 139–153

BERRY, S. STILLMAN (1912): A review of the cephalopods of western North America. *Bul. U.S. Bur. Fish.* **30**: 269–336

—— (1913): Notes on some West American cephalopods. *Proc. Acad. nat. Sci. Philad.* **65**: 72–77

—— (1914): The Cephalopoda of the Hawaiian Islands. *Bull. U.S. Bur. Fish.* **32**: 255–362

—— (1916): Cephalopoda of the Kermadec Islands. *Proc. Acad. nat. Sci. Philad.* **68**: 45–66

—— (1918): Report on the Cephalopoda. *Zool. Res. Fish. Exp. "Endeavour"* **4**: 203–298

—— (1920): Light production in cephalopods. *Biol. Bull., Woods Hole* **38**: 141–195

—— (1952): The flapjack devilfish, *Opisthoteuthis*, in California. *Calif. Fish Game* **38**: 183–188

BIERENS DE HAAN, J. A. (1926): Versuche über den Farbensinn und das psychische Leben von *Octopus vulgaris. Z. vergl. Physiol.* **4**: 766–796

BØGGILD, O. B. (1930): The shell structure of the mollusks. *K. danske vidensk. Selsk.* (9) **2**: 231–325

BORRADAILE, L. A., POTTS, F. A., EASTHAM, L. E. S. & SAUNDERS, J. T. (1958): *The Invertebrata.* Ed. revised by G. A. Kerkut. Cambridge: University Press

BOYCOTT, B. B. (1958): The cuttlefish—*Sepia. New Biol.* No. 25: 98–118

BRELAND, OSMOND P. (1953): Which are the biggest? *Nat. Hist., N.Y.* **62**: 67–71, 96

BRUUN, ANTON FR. (1943): The biology of *Spirula spirula* (L.). *Dana-Rep.* No. 24: 1–44

—— (1945): Cephalopoda. *Zoology of Iceland* 4 **64**: 1–15. Copenhagen: Carlsberg Fond.

—— (1955): New light on the biology of *Spirula*, a mesopelagic cephalopod. *Essays in the natural sciences in honor of Captain Allan Hancock:* 61–72. Los Angeles: University S. California Press

BRUUN, ANTON FR., Greve, Sv., Mielche, Hakon & Spärck, Ragnar (1956): *The "Galathea" Deep Sea Expedition 1950–1952.* Trans. by Spink, Reginald. New York: Macmillan

BUCHANAN, J. Y. (1919): *Accounts rendered.* Cambridge: University Press

BÜLOW-TRUMMER, E. v. (1920): Cephalopoda Dibranchiata in *Fossilium Catalogus I: Animalia.* Berlin: Junk

BUYTENDIJK, F. J. J. (1933): Das Verhalten von Octopus nach teilweiser Zerstörung des "Gehirns." *Arch. néerl. Physiol.* (3c) **18**: 24–70

[CHANG HSI & HSIANG-LI CHÜ] (n.d.): [*Maritime edible Mollusca of the Kiaochow Bay and adjacent Seas.*] Peking [in Chinese]

[CHANG HSI, CH'I CHUNG-YEN & LI CHIEH-MIN] (1955): [*Maritime economic Mollusca of North China.*] Peking [in Chinese]

CHUN, CARL (1910): Die Cephalopoden. *Wiss. Ergebn. "Valdivia"* **18**: 1–552

—— (1914): Cephalopoda from the "Michael Sars" North Atlantic Deep-Sea Expedition, 1910. *Rep. Sars N. Atl. Deep Sea Exped.* **3**:1–28

CLARK, AUSTIN H. (1948): *Animals alive.* New York: Van Nostrand

COTTON, BERNARD C. & GODFREY, FRANK K. (1938–40): *The molluscs of South Australia* Pt. 2. Adelaide: Frank Trigg

COZZI, SILVIA (1938): Prime ricerche sulla Seppia del Mar Ligure. *Boll. Mus. Zool. Anat. comp. Genova* **18**: 125–127

CUÉNOT, L. (1917): *Sepia officinalis* L. est une espèce en voie de dissociation. *Arch. Zool. exp. gén.* **56**: 315–346

—— (1933): Le seiche commune de la Méditerranée–étude sur la naissance d'une espèce. *Arch. Zool. exp. gén.* **75**: 319–330

DALL, WILLIAM H. (1885): The arms of the octopus, or devil fish. *Science* **6**: 432

DATHE, HEINRICH (1950): Uber Schulp-Missbildungen bei *Sepia officinalis*. *Arch. Molluskenk.* **79**: 21–24

DEAN, BASHFORD (1901): Notes on living *Nautilus*. *Amer. Nat.* **35**: 819–837, 1029

DEGNER, E. (1926): Cephalopoda. *Rep. Danish oceanogr. Exped. Medit.* **2**: 1–94

DELL, R. K. (1952): The recent Cephalopoda of New Zealand. *Dominion Mus. Bull.* No. 16

FÉRUSSAC, A. DE & ORBIGNY A. D' (1835–1848): *Histoire naturelle générale et particulière des céphalopodes acetabulifères vivants et fossiles.* Paris: Baillière (quarto), Lacour (folio)

FISCHER, P.–H. (1950): *Vie et moeurs des mollusques.* Paris: Payot

FLOWER, ROUSSEAU H. (1955): Status of endoceroid classification. *J. Paleont.* **29**: 329–371

FLOWER, ROUSSEAU H. & KUMMEL, B., JR. (1950): A classification of the Nautiloidea. *J. Paleont.* **24**: 604–616

FREDERICQ, LÉON (1878): Sur l'organisation et la physiologie du poulpe. *Bull. Acad. Belg. Cl. Sci.* **46**: 710–765 reprinted in *Léon Fredericq, un pionnier de la physiologie* (1953)—volume publié à l'occasion du centenaire de sa naissance. Physiologie et biochimie comparées: 149–166. Liège: Sciences et Lettres

GARSTANG, WALTER (1900): The plague of *Octopus* on the South Coast, and its effect on the crab and lobster fisheries. *J. Mar. biol. Ass. U.K.* **6**: 260–273

GIROD, P. (1883 & 1884): Recherches sur la peau des céphalopodes. *Arch. Zool. exp. gén.* (2) **1**: 225–226; (2) **2**: 379–401

GRIFFIN, L. E. (1900): On the anatomy of *Nautilus pompilius*. *Mem. nat. Acad. Sci.* **8**: 101–179

GRIMPE, GEORG (1921): Teuthologische Mitteilungen 7.–Systematische Ubersicht der Nordseecephalopoden. *Zool. Anz.* **52**: 296–304

—— (1922): Systematische Ubersicht der europaischen Cephalopoden. *S.B. naturf. Ges. Lpz.* **45–48**: 36–52

—— (1925): Zur Kenntnis der Cephalopodenfauna der Nordsee. *Wiss. Meeresuntersuchungen. Biol. Anst., Helgoland* **16** 3: 1–124

HARDY, ALISTER C. (1957): *The open sea.* Boston: Houghton Mifflin

HILLIG, R. (1912): Das Nervensystem von *Sepia officinalis* L. *Z. wiss. Zool.* **101**: 736–806

HOLDER, CHARLES FREDERICK (1909): First photographs ever made of a paper nautilus. *Country Life in Amer.* **15**: 356–358, 404, 406, 408

HOLMES, ARTHUR (1944): *Principles of physical geology.* London: Thomas Nelson

HOYLE, WILLIAM E. (1885): Report on the Cephalopoda. *Rep. sci. Res. H.M.S. "Challenger."* (Zool.) **16** 44: 1–245

—— (1902): British Cephalopoda: their nomenclature and identification. *J. Conch.* **10**: 197–206

HUXLEY, THOMAS H. (1859): On some points in the anatomy of *Nautilus pompilius*. *J. Linn. Soc. Lond.* (Zool.) **3**: 36–44

IREDALE, TOM (1944): Australian pearly nautilus. *Aust. Zool.* **10**: 294–298

—— (1954): Cuttle-fish "bones" again. *Aust. Zool.* **12**: 63–82

ISGROVE, ANNIE (1909): *Eledone. L.M.B.C. Mem.* No. 18

ISSEL, RAFFAELE (1931): Cefalopodi. *Enciclopedia Italiana* **9**: 638–646. Milan: Bestetti & Tumminelli

JAECKEL, SIEGFRIED G. A., JR. (1958): Cephalopoda in Remane's *Tierwelt der Nord-und Ostsee* **9**. Leipzig: Akademischen

JATTA, GIUSEPPE (1896): I cephalopodi viventi nel Golfo di Napoli. *Fauna u. Flora Neapel* Monogr. 23

254 BIBLIOGRAPHY

JOUBIN, LOUIS (1895): Contribution à l'étude des céphalopodes de l'Atlantique Nord. *Résult. Camp. sci. Monaco* No. 9: 1–63
—— (1900): Céphalopodes provenant des campagnes de la "Princesse-Alice." *Résult. Camp. sci. Monaco* No. 17: 1–135
—— (1920): Céphalopodes provenant des campagnes de la "Princesse-Alice." *Résult. Camp. sci. Monaco* No. 54: 1–95
—— (1924): Contribution à l'étude des céphalopodes de l'Atlantique Nord. *Résult. Camp. sci. Monaco* No. 67: 1–113
—— (1937): Les octopodes de la croisière du "Dana" 1921–22. *Dana-Rep.* No. 11: 1–49
KONDAKOV, N. N. (1941): [Cephalopods of Far Eastern Seas of U.S.S.R.] *Investigations of Far Eastern Seas of U.S.S.R.* 1: 216–256 [in Russian with English summary]
KURODA, T. & HABE, T. (1952): *Checklist and bibliography of the recent marine Mollusca of Japan.* Tokyo: Stach
LACAZE-DUTHIERS, H. DE (1892): Observation d'un argonaute de la Méditerranée. *Arch. Zool. exp. gén.* (2) 10: 37–56
LANDOIS, HERMANN (1895): Die Riesenammoniten von Seppenrade, *Pachydiscus* Zittel *seppenradensis* H. Landois. *Jber. westf. Prov.-Ver. Wiss. Kunst* 1894–1895: 99–108
LANKESTER, E. RAY (1891): *Zoological articles.* London: Adam & Charles Black
LEE, HENRY (1875): *The octopus.* London: Chapman & Hall
—— (1883): *Sea fables explained.* London: William Clowes
—— (1884): *Sea monsters unmasked.* London: William Clowes
LISSAJOUS, M. (1925): Répertoire alphabétique des bélemnites jurassiques précédé d'un essai de classification. *Trav. Lab. Géol. Lyon* 8 7: 3–173
MACGINITIE, G. E. & MACGINITIE, NETTIE (1949): *Natural history of marine animals.* New York: McGraw-Hill
MARSHALL, N. B. (1954): *Aspects of deep sea biology.* London: Hutchinson
MASSY, A. L. (1916): Mollusca. Pt. 2. Cephalopoda. *Brit. Antarct. "Terra Nova" Exped.* 1910 (Nat. Hist. Rep. Zool.) 2: 141–175
MILLER, A. K. (1947) Tertiary nautiloids of the Americas. *Mem. geol. Soc. Amer.,* No. 23: 1–234
MINER, ROY WALDO (1935): Marauders of the sea. *Nat. geogr. Mag.* 68: 185–207
—— (1937): What is a mollusk shell? *Nat. Hist.,* N.Y. 40:399–409
MOORE, RAYMOND C. (in press): *Treatise on invertebrate paleontology.* Pts. K, L & M. Lawrence, Kansas: Geological Society of America and University of Kansas Press
MOORE, RAYMOND C., LALICKER, CECIL G. & FISCHER, ALFRED G. (1952): *Invertebrate fossils.* New York: McGraw-Hill
MORTON, J. E. (1958): *Molluscs.* London: Hutchinson University Library
MUGGLIN, F. (1939): Beiträge zur Kenntnis der Anatomie von *Nautilus macromphalus* G. B. Sowerby. *Vjschr. naturf. Ges. Zürich* 84: 25–118
NAEF, ADOLF (1921–1928): Die Cephalopoden. *Fauna u. Flora Neapel* Monogr. 35
—— (1922): *Die fossilen Tintenfische.* Jena: Gustav Fischer
NICHOLS, JOHN T. & BARTSCH, PAUL (1946): *Fishes and shells of the Pacific World.* New York: Macmillan
OWEN, RICHARD (1832): *Memoir on the pearly nautilus* (Nautilus pompilius). London: Wood
—— (1839): On the paper nautilus (*Argonauta argo*). *Proc. zool. Soc. Lond.* 1839: 35–48
—— (1855): *Lectures on the comparative anatomy and physiology of invertebrate animals.* London: Longman
PARKER, T. JEFFREY & HASWELL, WILLIAM A. (1947): *A text-book of zoology.* Ed. revised by Otto Lowenstein. London: Macmillan

BIBLIOGRAPHY 255

PELSENEER, PAUL (1906): Mollusca in Lankester's *Treatise on zoology* Pt. 5. London: Adam & Charles Black

—— (1935): *Essai d'éthologie zoologique d'après l'étude des mollusques.* Bruxelles: Palais des Académies

PFEFFER, GEORG (1912): Die Cephalopoden der Plankton-Expedition. *Ergebn. Planktonexped.* Pt. 2. Kiel & Leipzig: Lipsius & Tischer

PICKFORD, GRACE EVELYN (1940): The Vampyromorpha, living-fossil Cephalopoda. *Trans. N.Y. Acad. Sci.* (2) **2**: 169–181

—— (1945): Le poulpe américain: a study of the littoral Octopoda of the Western Atlantic. *Trans. Conn. Acad. Arts Sci.* **36**: 701–782

—— (1946): *Vampyroteuthis infernalis* Chun. 1. Natural history and distribution. *Dana-Rep.* No. 29: 1–45

—— (1949): *Vampyroteuthis infernalis* Chun. 2. External anatomy. *Dana-Rep.* No. 32: 1–131

—— (1950): The Vampyromorpha (Cephalopoda) of the Bermuda Oceanographic Expeditions. *Zoologica* **35**: 87–95

—— (1952): The Vampyromorpha of the "Discovery" Expeditions. *Discovery Rep.* **26**: 197–210

—— (1955): A revision of the Octopodinae in the collections of the British Museum. *Bull. Brit. Mus. (nat. Hist.)* (Zool.) **3**: 151–167

PIERCE, MADELENE E. (1950): *Loligo pealeii* in Brown's *Selected invertebrate types.* New York: John Wiley

PORTMANN, ADOLPHE (in press): Céphalopodes in Grassé's *Traité de Zoologie* **5**. Paris: Masson

POWER, JEANETTE (1845): Further experiments and observations on the *Argonauta argo. Rep. Brit. Ass.* **1844**: 74–77

PRUVOT-FOL, ALICE (1937): Remarques sur le nautile. *Int. Congr. Zool.* **12**: 1652–1663

RAVEN, CHR. P. (in press): *Morphogenesis: the analysis of molluscan development.* London: Pergamon

REDFIELD, ALFRED C. (1934): The haemocyanins. *Biol. Rev.* **9**: 175–212

REDFIELD, ALFRED C. & GOODKIND, ROBERT (1929): The significance of the Bohr effect in the respiration and asphyxiation of the squid, *Loligo pealei. Brit. J. exp. Biol.* **6**: 340–349

REES, W. J. (1950): The distribution of *Octopus vulgaris* Lamarck in British waters. *J. Mar. biol. Ass. U.K.* **29**: 361–378

REES, W. J. & LUMBY, J. R. (1954): The abundance of *Octopus* in the English Channel. *J. Mar. biol. Ass. U.K.* **33**: 515–536

ROBSON, G. C. (1924): On the Cephalopoda obtained in South African waters by Dr. J. D. F. Gilchrist in 1920–21. *Proc. zool. Soc. Lond.* **1924**: 589–686

—— (1925): Cephalopoda in Hutchinson's *Animals of all countries* **4**: 2145–2177. London: Hutchinson

—— (1925): The deep-sea Octopoda. *Proc. zool. Soc. Lond.* **1925**: 1323–1356

—— (1929 & 1932): *A monograph of the recent Cephalopoda.* Octopoda. London: British Museum (Nat. Hist.)

—— (1954): Cephalopoda. *Encyclopaedia Britannica* **5**: 148–156. London: Encyclopaedia Britannica

ROCHE, J. (1933): La composition élémentaire des hémocyanines et leur spécificité. *C. R. Soc. Biol., Paris* **114**: 1190–1192

ROGERS, JULIA ELLEN (1951): *The shell book.* Boston, Mass.: Charles Branford

SASAKI, MADOKA (1929): A monograph of the dibranchiata cephalopods of the Japanese and adjacent waters. *J. Fac. Agric. Hokkaido Imp. Univ.* **20** Suppl.: 1–357

SCHMIDT, JOHANNES (1922): Live specimens of *Spirula. Nature, Lond.* **110**: 788–790

SHROCK, ROBERT R. & TWENHOFEL, WILLIAM H. (1953): *Principles of invertebrate paleontology*. New York: McGraw-Hill

SINEL, JOSEPH (1906): *An outline of the natural history of our shores*. London: Sonnenschein

SLEPZOV, M. M. (1955): On the biology of cephalopodan molluscs of the far eastern seas and the north west Pacific. *Trud. Inst. Okeanol.* 18: 69–77

SPATH, L. F. (1934 & 1951): *Catalogue of the fossil Cephalopoda in the British Museum (Natural History)*. London: British Museum (Nat. Hist.)

SQUIRES, H. J. (1957): Squid, *Illex illecebrosus* (LeSueur), in the Newfoundland fishing area. *J. Fish. Res. Bd. Canada* 14: 693–728

STEINBACH, H. B. (1951): The squid. *Sci. Amer.* 184 4:64–69

STEINMAN, G. (1925): Beiträge zur Stammesgeschichte der Cephalopoden. 1. Argonauta und die Ammoniten. *Z. indukt. abst.* 36: 350–416

STENZEL, H. B. (1948): Ecology of living nautiloids. *Nat. Res. Council, Rept. Comm. Treatise Marine Ecology and Paleoecology*, 1947–1948: 84–90

STEP, EDWARD (1945): *Shell life*. Ed. revised by A. Laurence Wells. London: Warne

STEPHEN, A. C. (1944): The Cephalopoda of Scottish and adjacent waters. *Trans. roy. Soc. Edinb.* 61: 247–270

THIELE, J. (1926): Mollusca in Kükenthal & Krumbach's *Handbuch der Zoologie* 5 2: 97–176; 5 3: 177–256. Berlin & Leipzig: Gruyter

—— (1929–1935): *Handbuch der systematischen Weichtierkunde*. Jena: Gustav Fischer

THOMPSON, D'ARCY WENTWORTH (1940): *Science and the classics*. Oxford: University Press

THOMSON, J. ARTHUR (1935): *Biology for everyman*. New York: Dutton

THORE, SVEN (1949): Investigations on the "Dana" Octopoda; Pt. 1. Bolitaenidae, Amphitretidae, Vitreledonellidae and Alloposidae. *Dana-Rep.* No. 33: 1–85

TINBERGEN, L. & VERWEY, J. (1945): Zur Biologie von *Loligo vulgaris* Lam. *Arch. néerl. Zool.* 7: 213–285

TOMPSETT, DAVID H. (1939): *Sepia*. *L.M.B.C. Mem.* No. 32

TRYON, GEORGE W., JR. (1879): *Manual of conchology*. 1. Cephalopoda. Philadelphia: Tryon

TUREK, R. (1933): Chemisch-analytische Untersuchungen an Molluskenschalen. *Arch. Naturgesch.* (N.F.) 2: 291–302

VALENCIENNES, ACHILLE (1841): Nouvelles recherches sur le nautile flambé (*Nautilus pompilius* Lam.). *Arch. Mus. Hist. nat., Paris* 2: 257–314

VERANY, JEAN BAPTISTE (1851): *Mollusques méditerranéens*. Geneva: Sourds-Muets

VERNEUIL, M. P. (1924): *Étude de la mer*. Paris: Albert Levy

VERRILL, A. E. (1879–1881): The cephalopods of the north-eastern coast of America. *Trans. Conn. Acad. Arts Sci.* 5: 177–446

VOSS, GILBERT L. (1955): The Cephalopoda obtained by the Harvard-Havana Expedition off the coast of Cuba in 1938–39. *Bull. Mar. Sci. Gulf Caribbean* 5: 81–115

—— (1956): A review of the cephalopods of the Gulf of Mexico. *Bull. Mar. Sci. Gulf Caribbean* 6: 85–178

WILLEY, ARTHUR (1902): *Zoological results*. Cambridge: University Press

WILLIAMS, LEONARD WORCESTER (1909): *The anatomy of the common squid, Loligo pealii, Lesueur*. Leiden: Brill

WILLIAMS, WOODY (1951): Friend octopus. *Nat. Hist. N.Y.* 60: 210–215

WINCKWORTH, R. (1932): The British marine Mollusca. *J. Conch.* 19: 211–252

—— (1950): Cephalopoda. *Chambers's Encyclopaedia* 3: 239–240. London: George Newnes

WINKLER, LINDSAY R. & ASHLEY, LAURENCE M. (1954): The anatomy of the common octopus of northern Washington. *Contr. Allan Hancock Fdn.* No. 143

YAMAMOTO, TAKAHARU (1942): On the distribution of cephalopods in Korea. *Venus, Kyoto* 11: 126–133

YONGE, C. M. (1947): The pallial organs in the aspidobranch Gastropoda and their evolution throughout the Mollusca. *Phil. Trans.* B.232: 443–518

CHAPTER II

FOOD

ADAM, W. (1941): Notes sur les céphalopodes. 15. Sur la valeur diagnostique de la radule chez les céphalopodes octopodes. *Bull. Mus. Hist. nat. Belg.* 17: No. 38

ALEXANDROWICZ, J. S. (1928): Notes sur l'innervation du tube digestif des céphalopodes. *Arch. Zool. exp. gén.* Notes & Rev. 67: 69–90

BACQ, Z. M. (1951): Isolement et perfusion des glandes salivaires postérieures des céphalopodes octopodes. *Arch. int. Physiol.* 59: 273–287

BACQ, Z. M., FISCHER, P. & GHIRETTI, FR. (1952): Action de la 5-hydroxytryptamine chez les céphalopodes. *Arch. int. Physiol.* 60: 165–171

BACQ, Z. M. & GHIRETTI, F. (1951): La sécrétion externe et interne des glandes salivaires postérieures des céphalopodes octopodes. *Bull. Acad. Belg. Cl. Sci.* (5) 37: 79–102

BARTSCH, PAUL (1917): Pirates of the deep—stories of the squid and octopus. *Rep. Smithson. Instn.* 1916: 347–375

—— (1931): The octopuses, squids, and their kin. *Smithson. Sci. Ser.* 10: 321–356. New York: published privately by the Smithsonian Institution Series, Inc.

BERGE, VICTOR & LANIER, HENRY WYSHAM (1930): *Pearl diver.* London: Heinemann

BERRY, S. STILLMAN & HALSTEAD, BRUCE W. (1954): Octopus bites—a second report. *Leafl. Malacol.* 1 11: 59–66

BIDDER, ANNA M. (1950): The digestive mechanism of the European squids, *Loligo vulgaris, Loligo forbesii, Alloteuthis media* and *Alloteuthis subulata. Quart. J. micr. Sci.* 91: 1–43

—— (1957): Evidence for an absorptive function in the "liver" of *Octopus vulgaris* Lam. *Pubbl. Staz. zool. Napoli* 29: 139–150

BORRADAILE, L. A., POTTS, F. A., EASTHAM, L. E. S. & SAUNDERS, J. T. (1958): *The Invertebrata.* Ed. revised by G. A. Kerkut. Cambridge: University Press

BOTAZZI, F. & VALENTINI, V. (1924): Nuove ricerche sul veleno della saliva di *Octopus macropus. Arch. Sci. biol., Napoli* 6: 153–168

BOURQUELOT, E. (1882): Digestion chez les céphalopodes. *Arch. Zool. exp. gén.* 10: 385–421

—— (1885): Recherches sur les phénomènes de la digestion chez les mollusques céphalopodes. *Arch. Zool. exp. gén.* (2) 3: 1–73

BOYCOTT, B. B. (1954): Learning in *Octopus vulgaris* and other cephalopods. *Pubbl. Staz. zool. Napoli* 25: 67–93

—— (1958): The cuttlefish—*Sepia. New Biol.* No. 25: 98–118

BRISTOWE, W. S. (1941): *The comity of spiders.* London: Ray Society

BURFORD, VIRGIL (1954): *North to danger.* New York: John Day

DAKIN, WILLIAM J. (1953): *Australian seashores.* London: Angus & Robertson

DALL, WILLIAM H. (1885): The arms of the octopus, or devil fish. *Science* 6: 432

DAVIS, J. CHARLES, 2ND (1949): *California salt water fishing.* New York: Barnes

DUNCAN, DAVID D. (1941): Fighting giants of the Humboldt. *Nat. geogr. Mag.* 79: 373–400

ENRIQUES, PAOLO (1901): Il fegato dei Molluschi e le sue funzioni. *Mitt. zool. Stat. Neapel* 15: 281–407

ERSPAMER, V. & ASERO, B. (1953): Isolation of enteramine from extracts of posterior salivary glands of *Octopus vulgaris* and of *Discoglossus pictus* skin. *J. biol. Chem.* **200**: 311–318

ERSPAMER, V. & OTTOLENGHI, A. (1950): Antidiuretic action of enteramine. *Experientia, Basel* **6** 1: 428

FALLOISE, A. (1905–1906): Contribution à la physiologie comparée de la digestion. La digestion chez les Céphalopodes. *Arch. int. Physiol.* **3**: 282–305

FISCHER, P.–H. (1939): Sur les terriers des poulpes. *Bull. Lab. marit. Dinard* No. 20: 92–94

FLECKER, H. & COTTON, BERNARD C. (1955): Fatal bite from octopus. *Med. J., Austr.* **2** (42nd year): 429–431

FRITSCH, RUDOLF H. (1938): Das "Bauen" des *Octopus* und andere Beobachtungen an Cephalopoden. *Zool. Anz.* Suppl. **11**: 119–126

GARIAEFF, V. P. (1916): [The structure of the digestive tract of certain cephalopods.] *Trav. Soc. Nat. Kharkov* **48** 2: 1–122 [in Russian]

GIBBINGS, ROBERT (1949): *Over the reefs.* New York: Dutton

GIBSON, JOHN (1887): *Monsters of the sea.* London: Thomas Nelson

GILL, WILLIAM WYATT (1876): *Life in the Southern Isles.* London: Religious Tract Society

GILPATRIC, GUY (1938): *The compleat goggler.* New York: Dodd, Mead

GORSKY, BERNARD (1954): *Mediterranean hunter.* London: Souvenir Press

GOSSE, PHILIP HENRY (1854): *The aquarium.* London: Van Voorst

GRIMBLE, ARTHUR (1952): *We chose the islands.* New York: William Morrow

GUÉRIN, J. (1908): Contribution à l'étude des systèmes cutané, musculaire et nerveux de l'appareil tentaculaire des céphalopodes. *Arch. Zool. exp. gén.* (4) **8**: 1–178

HALSTEAD, BRUCE W. (1949): Octopus bites in human beings. *Leafl. Malacol.* **1** 5: 17–22

HANSTROM, B. (1939): *Hormones in invertebrates.* Oxford: Clarendon Press

HOLDER, CHARLES FREDERICK (1899): Some Pacific cephalopods. *Sci. Amer.* **80**: 253

—— (1908): *Big game at sea.* London: Hodder & Stoughton

HOLZLÖHNER, E. & NIESSING, K. (1938): Über den Feinbau und die Sekretion der hinteren Speicheldrüsen von Octopoden. *Anat. Anz.* **87**: 113–125

HORNELL, JAMES (1893): Observations on the habits of marine animals. Ser. 1. *J. mar. Zool.* **1**: 9–12

HUGO, VICTOR (1866): *Toilers of the sea.* Translated by W. Moy Thomas. London: Sampson Low

ISGROVE, ANNIE (1909): *Eledone. L.M.B.C. Mem.* No. 18.

JEFFREYS, JOHN GWYN (1869): *British conchology* **5**: 121–148. London: Van Voorst

KLINGEL, GILBERT C. (1940): *Inagua.* New York: Dodd, Mead

LANGE, MATHILDE M. (1920): On the regeneration and finer structure of the arms of the cephalopods. *J. exp. Zool.* **31**: 1–40

LAWRENCE, D. H. (1956): *Sea and Sardinia.* New York: Viking Press

LEE, HENRY (1875): *The octopus.* London: Chapman & Hall

LO BIANCO, SALVATORE (1909): Notizie biologiche riguardanto specialmente il periodo di maturitá sessuale degli animali del Golfo di Napoli. *Mitt. zool. Stat. Neapel* **19**: 513–761

MACGINITIE, G. E. (1938): Notes on the natural history of some marine animals. *Amer. Midl. Nat.* **19**: 207–219

MACGINITIE, G. E. & MACGINITIE, NETTIE (1949): *Natural history of marine animals.* New York: McGraw-Hill

MASSY, A. L. (1916): Mollusca. Pt. 2. Cephalopoda. *Brit. Antarct. "Terra Nova" Exped. 1910* (Nat. Hist. Rep. Zool.) **2**: 141–175

MENARD, WILMON (1947): Hunting the giant octopus. *Wide World Mag.* **99**: 203–207

BIBLIOGRAPHY 259

MEYER, WERNER TH. (1913): Tintenfische in Ziegler & Woltereck's *Monographien einheimischer Tiere* 6. Leipzig: Klinkhardt

NAEF, ADOLF (1921): Die Cephalopoden. *Fauna u. Flora Neapel* Monogr. 35, Pt. 1

NAKAZIMA, MASAO (1956): On the structure and function of the midgut gland of Mollusca, with a general consideration of the feeding habits and systematic relations. *Jap. J. Zool.* 11: 469–566

OWEN, RICHARD (1855): *Lectures on the comparative anatomy and physiology of the invertebrate animals*. London: Longman

—— (1885): Descriptions of some new and rare Cephalopoda. *Trans. zool. Soc. Lond.* 11: 131–170

PARKER, G. H. (1921): The power of adhesion in the suckers of *Octopus bimaculatus* Verrill. *J. exp. Zool.* 33: 391–394

PEILE, A. J. (1936): Some radula problems. *J. Conch.* 20: 292–304

PHILLIPS, J. B. (1933): Octopi of California. *Calif. Fish Game* 20 1: 20–29

PHISALIX, MARIE (1922): *Animaux venimeux et venins*. Paris: Masson

ROBSON, G. C. (1925): On seriation and asymmetry in the cephalopod radula. *J. Linn. Soc. Lond.* (Zool.), 36: 99–108

—— (1929 & 1932): *A monograph of the recent Cephalopoda*. Octopoda. London: British Museum (Nat. Hist.)

—— (1930): Cephalopoda. 1. Octopoda. *Discovery Rep.* 2: 371–402

—— (1932): Report on the Cephalopoda in the Raffles Museum. *Bull. Raffles Mus.* 7: 21–33

—— (1954): Cephalopoda. *Encyclopaedia Britannica* 5: 148–156. London: Encyclopaedia Britannica

ROMANINI, M. G. (1952): Osservazioni sulla ialuronidasi delle ghiandole salivari anteriori e posteriori degli octopodi. *Pubbl. Staz. zool. Napoli* 23: 251–270

ROMIJN, C. (1935): Die Verdauungsenzyme bei einigen Cephalopoden. *Arch. néerl. Zool.*, 1: 373–431

ROSSI, FERDINANDO & GRAZIADEI, PASQUALE (1954): Nouvelles recherches sur le système nerveux du bras des céphalopodes avec des méthodes spécifique pour le tissu nerveux. *Acta anat.* 22: 202–215

ROUVILLE, E. DE (1910): Études physiologiques sur les glandes salivaires des céphalopodes, et, en particulier, sur la toxicité de leurs extraits. *C. R. Soc. Biol., Paris* 68: 834–836

—— (1910): Sur la toxicité des extraits des glandes salivaires des céphalopodes pour les mammifères. *C. R. Soc. Biol., Paris* 68: 878–880

SIMPSON, DONALD A. (1948): The octopus is an odd oaf. *Aquarium J.* 19 10: 18–21, 25

SINEL, JOSEPH (1906): *An outline of the natural history of our shores*. London: Sonnenschein

SQUIRES, H. J. (1957): Squid, *Illex illecebrosus* (LeSueur), in the Newfoundland fishing area. *J. Fish. Res. Bd. Canada* 14: 693–728

STEINBACH, H. B. (1951): The squid. *Sci. Amer.* 184 4: 64–69

STREET, PHILIP (1952): *Between the tides*. London: University Press

TAKI, IWAO (1941): On keeping octopods in an aquarium for physiological experiments with remarks on some operative techniques. *Venus, Kyoto* 10: 140–156

TINBERGEN, N. (1951): *The study of instinct*. New York: Oxford

TOMPSETT, DAVID H. (1939): *Sepia. L.M.B.C. Mem.* No. 32

TRYON, GEORGE W., JR. (1879): *Manual of conchology*, 1. Cephalopoda. Philadelphia: Tryon

VERRILL, A. E. (1879–1881): The cephalopods of the north-eastern coast of America. *Trans. Conn. Acad. Arts Sci.* 5: 177–446

VLÉS, FRED (1914): Notes sur l'alimentation artificielle du poulpe. *Bull. Soc. zool. Fr.* 39: 19–23

WELLS, M. J. & WELLS, J. (1956): Tactile discrimination and the behaviour of blind *Octopus*. *Pubbl. Staz. zool. Napoli* **28**: 94–126
WICKSTEAD, J. (1956): An unusual method of capturing prey by a cuttlefish. *Nature, Lond.* **178**: 929
WILLIAMS, LEONARD WORCESTER (1909): *The anatomy of the common squid, Loligo pealii, Lesueur.* Leiden: Brill
WILSON, DOUGLAS P. (1946): A note on the capture of prey by *Sepia officinalis* L. *J. Mar. biol. Ass. U.K.* **26** 421–425
—— (1947): *They live in the sea.* London: Collins

CHAPTER III

ENEMIES

ADAM, W. (1937): Notes sur les céphalopodes. 7. Sur un cas de régénération chez *Sepioteuthis lessoniana* Lesson, 1830. *Bull. Mus. Hist. nat. Belg.* **13** No. 45
ANON (1957): Article in *The Times*, London June 17
BARTSCH, PAUL (1945): Mollusks of the U.S. Antarctic Science Expedition. *Proc. Amer. phil. Soc.* **89**:1–294
BATHER, FRANCIS A. (1895): The habits of the young *Sepia*. *J. Malacol.* **2**: 33
BERGE, VICTOR (1954): *Danger is my life.* London: Hutchinson
BOONE, L. (1933): Scientific results of cruises of the yachts *Eagle* and *Ara*, 1921–1928, William K. Vanderbilt, commanding. Mollusca: Systematic discussion. *Bull. Vanderbilt oceanogr. (Mar.) Mus.* **4**: 165–210
BOWIE, BEVERLEY M. (1954): Bermuda, cradled in warm seas. *Nat. geogr. Mag.* **105**: 203–238
BOYCOTT, B. B. (1958): The cuttlefish—*Sepia*. *New Biol.* No. 25: 98–118
BRUUN, ANTON FR. (1943): The biology of *Spirula spirula* (L.). *Dana-Rep.* No. 24: 1–44
CLARK, AUSTIN H. (1948): *Animals alive.* New York: Van Nostrand
COUSTEAU, JACQUES-YVES (1953): *The silent world.* New York: Harper
COWDRY, E. V. (1911): Colour changes of *Octopus vulgaris* Lmk. *Univ. Toronto Stud. Biol.* No. 10: 1–53
CUMMINGS, BRUCE (1936): Encounter between cone shell and octopus. *N. Queensland Nat.* **4**: 47: 42
DARWIN, CHARLES (1955): *A naturalist's voyage.* New York: Dutton
DENYS DE MONTFORT, P. (1808–1810): *Conchyliogie systématique.* Paris: Schoell
DOBELL, C. C. (1909): Some observations on the infusoria parasitic in Cephalopoda. *Quart. J. micr. Sci.* **53**: 183–199
DUNCAN, DAVID, D. (1941): Fighting giants of the Humboldt. *Nat. geogr. Mag.* **79**: 373–400
FIGGE, FRANK H. J. (1940): Squid melanin: a naturally occurring reversibly oxidizable pigment. *Proc. Soc. exp. Biol. N.Y.* **44**: 293–294
FOX, DENIS L. & CRANE, SHELDON C. (1942): Concerning the pigments of the two-spotted octopus and the opalescent squid. *Biol. Bull., Woods Hole* **82**: 284–291
GESSARD, C. (1903): Sur les oxydases des seiches. *C. R. Acad. Sci., Paris* **136**: 631–632
GIBSON, JOHN (1887): *Monsters of the sea.* London: Thomas Nelson
GILPATRIC, GUY (1938): *The compleat goggler.* New York: Dodd, Mead
GIROD, PAUL (1882): Recherches sur la poche de noir des céphalopodes des côtes de France. *Arch. Zool. exp. gén.* **10**: 1–100
GORSKY, BERNARD (1954): *Mediterranean hunter.* London: Souvenir Press
GRAUPNER, HEINZ & FISCHER, ILSE (1934): Das Tintendrüsenepithel von *Sepia* vor, während und nach der Pigmentbildung. *Z. Zellforsch.* **21**: 329–341

HAGENBECK, LORENZ (1956): *Animals are my life*. London: Bodley Head

HALL, D. N. F. (1956): Ink ejection by Cephalopoda. *Nature, Lond.* **177**: 663

HALSTEAD, BRUCE W. (1949): Octopus bites in human beings. *Leafl. Malacol.* **1** 5: 17–22

HEATH, HAROLD (1917); Devilfish and squid. *Calif. Fish Game* **3** 3: 1–6

HERMITTE, L. C. D. (1946): Venomous marine molluscs of the genus *Conus. Trans. R. Soc. trop. Med. Hyg.* **39**: 485–512

HOLDER, CHARLES FREDERICK (1899): Some Pacific cephalopods. *Sci. Amer.* **80**: 253

—— (1908): *Big game at sea*. London: Hodder & Stoughton

HOLMES, WILLIAM (1940): The colour changes and colour patterns of *Sepia officinalis* L. *Proc. zool. Soc. Lond.* **110A**: 17–35

KLINGEL, GILBERT C. (1940): *Inagua*. New York: Dodd, Mead

KUENTZ, L. (1934): La pêche et le commerce des seiches en Tunisie. *Nature, Paris* No. 2925: 270–271

LANGE, MATHILDE M. (1920): On the regeneration and finer structure of the arms of the cephalopods. *J. exp. Zool.* **31**: 1–40

LEE, HENRY (1875): *The octopus*. London: Chapman & Hall

MacGINITIE, G. E. (1938): Notes on the natural history of some marine animals. *Amer. Midl. Nat.* **19**: 207–219

MacGINITIE, G. E. & MacGINITIE, NETTIE (1949): *Natural history of marine animals*. New York: McGraw-Hill

MAY, RAOUL M. (1933): The formation of nerve endings in the suckers of regenerated arms of the cephalopod *Octopus vulgaris* Lam. *Anat. Rec.* **57**: 70 (No. 4 Suppl.)

MENARD, WILMON (1947): Hunting the giant octopus. *Wide World Mag.* **99**: 203–207

MEYER, WERNER TH. (1913): Tintenfische in Ziegler & Woltereck's *Monographien einheimischer Tiere* 6. Leipzig: Klinkhardt

MORITA, J. (1931): On the ink-sac of the cephalopod. *Dobuts. Zasshi Tokyo* (*Zool. Mag., Tokyo*) **43**: 150–162

MURPHY, ROBERT CUSHMAN (1936): *Oceanic birds of South America*. New York: American Museum of Natural History

NAEF, ADOLF (1921): Die Cephalopoden. *Fauna u. Flora Neapel* Monogr. 35, Pt. 1

PIETTRE, MAURICE (1911): Sur les pigments mélaniques d'origine animale. *C. R. Acad. Sci., Paris* **153**: 782–785

—— (1911): Sur les mélanines. *C. R. Acad. Sci., Paris* **153**: 1037–1040

PORTMANN, ADOLPHE (1952): Les bras dorsaux de *Tremoctopus violaceus* Delle Chiaje. *Rev. suisse Zool.* **59**: 288–293

RIES, ERICH (1936): Die Pigmentbildung in der Tintendrüse von *Sepia officinalis* L. *Z. Zellforsch.* **25**: 1–13

ROBSON, G. C. (1929 & 1932): *A monograph of the recent Cephalopoda*. Octopoda. London: British Museum (Nat. Hist.)

—— (1954): Cephalopoda. *Encyclopaedia Britannica* **5**: 148–156. London: Encyclopaedia Britannica

SCHÄFER, WILHELM (1956): Die Schutzwirkung der Tintenfisch-Tinte. *Natur u. Volk:* **86** 1:24–26

SCHULTZ, LEONARD P. (1949): At grips with a giant moray eel. *Nat. Hist., N.Y.* **58**: 42–43

SQUIRES, H. J. (1957): Squid, *Illex illecebrosus* (LeSueur), in the Newfoundland fishing area. *J. Fish. Res. Bd. Canada* **14**: 693–728

STEENSTRUP, JOH. JAPETUS (1857): Hectocotylus-formation in *Argonauta* and *Tremoctopus* explained by observations on a similar formation in the Cephalopoda in general. *Ann. Mag. nat. Hist.* (2) **2**: 81–114

STEINBACH, H. B. (1951): The squid. *Sci. Amer.* **184** 4: 64–69

STEP, EDWARD (1945): *Shell life*. Ed. revised by A. Laurence Wells. London: Warne

SUNTER, GEORGE HERBERT (1937): *Adventures of a trepang fisher*. London: Hurst & Blackett.

TOMPSETT, DAVID H. (1939): *Sepia. L.M.B.C. Mem.* No. 32

TRYON, GEORGE W., JR. (1879): *Manual of conchology*. 1 Cephalopoda. Philadelphia: Tryon

TURCHINI, J. (1922): Nature muqueuse des cellules à mélanine de la glande du noir de la seiche (*Sepia officinalis* L.) et mécanisme de l'excrétion du pigment. *C. R. Soc. Biol., Paris* 86: 480–482

VERRILL, A. E. (1879–1881): The cephalopods of the north-eastern coast of America. *Trans. Conn. Acad. Arts Sci.* 5: 177–446

VOSS, GILBERT L. (1954): Cephalopoda of the Gulf of Mexico. *Fish. Bull. U.S. Wildl. Serv.* 55: 475–478

WALLACE, DAVID H. & WALLACE, ELIZABETH M. (1942): Observations of the feeding habits of the white marlin. *Publ. State Maryland dept. Res. Educ.* 50: 3–10

WELLS, M. J. & WELLS, J. (1956): Tactile discrimination and the behaviour of blind *Octopus. Pubbl. Staz. zool. Napoli* 28: 94–126

WENYON, C. M. (1926): *Protozoology. A manual for medical men, veterinarians and zoologists*. London: Ballière, Tindall & Cox

WINCKWORTH, R. (1950): Cephalopoda. *Chambers's Encyclopaedia* 3: 239–240. London: George Newnes

CHAPTER IV

LOCOMOTION

ABBOTT, R. TUCKER (1954): *American seashells*. New York: Van Nostrand

AKIMUSHKIN, I. I. (1954): [New data on the geographical distribution of cephalopod molluscs in the far eastern waters.] *Dokl. Akad. nauk S.S.S.R.* 94: 1181–1184 [in Russian]

ALLCARD, E. C. (1950): *Singlehanded passage*. New York: Norton

ARATA, GEORGE F., JR. (1954): A note on the flying behaviour of certain squids. *Nautilus* 68: 1–3

ARISTOTLE (c. 330 B.C.): *Historia animalium*. Translation by D'Arcy Wentworth Thompson (1910). Oxford: Clarendon Press

BARTSCH, PAUL (1917): Pirates of the deep—stories of the squid and octopus. *Rep. Smithson. Instn.* 1916: 347–375

BEALE, THOMAS (1839): *The natural history of the sperm whale*. London: Van Voorst

BERRY, S. STILLMAN (1952): The flapjack devilfish, *Opisthoteuthis*, in California. *Calif. Fish Game* 38: 183–188

BIGELOW, HENRY B. (1926): Plankton of the offshore waters of the Gulf of Maine. *Bull. U.S. Bur. Fish.* 40 2: 1–509

BOONE, L. (1933): Scientific results of the cruises of the yachts Eagle and Ara, 1921–1928, William K. Vanderbilt, commanding. Mollusca: Systematic discussion. *Bull. Vanderbilt oceanogr. (Mar.) Mus.* 4: 165–210

BOYCOTT, B. B. (1958): The cuttlefish—*Sepia. New Biol.* No. 25: 98–118

CARSON, RACHEL L. (1951): *The sea around us*. New York: Oxford

CLARK, AUSTIN H. (1948): *Animals alive*. New York: Van Nostrand

DAETZ, GARY (1955): Meet and eat the octopus. *Nat. Hist., N.Y.* 64: 210–213

DAKIN, WILLIAM J. (1953): *Australian seashores*. London: Angus & Robertson

DANIEL, R. J. (1925): *Animal life in the sea*. London: Hodder & Stoughton

DAVIS, GRACE SHULTS (1952): The paper nautilus. *Nature Mag.* 45: 355–356

DENTON, E. J., etc. (1958): Bathyscaphoid squid. *Nature, Lond.* 182: 1810

FIELDS, W. GORDON (1950): A preliminary report on the fishery and on the biology of the squid, *Loligo opalescens*. *Calif. Fish Game* **36**: 365–377

FRITSCH, RUDOLF H. (1938): Das "Bauen" des *Octopus* und andere Beobachtungen an Cephalopoden. *Zool. Anz.* Suppl. **11**: 119–126

GIBSON, JOHN (1887): *Monsters of the sea*. London: Thomas Nelson

GILPATRIC, GUY (1938): *The compleat goggler*. New York: Dodd, Mead

GRIMBLE, ARTHUR (1952): *We chose the islands*. New York: William Morrow

HAMLYN-HARRIS, R. (1903): Die Statocysten der Cephalopoden. *Zool. Jb.* (Anat.) **18**: 327–358

HARDY, ALISTER C. (1957): *The open sea*. Boston: Houghton Mifflin

HEYERDAHL, THOR (1950): *The Kon-Tiki expedition*. Chicago: Rand McNally

ISGROVE, ANNIE (1909): *Eledone*. *L.M.B.C. Mem.* No. 18

ISHIKAWA, MASASHI (1929): On the statocyst of the American cephalopod genera. *J. Morph.* **48**: 563–584

JAECKEL, SIEGFRIED G. A., JR. (1958): Cephalopoda in Remane's *Tierwelt der Nord- und Ostsee* 9. Leipzig: Akademischen

JATTA, GIUSEPPE (1896): I cefalopodi viventi nel Golfo di Napoli. *Fauna u. Flora Neapel* Monogr. 23

KLEIN, KLEMENS (1931): Die Nervenendigungen in der Statocyste von *Sepia*. *Z. Zelforsch.* **14**: 481–516

KLINGEL, GILBERT C. (1940): *Inagua*. New York: Dodd, Mead

KOLLMANN, J. (1877): Aus dem Leben der Cephalopoden. *Vjschr. wiss. Phil.* **1**: 136–155

KONDAKOV, N. N. (1941): [Cephalopods of Far Eastern Seas of U.S.S.R.] *Investigations of Far Eastern Seas of U.S.S.R.* **1**: 216–256. Acad. Nat. Sci. U.S.S.R. [in Russian with English summary]

LA PYLAIE, M. DE (1824): Notice sur l'encornet des pêcheurs (*Loligo piscatorum*, N.) *Ann. Sci. Nat.* **4**: 319–335

LANE, FRANK W. (1954): *Nature parade*. New York: Sheridan House

LEE, HENRY (1875): *The octopus*. London: Chapman & Hall

LORD, JOHN KEAST (1866): *The naturalist in Vancouver Island and British Columbia*. London: Richard Bentley

MACGINITIE, G. E. & MACGINITIE, NETTIE (1949): *Natural history of marine animals*. New York: McGraw-Hill

MALACOLOGICAL SOCIETY OF LONDON (1956): Discussion meeting on pelagic Mollusca. *Nature, Lond.* **177**: 1023–1025

MILNE, LORUS J. (1947): Squid. *Atlant. Mon.* **180** 2: 104–106

NISHIZAWA, SATOSHI (1954): Preliminary study on the diffusive movements of squid population. *Bull. Fac. Fish. Hokkaido* **5** 1: 29–35

PIERCE, MADELENE E. (1950): *Loligo pealeii* in Brown's *Selected invertebrate types*. New York: John Wiley

PROSSER, C. LADD (Editor) (1950): *Comparative animal physiology*. Philadelphia: Saunders

PUMPHREY, R. J. & YOUNG, J. Z. (1938): The rates of conduction of nerve fibres of various diameters in cephalopods. *J. exp. Biol.* **15**: 453–466

RAO, K. VIRABHADRA (1954): Biology and fishery of the Palk-bay squid, *Sepioteuthis arctipinnis* Gould. *Indian J. Fish.* **1**: 37–66

REES, W. J. (1949): Note on the hooked squid, *Onychoteuthis banksi*. *Proc. malacol. Soc. Lond.* **28**: 43–45

—— (1950): The distribution of *Octopus vulgaris* Lamarck in British waters. *J. Mar. biol. Ass. U.K.* **29**: 261–378

—— (1952): Octopuses in the Channel. *New Biology* No. 12: 58–67

—— (1953): The *Octopus* larvae of the Thor. *Proc. malacol. Soc. Lond.* **29**: 215–218

REES, W. J. & LUMBY, J. R. (1954): The abundance of *Octopus* in the English Channel. *J. Mar. biol. Ass. U.K.* **33**: 515–536

ROBSON, G. C. (1925): Cephalopoda in Hutchinson's *Animals of all countries* 4: 2145–2177. London: Hutchinson

—— (1929 & 1932): *A monograph of the recent Cephalopoda*. Octopoda. London: British Museum (Nat. Hist.)

—— (1932): The closure of the mantle cavity in the Cephalopoda. *Jena. Z. Naturw.* 67: 14–18

RUSH, WILLIAM H. (1892): Letter in *Nautilus* 6: 81–82

RUSSELL, F. S. & STEVEN, G. A. (1930): The swimming of cuttlefish. *Nature, Lond.* 125: 893

SCHMIDT, JOHANNES (1922): Live specimens of *Spirula. Nature, Lond.* 110: 788–790

SINEL, JOSEPH (1893): On the locomotion of the Mollusca. Ser. 1. *J. mar. Zool.* 1: 31–32

—— (1906): *An outline of the natural history of our shores*. London: Sonnenschein

SOEDA, J. (1950): The migration of the squid (*Ommastrephes sloani pacificus* Steenstrup) in the coastal waters of Japan. *Sci. Pap. Hokkaido Fish. Sci. Inst.* No. 4

SPRATT, THOMAS ABEL BREMAGE & FORBES, EDWARD (1847): *Travels in Lycia, Milyas, and the Cibyratis*. London: Van Voorst

STEINBACH, H. B. (1951): The squid. *Sci. Amer.* 184 4:64–69

STEP, EDWARD (1945): *Shell life*. Ed. revised by A. Laurence Wells. London: Warne

TEN CATE, J. (1929): Contributions à l'innervation des nageoires chez *Sepia officinalis. Arch. néerl. Sci.* (3c) 14: 501–510

THOMSON, J. ARTHUR (1935): *Biology for everyman*. New York: Dutton

TINBERGEN, L. (1939): Zur Fortpflanzungsethologie von *Sepia officinalis* L. *Arch. néerl. Zool.* 3: 323–364

TINBERGEN, L. & VERWEY, J. (1945–1946): Zur Biologie von *Loligo vulgaris* Lam. *Arch. néerl. Zool.* 7: 213–286

TOMPSETT, DAVID H. (1939): *Sepia L.M.B.C. Mem.* No. 32

TRYON, GEORGE W., JR. (1879): *Manual of conchology.* 1 Cephalopoda. Philadelphia: Tryon

VERANY, JEAN BAPTISTE (1851): *Mollusques méditerranéens*. Geneva: Sourds-Muets

VERRILL, A. E. (1879–1882): The cephalopods of the north-eastern coast of America. *Trans. Conn. Acad. Arts Sci.* 5: 177–446

—— (1897): Nocturnal and diurnal changes in the colors of certain fishes and of the squid (*Loligo*), with notes on their sleeping habits. *Amer. J. Sci.* (4) 3: 135–136

WILSON, DOUGLAS P. (1951): *Life of the shore and shallow sea*. London: Nicholson & Watson

YOUNG, J. Z. (1938): The functioning of the giant nerve fibres of the squid. *J. exp. Biol.* 15: 170–185

—— (1944): Giant nerve-fibres. *Endeavour* 3: 108–113

ZAHL, PAUL A. (1954): Night life in the Gulf Stream. *Nat. geogr. Mag.* 105: 391–418

CHAPTER V

BEHAVIOR

ABEL, O. (1916): *Paläobiologie der Cephalopoden aus der Gruppe der Dibranchiaten*. Jena: Gustav Fischer

ALEXANDROWICZ, J. S. (1927): Contribution à l'étude des *Dibranchiaten* muscles, des nerfs et du mécanisme de l'accommodation de l'oeil des céphalopodes. *Arch. Zool. exp. gén.* 66: 71–134

BAGLIONI, S. (1909): Contributions expérimentales à la physiologie du sens olfactif et du sens tactile des animaux marins (*Octopus* et quelques poissons). *Arch. ital. biol., Torino* **52**: 225–230

—— (1909): Zur Kenntnis der Leistungen einiger Sinnesorgane (Gesichtssinn, Tastsinn und Geruchssinn) und des Zentralnervensystems der Cephalopoden und Fische. *Z. Biol., Munchen* **53**: 255–286

BAUER, V. (1908): Einführung in die Physiologie der Cephalopoden. *Mitt. zool. stat. Neapel* **19**: 149–268

BEACH, FRANK A. (1947): Of course animals can think. *Nat. Hist., N.Y.* **56**: 116–118, 144

BEEBE, WILLIAM (1932): The depths of the sea. *Nat. geogr. Mag.* **61**: 65–68

BERGE, VICTOR & LANIER, HENRY WYSHAM (1930): *Pearl diver*. London: Heinemann

BERRILL, N. J. (1951): *The living tide*. New York: Dodd, Mead

BIERENS DE HAAN, J. A. (1926): Versuche über den Farbensinn und das psychische Leben von *Octopus vulgaris*. *Z. vergl. Physiol.* **4**: 766–796

—— (1929): *Animal psychology for biologists*. London: University Press

—— (1948): *Animal psychology*, London: Hutchinson

BOULET, P. (1954): Expériences sur la perception visuelle du mouvement chez *Sepia officinalis L. C. R. Soc. Biol., Paris* **148**: 1486–1489

BOYCOTT, B. B. (1953): The chromatophore system of cephalopods. *Proc. Linn. Soc. Lond.* **164**: 235–240

—— (1954): Learning in *Octopus vulgaris* and other cephalopods. *Pubbl. Staz. zool. Napoli* **25**: 67–93

—— (1956): The neural basis of learning in *Octopus vulgaris*. (Presented at the discussion initiated by the Section of Comparative Medicine of the Royal Society of Medicine on "Learning in Man and Animals.") *Nature, Lond.* **177**: 1147

—— (1957): How does an animal store information? *New Scientist*, London No. 15: 30–32

BOYCOTT, B. B. & YOUNG, J. Z. (1950): The comparative study of learning. *Symp. Soc. exp. Biol.* No. 4: 432–453

—— —— (1955a): A memory system in *Octopus vulgaris* Lamarck. *Proc. roy. Soc.* (B) **143**: 449–480

—— —— (1955b): Memories controlling attacks on food objects by *Octopus vulgaris* Lamarck. *Pubbl. Staz. zool. Napoli* **27**: 232–249

—— —— (1956): Reactions to shape in *Octopus vulgaris* Lamarck. *Proc. zool. Soc. Lond.* **126**: 491–547

—— (1956): The subpedunculate body and nerve and other organs associated with the optic tract of cephalopods. *Bertil Hanström, zoological papers in honour of his 65th birthday*: 76–105. Lund, Sweden: Zoological Institute.

BUYTENDIJK, F. J. J. (1933): Das Verhalten von *Octopus* nach teilweiser Zerstörung des "Gehirns." *Arch. néerl. Physiol.* (3c) **18**: 24–70

—— (1953): *Toucher et être touché*. (Volume jubilaire dédie à J. A. Bierens de Haan.) Leiden: Brill

CAMPBELL, ROY (1952): *Light on a dark horse*. Chicago: Regnery

COUSTEAU, JACQUES-YVES (1953): *The silent world*. New York: Harper

—— (1954): Fish men discover a 2,200-year-old Greek ship. *Nat. geogr. Mag.* **105**: 1–36

DUNTON, SAM (1957): *Hold that tiger!* New York: Greenberg

FISCHER, P.-H. (1939): Sur les terriers des poulpes. *Bull. Lab. marit. Dinard* No. 20: 92–94

FRITSCH, RUDOLF H. (1938): Das "Bauen" des *Octopus* und andere Beobachtungen an Cephalopoden. *Zool. Anz.* Suppl. **11**: 119–126

GIBBINGS, ROBERT (1949): *Over the reefs*. New York: Dutton

GIERSBERG, H. (1925): Über den chemischen Sinn von *Octopus vulgaris*. *Z. vergl. Physiol.* **3**: 827–838

GILPATRIC, GUY (1938): *The compleat goggler*. New York: Dodd, Mead

GOLDSMITH, MARIE (1927): *La psychologie comparée*. Paris: Alfred Costes

GRIMPE, GEORG (1913): Das Blutgefässsystem der dibranchiaten Cephalopoden. *Z. wiss. Zool.* **104**: 531–621

—— (1928): Pflege, Behandlung und Zucht der Cephalopoden etc. in Abderhalden's *Handbuch der Biologischen Arbeitsmethoden* **9** 5: 331–402. Berlin: Urban & Schwarzenberg

GUÉRIN, JOSEPH (1908): Contribution à l'étude des systèmes cutané, musculaire et nerveux de l'appareil tentaculaire des céphalopodes. *Arch. Zool. exp. gén.* (4) **8**: 1–178

HARDY, ALISTER C. (1957): *The open sea*. Boston: Houghton Mifflin

HEMPELMANN, F. (1926): *Tierpsychologie: vom Standpunkte des Biologen*. Leipzig: Akademische

HILLIG, R. (1912): Das Nervensystem von *Sepia officinalis* L. *Z. wiss. Zool.* **101**: 736–806

HILTON, W. A. (1941): Cephalopoda. *J. Ent. Zool.* **33**: 32–40

HOLDER, CHARLES FREDERICK (1908): *Big game at sea*. London: Hodder & Stoughton

JEFFREYS, JOHN GWYN (1869): *British conchology* **5**: 121–148. London: Van Voorst

KLINGEL, GILBERT C. (1940): *Inagua*. New York: Dodd, Mead

KOLLMANN, J. (1875): Die Cephalopoden in der Zoologischen Station des Dr. Dohrn. *Z. wiss. Zool.* **26**: 1–23

KRUSZYŃSKI, J. (1933): Entwicklung, Cytologie und Histochemie der Knorpel und der chondroiden Gewebe des Auges der Sepia (*Sepia officinalis*). *Z. Zellforsch.* **19**: 403–440

LANE, FRANK W. (1951): *Animal wonder world*. New York: Sheridan House

LANGE, MATHILDE M. (1920): On the regeneration and finer structure of the arms of the cephalopods. *J. exp. Zool.* **31**: 1–40

LEE, HENRY (1875): *The octopus*. London: Chapman & Hall

LO BIANCO, SALVATORE (1899): Notizie biologiche riguardanti specialmente il periodo di maturità sessuale degli animali del Golfo di Napoli. *Mitt. zool. Stat. Neapel* **13**: 448–573

MACGINITIE, G. E. & MACGINITIE, NETTIE (1949): *Natural history of marine animals*. New York: McGraw-Hill

MAIER, N. R. F. & SCHNEIRLA, T. C. (1935): *Principles of animal psychology*. New York: McGraw-Hill

MENARD, WILMON (1947): Hunting the giant octopus. *Wide World Mag.* **99**: 203–207

—— (1948): Never again. *Nat. Hist., N.Y.* **57**: 324

MIKHAÏLOFF, SERGE (1920 & 1921): Expériences réflexologiques. 2 & 3. Expériences nouvelles sur *Eledone moschata*. *Bull. Inst. océanogr. Monaco* Nos. 379 & 398

MINER, ROY WALDO (1935): Marauders of the sea. *Nat. geogr. Mag.* **68**: 185–207

MORGAN, C. LLOYD (1894): *An introduction to comparative psychology*. London: Walter Scott

PFEFFERKORN, ALFRED (1915): Das Nervensystem der Octopoden. *Z. wiss. Zool.* **114**: 425–531

PIERON, H. (1911): Contribution à la psychologie du poulpe. *Bull. Inst. gén. psychol.* **11**: 111–119

[PLINY] PLINIUS, GAIUS SECUNDUS (A.D. 77): *Pliny—natural history*. With an English translation by H. Rackham & W. H. S. Jones (1947) **3** Libri 8–11: 223. London: Heinemann

POWER, JEANETTE (1857): Observations on the habits of various marine animals. *Ann. Mag. nat. Hist.* (2) **20**: 334–336

PRICE, WILLARD (1955): *Adventures in paradise.* New York: John Day

PRINCE, JACK H. (1949): *Visual development.* 1. Edinburgh: Livingstone

ROBSON, G. C. (1929 & 1932): *A monograph of the recent Cephalopoda.* Octopoda. London: British Museum (Nat. Hist.)

ROSSI, FERDINANDO & GRAZIADEI, PASQUALE (1954): Nouvelles recherches sur le système nerveux du bras des céphalopodes avec des méthodes spécifiques pour le tissu nerveux. *Acta anat.* **22**: 202–215

SANDERS, F. K. & YOUNG, J. Z. (1940): Learning and other functions of the higher nervous centres of *Sepia. J. Neurophysiol.* **3**: 501–526

SCHILLER, PAUL H. (1949): Delayed detour response in the octopus. *J. comp. physiol. Psychol.* **42**: 220–225

SERENI, E. & YOUNG, J. Z. (1932): Nervous degeneration and regeneration in cephalopods. *Pubbl. Staz. zool. Napoli* **12**: 173–208

SINEL, JOSEPH (1906): *An outline of the natural history of our shores.* London: Sonnenschein

SUTHERLAND, N. S. (1957): Visual discrimination of orientation and shape by the octopus. *Nature, Lond.* **179**: 11–13

—— (1957): Visual discrimination of orientation by *Octopus. Brit. J. Psychol.* **48** 1: 55–71

TAKI, IWAO (1941): On keeping octopods in an aquarium for physiological experiments with remarks on some operative techniques. *Venus, Kyoto* **10**: 140–156

TEN CATE, J. (1928a): Contribution à l'innervation des ventouses chez *Octopus vulgaris. Arch. néerl. Physiol.* **13**: 407–422

—— (1928b): Nouvelles observations sur l'hypnose dite animal. Etat d'hypnose chez *Octopus vulgaris. Arch. néerl. Physiol.* **13**: 402–406

TEN CATE, J. & TEN CATE-KAZEEWA, B. (1938): Les *Octopus vulgaris* peuventils discerner les formes? *Arch. néerl. Physiol.* **23**: 541–551

THORE, SVEN (1939): Beiträge zur Kenntnis der vergleichenden Anatomie des zentralen Nervensystems der dibranchiaten Cephalopoden. *Pubbl. Staz. zool. Napoli* **17**: 313–506

THORPE, W. H. (1956): *Learning and instinct in animals.* London: Methuen

WELLS, M. J. & WELLS, J. (1956): Tactile discrimination and behaviour of blind *Octopus. Pubbl. Staz. zool. Napoli* **28**: 94–126

WIGGLESWORTH, V. B. (1955): The contribution of pure science to applied biology. *Ann. appl. Biol.* **42**: 34–44

WILLEY, ARTHUR (1902): *Zoological results.* Cambridge: University Press

WILLIAMS, LEONARD WORCESTER (1909): *The anatomy of the common squid, Loligo pealii, Lesueur.* Leiden: Brill

YOUNG, J. Z. (1945): *The structure, degeneration and repair of nerve fibres.* Royal Instn. Gt. Brit. Weekly Evening Meeting March 18, 1945. 11 pp.

—— (1951): *Doubt and certainty in science.* New York: Oxford

—— (1955): Memory systems in the brain. *The Listener* **1955**: 929–932

CHAPTER VI

COLOR

ADAM, W. (1937): Céphalopodes des Îles Bonaire et Curaçao. *Capita Zoologica* **8** 3: 1–29

ALLAN, JOYCE (1950): *Australian shells.* Melbourne: Georgian House

BACQ, Z. M. (1932–1934): Series of papers. *C. R. Soc. Biol. Paris.*

268 BIBLIOGRAPHY

BEEBE, WILLIAM (1926): *The Arcturus adventure.* New York: Putnam
BOYCOTT, B. B. (1953): The chromatophore system of cephalopods. *Proc. Linn. Soc. Lond.* **164:** 235–240
—— (1954): Learning in *Octopus vulgaris* and other cephalopods. *Pubbl. Staz. zool. Napoli* **25:** 67–93
BOZLER, EMIL (1931): Über die Tätigkeit der einzelnen glatten Muskelfaser bei der Kontraktion. *Z. vergl. Physiol.* **13:** 762–772
CHUN, CARL (1902): Ueber die Natur und die Entwicklung der Chromatophoren bei den Cephalopoden. *Verh. dtsch. zool. Ges.* **12:** 162–182
COTT, HUGH B. (1940): *Adaptive coloration in animals.* London: Methuen
COWDRY, E. V. (1911): The colour changes of *Octopus vulgaris* Lmk. *Univ. Toronto Stud. Biol.* No. 10: 1–53
DAKIN, WILLIAM J. (1953): *Australian seashores.* London: Angus & Robertson
FOX, DENIS L. (1953): *Animal biochromes and structural colours.* Cambridge: University Press
FOX, DENIS L. & CRANE, SHELDON C. (1942): Concerning the pigments of the two-spotted octopus and the opalescent squid. *Biol. Bull., Woods Hole* **82:** 284–291
GIBBINGS, ROBERT (1949): *Over the reefs.* New York: Dutton
GILPATRIC, GUY (1938): *The compleat goggler.* New York: Dodd, Mead
GIROD, PAUL (1883): Recherches sur la peau des céphalopodes. *Arch. Zool. exp. gén.* (2) **1:** 225–266
HALL, D. N. F. (1956): Ink ejection by Cephalopoda. *Nature, Lond.* **177:** 663
HILL, A. V. & SOLANDT, D. Y. (1935): Myograms from the chromatophores of *Sepia. J. Physiol.* **83:** 13P–14P
HOLDER, CHARLES FREDERICK (1908): *Big game at sea.* London: Hodder & Stoughton
—— (1909): First photographs ever made of a paper nautilus. *Country Life in Amer.* **15:** 356–358, 404, 406, 408
HOLMES, WILLIAM (1940): The colour changes and colour patterns of *Sepia officinalis* L. *Proc. zool. Soc. Lond.* **110A:** 17–35
—— (1955): The colour changes of cephalopods. *Endeavour* **14:** 78–82
HORNELL, JAMES (1893): Notes on animal colouration. Ser. 1. *J. Mar. Zool.* **1:** 3–8
ISSEL, RAFFAELE (1920): Distribuzione e significato biologico del pigmento cefalico nelle giovani larve di cefalopodi egopsidi. *Mem. R. Com. talassogr. ital.* No. 76
JOUBIN, L. (1893): Recherches sur la coloration du tégument chez les céphalopodes. *Arch. Zool. exp. gén.* (2) **10:** 277–303
KLINGEL, GILBERT C. (1940): *Inagua.* New York: Dodd, Mead
KÜHN, A. (1950): Über Farbenwechsel und Farbensinn von Cephalopoden. *Z. vergl. Physiol.* **32:** 572–598
KÜHN, A. & HEBERDEY, R. F. (1929): Über die Anpassung von *Sepia officinalis* L. an Helligkeit und Farbton der Umgebung. *Verh. dtsch. zool. Ges.* **33:** 231–237
LEE, HENRY (1875): *The octopus.* London: Chapman & Hall
MILNE, LORUS J. (1947): Squid. *Atlant. Mon.* **180** 2: 104–106
PARKER, GEORGE HOWARD (1930): Chromatophores. *Biol. Rev.* **5:** 59–90
—— (1948): *Animal colour changes and their neurohumours.* Cambridge: University Press
SCHÄFER, W. (1937): Bau, Entwicklung und Farbenentstehung bei den Flitterzellen von *Sepia officinalis. Z. Zellforsch.* **27:** 222–245
—— (1938): Über die Zeichnung in der Haut einer *Sepia officinalis* von Helgoland. *Z. Morph. Ökol. Tiere* **34:** 128–134
SERENI, ENRICO (1930): Sui cromatofori dei cefalopodi. 3. Azione di alcuni verlerie *in vitro. Z. vergl. Physiol.* **12:** 329–503

—— (1930): The chromatophores of the cephalopods. *Biol. Bull., Woods Hole* **59**: 247–268

SINEL, JOSEPH (1906): *An outline of the natural history of our shores.* London: Sonnenschein

STEVENSON, J. A. (1934): On the behaviour of the long-finned squid (*Loligo pealii* Lesueur). *Canad. Field Nat.* **48**: 4–7

TEN CATE, J. (1928): Contribution à la question de l'innervation des chromatophores chez *Octopus vulgaris. Arch. néerl. Physiol.* **12**: 568–599

TINBERGEN, L. (1939): Zur Fortpflanzungsethologie von *Sepia officinalis* L. *Arch. néerl. Zool.* **3**: 323–364

TOMPSETT, DAVID H. (1939): *Sepia. L.M.B.C. Mem.* No. 32

VERRILL, A. E. (1879–1881): The cephalopods of the north-eastern coast of America. *Trans. Conn. Acad. Arts Sci.* **5**: 177–446

VOSS, GILBERT L. (1953): Observations on a living specimen of *Octopus hummelincki* Adam. *Nautilus* **66**: 73–76

WENDT, HERBERT (1952): Das Haupt der Medusa. *Kosmos* **48**: 15–21

WICKSTEAD, J. (1956): An unusual method of capturing prey by a cuttlefish. *Nature, Lond.* **178**: 929

WILSON, DOUGLAS P. (1946): A note on the capture of prey by *Sepia officinalis* L. *J. Mar. biol. Ass. U.K.* **26**: 421–425

CHAPTER VII

LUMINESCENCE

BERRY, S. STILLMAN (1920): Light production in cephalopods. *Biol. Bull., Woods Hole* **38**: 141–195

—— (1926): A note on the occurrence and habits of a luminous squid (*Abralia veranyi*) at Madeira. *Biol. Bull., Woods Hole* **51**: 257–268

BRUUN, ANTON FR. (1943): The biology of *Spirula spirula* (L.) *Dana-Rep.* 4 **24**: 1–44

BUCHNER, P. (1953): *Endosymbiose der Tiere mit Pflanzlichen Microorganismen.* Berlin: Birkhauser

CHUN, CARL (1903): Ueber Leuchtorgane und Augen von Tiefsee-Cephalopoden. *Verh. dtsch. zool. Ges.* **13**: 67–91

—— (1914): Cephalopoda from the "Michael Sars" North Atlantic Deep-Sea Expedition. *Rep. Sars N. Atl. Deep Sea Exped.* **3**: 1–28

COUSTEAU, JACQUES-YVES (1954): To the depths of the sea by bathyscaphe. *Nat. geogr. Mag.* **106**: 67–79

DAHLGREN, U. (1916): Light production in cephalopods. *J. Franklin Inst.* **181**: 525–556

GIROD, PAUL (1882): Recherches sur la poche de noir des céphalopodes des côtes de France. *Arch. Zool. exp. gén.* **10**: 1–100

—— (1883 & 1884): Recherches sur la peau des céphalopodes. *Arch. Zool. exp. gén.* (2) **1**: 225–266; (2) **2**: 379–401

GRIMPE, G. & HOFFMANN, H. (1921): Über die Postembryonalentwicklung von *Histioteuthis* und über ihre sogennanten "Endorgane." *Arch. Naturgesch.* 87 **12A**: 179–219

HANEDA, YATA (1955): Luminous organisms of Japan and the Far East in Johnson's *The luminescence of biological systems.* Washington: Amer. Ass. Adv. Sci.

—— (1956): Squid producing an abundant luminous secretion found in Suruga Bay, Japan. *Sci. Rep. Yokosuka City Mus.* **1**: 27–32

HARDY, ALISTER C. (1957): *The open sea.* Boston: Houghton Mifflin

HARVEY, E. NEWTON (1950): Luminescence, animal. *Chambers's Encyclopaedia* **8**: 726–727. London: George Newnes

—— (1952): *Bioluminescence.* New York: Academic Press

HOYLE, WILLIAM E. (1908): Presidential address to Section D (Zoology) of the British Association. *Rep. Brit. Ass.* 1907: 520–539

ISHIKAWA, C. (1913): Einige Bemerkungen über den leuchtenden Tintenfisch, *Watasea* nov. gen. (*Abraliopsis* der Autoren) *scintillans*, Berry, aus Japan. *Zool. Anz.* 43: 162–172

JOHNSON, FRANK H. (1955): *The luminescence of biological systems.* Washington: Amer. Ass. Adv. Sci.

JOUBIN, L. (1893): Recherches sur l'appareil lumineux d'un céphalopode: *Histioteuthis ruppellii,* Verany. *Bull. Soc. sci. méd. Ouest* 2: 49–78

KISHITANI, TEIJIRO (1932): Studien über Leuchtsymbiose von japanischen Sepien. *Folia anat. jap.* 10: 315–418

MARSHALL, N. B. (1954): *Aspects of deep sea biology.* London: Hutchinson

MEYER, WERNER TH. (1906): Ueber das Leuchtorgan der Sepiolini. *Zool. Anz.* 30: 388–392

MURRAY, JOHN & HJORT, JOHAN (1912): *The depths of the ocean.* London: Macmillan

PIERANTONI, U. (1939): Le radiazioni luminose di origine biologica (biofotogenesi). *Trattato Radiobiologia* 3. Rome: Società italiana di Radiobiologia medica.

REES, W. J. & MAUL, G. E. (1956): The Cephalopoda of Madeira. *Bull. Brit. Mus. (nat. Hist.)* (Zool.) 3: 259–281

SASAKI, MADOKA (1914): Observations on Hotaru-ika *Watasenia scintillans. J. Coll. Agric. Sapporo* 6: 75–105

SCHMIDT, JOHANNES (1922): Live specimens of *Spirula. Nature, Lond.* 110: 788–790

SPARTÀ, A. (1933): Osservazioni compiute nello Stretto di Messina sul comportamento dei Pesci e Cefalopodi all' azione di sorgenti luminose. *Mem. R. Com. talassogr. ital.* No. 206: 3–22

VERANY, JEAN BAPTISTE (1851): *Mollusques meditérranéens.* Geneva: Sourds-Muets

VOSS, GILBERT L. (1956): A review of the cephalopods of the Gulf of Mexico. *Bull. Mar. Sci. Gulf Carribbean* 6: 85–178

WATASÉ, S. (1905): [On the luminous organs of *Abraliopsis*]. *Zool. Mag., Tokyo* 17: 119–122 [in Japanese]

ZAHL, PAUL A. (1953): Fishing in the whirlpool of Charybdis. *Nat geogr. Mag.* 104: 579–618

ZIRPOLO, GIUSEPPE (1917–1932): Series of papers. *Boll. Soc. Nat. Napoli*

CHAPTER VIII

REPRODUCTION

ADAM, W. & BRETSCHNEIDER, L. H. (1939): Résultats scientifiques des croisières du navire-école belge "*Mercator.*" 2 No. 9: À propos des organes épithéliaux (*Köllikersche Büschel*) chez une larve d'octopode. *Mem. Mus. Hist. nat. Belge* (2) 15: 123–134

ALLAN, JOYCE (1950): *Australian seashells.* Melbourne: Georgian House

ANON (1957): The Zoo's octopus eggs have hatched. *New Scient.* 2 49: 9–10

ARISTOTLE (c. 330 B.C.): *Historia animalium.* Translation by D'Arcy Wentworth Thompson (1910). Oxford: Clarendon Press

BARTSCH, PAUL (1931): The octopuses, squids and their kin. *Smithson. Sci. Ser.* 10: 321–356. New York, published privately by the Smithsonian Institution Series, Inc.

BATHAM, E. J. (1957): Care of eggs by *Octopus maorum*. *Trans. roy. Soc. N. Z.* 84: 629–638

BERRILL, N. J. (1951): *The living tide*. New York: Dodd, Mead

BERT, P. (1867): Mémoire sur la physiologie de la Seiche (*Sepia officinalis* L.) *Mem. Soc. Sci. phys. nat., Bordeaux* 5: 115–138

BLANCQUAERT, T. (1925): L'origine et la formation des spermatophores chez les céphalopodes décapodes. *Cellule* 36: 315–356

BOHADSCH, JOHANN BAPTISTE (1761): *De quibusdam Animalibus marinis eorumque proprietatibus*. Dresden: Walther

BOTT, RICHARD (1938): Kopula und Eiablage von *Sepia officinalis* L. *Z. Morph. Ökol. Tiere* 34: 150–160

BOYCOTT, B. B. (1957): An octopus lays eggs at London Zoo. *New Scient.* 2 47: 12–13

BROWN, BARNUM (1945): The mystery of the eight-pointed stars. *Nat. Hist., N.Y.* 54: 328–331

CHING, M. YUNG KO (1930): Contribution à l'étude cytologique de l'ovogénèse du développement et de quelques organes chez les céphalopodes. *Ann. Inst. Océanogr.* 7: 299–364

CHUN, CARL (1910): Die Cephalopoden. *Wiss. Ergebn. "Valdivia"* 18: 1–552

—— (1914): Cephalopoda from the "Michael Sars" North Atlantic Deep-Sea Expedition, 1910. *Rep. Sars N. Atl. Deep Sea Exped.* 3: 1–28

COLE, F. J. (1944): *A history of comparative anatomy*. New York: Macmillan

COTTON, BERNARD C. (1938): The Sir Joseph Banks Islands. Reports of the Expedition of the McCoy Society for Field Investigation and Research. 5. Mollusca, Pt. 1: The spermatophore of *Rossia australis* Berry. *Proc. roy. Soc. Vict.* (N.S.) 50: 338–340

COTTON, BERNARD C. & GODFREY, FRANK K. (1940): *The molluscs of South Australia*. Pt. 2. Adelaide: Frank Trigg

COWDRY, E. V. (1911): The colour changes of *Octopus vulgaris*. *Univ. Toronto Stud. Biol.* No. 10: 1–53

CUÉNOT, L. (1917): *Sepia officinalis* L. est une espèce en voie de dissociation. *Arch. Zool. exp. gén.* 56: 315–346

CUVIER, GEORGES (1829): Mémoire sur un ver parasite d'un nouveau genre (*Hectocotylus octopodis*). *Ann. Sci. nat.* 18: 147–156

CUVIER, GEORGES & VALENCIENNES, A. (1828): *Histoire naturelle des poissons*. Paris: Levrault

DELLE CHIAJE, STEFANO (1822–1830): *Memorie sulla storia e notomia degli animali senza vertebre del regno di Napoli*. Naples: Fratelli Fernandes

—— (1841): *Descrizione e notomia degli animali invertebrati della Sicilia citeriore.* 1. Naples: Stabilimento Tipografico di C. Batelli

DREW, GILMAN A. (1911): Sexual activities of the squid, *Loligo pealii* (Les.). 1. Copulation, egg-laying and fertilization. *J. Morph.* 22: 327–359

—— (1919): Sexual activities of the squid, *Loligo pealii* (Les.). 2. The spermatophore, its structure, ejaculation and formation. *J. Morph.* 32: 379–435

FISCHER, P.–H. (1950): *Vie et moeurs des mollusques*. Paris: Payot

FISHER, W. K. (1923): Brooding habits of a cephalopod. *Ann. Mag. nat. Hist.* (9) 12: 147–149

FORT, GUY (1937): Le spermatophore des céphalopodes. Étude du spermatophore d'*Eledone cirrhosa* Lmk. *Bull. biol.* 71: 357–373

—— (1941): Le spermatophore des céphalopodes. Étude du spermatophore d'*Eledone moschata* (Lamarck, 1799). *Bull. biol.* 75: 249–256

FOX, DENIS L. (1938): An illustrated note on the mating and egg-brooding habits of the two-spotted octopus. *Trans. S. Diego Soc. nat. Hist.* 9 7: 31–34

GHIRARDELLI, ELVEZIO (1947a): Nota sulla variazione di dimensioni delle Seppie durante il periodo estivo. *Boll. Pesca Piscic. Idrobiol.* (N.S.) 2: 116–124

—— (1947b): Considerazioni sull'influenza della pesca con le nasse sulla biologia delle specie costiere. *Boll. Pesca Piscic. Idrobiol.* (N.S.) 2: 129–134

GIROD, PAUL (1882): Recherches sur la poche du noir des céphalopodes des côtes de France. *Arch. Zool. exp. gén.* 10: 1–100

GRAVELY, F. H. (1908): Notes on the spawning of *Eledone* and on the occurrence of *Eledone* with the suckers in double rows. *Mem. Manchr. lit. phil. Soc.* 53 4: 1–14

GRIMPE, GEORG (1915): Zur Kenntnis der Cephalopodenfauna der Nordsee. *Wiss. Meeresuntersuch.,* Abt. Kiel (N.F.) 16 3: 1–124

—— (1926): Biologische Beobachtungen an *Sepia officinalis. Verh. dtsch. zool. Ges.* 31: 148–153

—— (1928): Über zwei jugendliche Männchen von *Argonauta argo* L. *Zool. Jb.* (Zool.) 45: 77–98

GUDGER, E. W. (1953): On certain small terrestrial mammals that are alleged to fish with the tail. *Amer. Midl. Nat.* 50: 189–201

HAMON, M. (1942): Recherches sur les Spermatophores. Thèses Fac. Sci. Univ. Alger.

HARVEY, E. NEWTON (1952): *Bioluminescence.* New York: Academic Press

HELDT, J. H. (1948): Observations sur un ponte d'*Octopus vulgaris* Lmk. *Bull. Soc. Sci. Nat. Tunisie* 1: 87–90

HOLDER, CHARLES FREDERICK (1909): First photographs ever made of a paper nautilus. *Country Life in Amer.* 15: 356–358, 404, 406, 408

HOLMES, WILLIAM (1955): The colour changes of cephalopods. *Endeavour* 14: 78–82

HOYLE, WILLIAM E. (1908): Presidential address to Section D (Zoology) of the British Association. Cephalopoda. *Rep. Brit. Ass.* 1907: 520–539

ISGROVE, ANNIE (1909): *Eledone. L.M.B.C. Mem.* No. 18

JOUBIN, L. (1929): Notes préliminaires sur les céphalopodes des croisières du "Dana" (1921–1922). Octopodes 2e partie. *Ann. Inst. océanogr., Paris* (N.S.) 7

JULLIEN, A. (1926): Observations sur la biologie de *Sepia officinalis* L. *C. R. Soc. biol., Paris* 94: 194–195

KLINGEL, GILBERT C. (1940): *Inagua.* New York: Dodd, Mead

KÖLLIKER, ALBERT (1845): Some observations upon the structure of two new species of *Hectocotyle* parasitic upon *Tremoctopus violaceus,* Delle Chiaje, and *Argonauta argo,* L., with an exposition of the hypothesis that these *Hectocotylae* are the males of the *Cephalopoda* upon which they are found. *Proc. Linn. Soc. Lond.* 1: 237–238

—— (1846): Some observations upon the structure of two new species of *Hectocotyle,* parasitic upon *Tremoctopus violaceus,* D.Ch., and *Argonauta argo,* Linn.; with an exposition of the hypothesis that these *Hectocotylae* are the males of the *Cephalopoda* upon which they are found. *Trans. Linn. Soc. Lond.* 20: 9–21

—— (1849): *Hectocotylus argonautae* D.Ch. und *Hectocotylus tremoctopodis* Köll., die Männchen von *Argonauta argo* und *Tremoctopus violaceus* D.Ch. *Ber. könig. zootom. Anstalt Wurzburg* No. 2: 67–89

—— (1853): Note in Henfrey, Arthur & Huxley, Thomas Henry—*Scientific Memoirs* p. 90. London: Taylor & Francis

KONOPACKI, M. (1933): Histophysiologie du développement de *Loligo vulgaris. Bull. int. Acad. polon. Sci.* (B2) 1933: 51–69

KORSCHELT, E. & HEIDER, K. (1900): *Textbook of the embryology of invertebrates* 4. trans. Bernard, Matilda. Rev. & ed. Woodward, Martin F. London: Sonnenschein

KRUSZYŃSKI, J. (1933): Entwicklung, Cytologie und Histochemie der Knorpel und der chondroiden Gewebe des Auges der Sepia (*Sepia officinalis*). *Z. Zellforsch.* 19: 403–440

BIBLIOGRAPHY 273

Le Soueff, A. S. & Allan, Joyce K. (1933): Habits of the Sydney octopus (*Octopus cyaneus*) in captivity. *Aust. Zool.* 7: 373–376

Lee, Henry (1875): *The octopus*. London: Chapman & Hall

Levy, Fritz (1912): Über die Copula von *Sepiola atlantica* D'Orb. *Zool. Anz.* 39: 284–290

Lo Bianco, Salvatore (1899 & 1909): Notizie biologiche riguardanti specialmente il periodo di maturità sessuale degli animali del Golfo di Napoli. *Mitt. zool. Stat. Neapel* 13: 448–573, 19: 513–761

MacGinitie, G. E. & MacGinitie, Nettie (1949): *Natural history of marine animals*. New York: McGraw-Hill

Marchand, Werner T. (1907): Studien über Cephalopoden 1. Der männliche Leitungsapparat der Dibranchiaten. *Z. wiss. Zool.* 86: 311–415

—— (1913): Studien über Cephalopoden 2. Ueber die Spermatophoren. *Zoologica, Stuttgart* 26: 171–200

McGowan, John A. (1954): Observations on the sexual behaviour and spawning of the squid, *Loligo opalescens*, at La Jolla, California. *Calif. Fish Game* 40: 47–54

Müller, Heinrich (1853): Ueber das Männchen von *Argonauta argo* und die Hectocotylen. *Z. wiss. Zool.* 4: 1–35

Naef, Adolf (1921–1928): Die Cephalopoden. *Fauna u. Flora Neapel* Monogr. 35

Pelseneer, Paul (1906): Mollusca in Lankester's *Treatise on Zoology* Pt. 5. London: Adam & Charles Black

—— (1935): *Essai d'éthologie zoologique*. Brussels: Palais des Academies

Pfeffer, Georg (1912): Die Cephalopoden der Plankton-Expedition. *Ergebn. Planktonexped.* Pt. 2. Kiel & Leipzig: Lipsius & Tischer

Pickford, Grace E. (1949): The distribution of the eggs of *Vampyroteuthis infernalis* Chun. *J. Mar. Res.* 8: 73–83

Portmann, Adolphe (1933): Observations sur la vie embryonnaire de la pieuvre (*Octopus vulgaris* Lam.) *Arch. Zool. exp. gén.* Notes & Rev. 76: 24–36

—— (1952): Les bras dorsaux de *Tremoctopus violaceus* Delle Chiaje. *Rev. suisse Zool.* 59: 288–293

—— (in press): Céphalopodes in Grassé's *Traité de Zoologie* 5. Paris: Masson

Pruvot-Fol, A. (1946): Quelques observations sur la ponte de la seiche (*Sepia officinalis* L.). *Bull. Soc. zool. Fr.* 71: 113–115

Querner, F. R. von (1926): Die Köllikerschen Büschel jugendlicher Octopoden nebst einiger Bemerkungen zur Histologie der Haut dieser Formen. *Z. Zellforsch.* 4: 237–265

Racovitza, Émile G. (1894a): Sur l'accouplement des quelques céphalopodes *Sepiola rondeletii* (Leach), *Rossia macrosoma* (D. Ch.) et *Octopus vulgaris* (Lam.). *C. R. Acad. Sci., Paris* 118: 722–724

—— (1894b): Notes de biologie. 1. Accouplement et fécondation chez l'*Octopus vulgaris* (Lam.). *Arch. Zool. exp. gén.* (3) 2: 23–49

—— (1894c): Notes de biologie. 3. Moeurs et reproduction de la *Rossia macrosoma* (D. Ch.). *Arch. Zool. exp. gén.* (3) 2: 491–539

Rees, W. J. (1950): The distribution of *Octopus vulgaris* Lamarck in British waters. *J. Mar. biol. Ass. U.K.* 29: 361–378

—— (1952): Octopuses in the Channel. *New Biology* No. 12: 58–67

—— (1953): The *Octopus* larvae of the Thor. *Proc. malacol. Soc. Lond.* 29: 215–218

—— (1954): The *Macrotritopus* problem. *Bull. Brit. Mus.* (*nat. Hist.*) (Zool.) 2: 69–99

—— (1955): The larvae and late-larval stages of *Octopus macropus* Risso. *Proc. malacol. Soc. Lond.* 31: 185–189

—— (1956): Notes on the European species of *Eledone*. *Bull. Brit. Mus.* (*nat. Hist.*) (Zool.) 3: 283–293

274 BIBLIOGRAPHY

—— (1958): [Review of British edition of *Kingdom of the octopus*] *J. Conchol.* 24: 289–290

REES, W. J. & LUMBY, J. R. (1954): The abundance of *Octopus* in the English Channel. *J. Mar. biol. Ass. U.K.* 33: 515–536

ROBSON, G. C. (1926): On the hectocotylus of the Cephalopoda—a reconsideration. *Proc. malacol. Soc. Lond.* 17: 117–122

—— (1929 & 1932): *A monograph of the recent Cephalopoda.* Octopoda. London: British Museum (Nat. Hist.)

RULLIER, F. (1953): Répartition et réproduction d'*Octopus vulgaris* Lamarck dans les eaux françaises. *Bull. Lab. marit. Dinard* No. 39: 22–33

RUSSO, ACHILLE (1926): Le nasse, con particolare riguardo alla pesca delle Seppie. *Boll. Pesca Piscic. Idrobiol.* 2: 3–47

SACARRÃO, G. DA FONSECA (1952): Ontogenetic evolution in the embryo-yolk organ relations of Cephalopoda. *Arch. Mus. Bocage* No. 23: 39–42

SASAKI, MADOKA (1921): On the life history of an economic cuttlefish of Japan, *Ommastrephes sloani pacificus. Trans. Wagner Free Inst.* 9 2: 1–25

—— (1929): A monograph of the dibranchiata cephalopods of the Japanese and adjacent waters. *J. Fac. Agric. Hokkaido Imp. Univ.* 20 Suppl.: 1–357

SAVASTANO, AMALIA (1927): Contributo alla conoscenza dei caratteri sessuali secondari dei cefalopodi (*Sepia officinalis* L. and *Sepia orbygnana* Fer.) *Riv. Biol.* 9: 179–212

SIEBOLD, C. TH. VON (1852): Einige Bemerkungen uber Hectocotylus. *Z. wiss. Zool.* 4: 122–124

SOEDA, J. (1956): Studies on the ecology and the breeding habits of the squid, *Ommastrephes sloani pacificus. Bull. Hokkaido Reg. Fish. Res. Lab.* No. 14: 1–24

STEENSTRUP, JOH. JAPETUS (1857): Hectocotylus-formation in *Argonauta* and *Tremoctopus* explained by observations on similar formations in the Cephalopoda in general. *Ann. Mag. nat. Hist.* (2) 20: 81–114

TAUTI, MORISABURO & MATSUMOTO, IWAO (1954): On the protection of spawner of octopus (*Polypus vulgaris* Lamarck) in Hyogo Prefecture. *Bull. Jap. Soc. sci. Fish.* 20: 479–482 [in Japanese with English summary]

THOMPSON, D'ARCY WENTWORTH (1928): How to catch cuttlefish. *Classical Rev.* 42: 14–18

THORE, SVEN (1949): Investigations on the "Dana" Octopoda; Pt. 1. Bolitaenidae, Amphitretidae, Vitreledonellidae and Alloposidae. *Dana-Rep.* No. 33: 1–85

TINBERGEN, L. (1939): Zur Fortpflanzungsethologie von *Sepia officinalis. Arch. néerl. Zool.* 3: 323–364

TINBERGEN, L. & VERWEY, J. (1945): Zur Biologie von *Loligo vulgaris* Lam. *Arch. néerl. Zool.* 7: 213–285

TOMPSETT, DAVID H. (1939): *Sepia. L.M.B.C. Mem.* No. 32

VAN OORDT, G. J. (1938): The spermatheca of *Loligo vulgaris.* 1. Structure of the spermatheca and function of its unicellular glands. *Quart. J. R. micr. Soc.* (N.S.) 80: 593–599

VERANY, J. & VOGT, L. (1852): Mémoire sur les hectocotyles et les males de quelques céphalopodes. *Ann. Sci. nat.* (Zool.) (3) 17: 147–188

VERCO, JOSEPH C. & COTTON, BERNARD C. (1931): The spermatophore of *Sepioteuthis australis* (Quoy & Gaimard). *Proc. malacol. Soc. Lond.* 19: 168–170

VERRILL, A. E. (1885): Third catalogue of Mollusca, recently added to the fauna of the New England coast and the adjacent parts of the Atlantic, consisting mostly of deep sea species, with notes on others previously recorded. *Trans. Conn. Acad. Arts Sci.* 6: 395–452

WEILL, R. (1927): Recherches sur la structure, la valeur systématique et le fontionnement du spermatophore de *Sepiola atlantica* D'Orb. *Bull. biol.* 61: 59–92

WELLS, M. J. (1958): Factors affecting reactions to *Mysis* by newly hatched *Sepia*. *Behaviour* 13: 96–111
WELLS, MORRIS M. (1928): Breeding habits of *Octopus*. *Science* 68: 482
WILLEY, ARTHUR (1897): The oviposition of *Nautilus macromphalus*. *Proc. roy. Soc. Lond.* 60: 467–471
—— (1902): *Zoological results*. Cambridge: University Press
WILSON, DOUGLAS P. (1947): *They live in the sea*. London: Collins
YAMADA, T. (1937): On the spawning of the squid *Watasenia scintillans*, in the waters of the east coast of Tyosen. *Bull. Jap. Soc. sci. Fish.* 6: 75–78 [in Japanese with English summary]

CHAPTER IX

FISHING

ACKERMAN, BILL (1946): Under-water jet job. *Outdoors*, Boston, Mass. 14 5: 31–33, 57
APOSTOLIDÈS, NICOLAS CHR. (1883): *La pêche en Grèce*. Athens: Ministère de l'Intérieur
BARTSCH, PAUL (1917): Pirates of the deep—stories of the squid and octopus. *Rep. Smithson. Instn.* 1916: 347–375
BOYCOTT, B. B. (1954): Learning in *Octopus vulgaris* and other cephalopods. *Pubbl. Staz. zool. Napoli* 25: 67–93
BRANDER, M. S. (1954): Hunting the eight-legged wonder. *BEA* [British European Airways] *Mag.* No. 72: 15
BURNETT, F. (1911): *Through Polynesia and Papua*. London: Francis Griffiths
COLLINS, J. W. (1892): Report on the fisheries of the Pacific coast of the United States. *Rep. U.S. Comm. Fish.* 1888: 3–269
CRILE, JANE & CRILE, BARNEY (1954): *Treasure diving holidays*. New York: Viking Press
DAVIS, J. CHARLES, 2ND (1942): Ever catch a polypus? *Westways*, Beverly Hills, Calif. February: 16–17
—— (1949): *California salt water fishing*. New York: Barnes
DEAN, BASHFORD (1901): Notes on living *Nautilus*. *Amer. Nat.* 35: 819–837, 1029
DUNCAN, DAVID D. (1941): Fighting giants of the Humboldt. *Nat. geogr. Mag.* 79: 373–400
FIELDS, W. GORDON (1950): A preliminary report on the fishery and on the biology of the squid, *Loligo opalescens*. *Calif. Fish Game* 36: 366–377
FISCHER, P.–H. (1943): Poissons et crustacés trouvés dans la cavité palléale de calmars. *Bull. Soc. zool. Fr.* 68: 107–110
GHIRARDELLI, ELVEZIO (1947): La pesca delle seppie con le nasse nella Provincia di Pesaro. *Pesca Ital.* (N.S.) 8 5: 7–8
—— (1947): Considerazioni sull'influenza della pesca con le nasse sulla biologia delle specie costiere. *Boll. Pesca Piscic. Idrobiol.* (N.S.) 2: 129–134
GIBBINGS, ROBERT (1949): *Over the reefs*. New York: Dutton
GIBSON, JOHN (1887): *Monsters of the sea*. London: Thomas Nelson
GILL, WILLIAM WYATT (1892): *The South Pacific and New Guinea*. Sydney: Commissioners for the World's Columbian Exposition, Chicago
GORSKY, BERNARD (1954): *Mediterranean hunter*. London: Souvenir Press
GRIMBLE, ARTHUR (1952): *We chose the islands*. New York: William Morrow
GRIMPE, GEORG (1928): Pflege, Behandlung, und Zucht der Cephalopoden etc. in Abderhalden's *Handbuch der Biologischen Arbeitsmethoden* 9 5: 331–402
GRIVET, J. (1944): Hôtes de la cavité palléale de calmars. *Bull. Soc. zool. Fr.* 69: 163–167
GRUVEL, A. (1926): L'industrie des pêches sur les côtes tunisiennes. *Bull. Sta. océanogr. Salammbô* No. 4: 1–135

HORNELL, JAMES (1918): The edible molluscs of the Madras Presidency. *Madras Fish. Bull.* 11: 1-51
—— (1931): *The fishing industry in Malta.* Malta: Government Printing Office
—— (1950): *Fishing in many waters.* Cambridge: University Press
HOSAKA, EDWARD Y. (1944): *Sport fishing in Hawaii.* Honolulu: Bond
KUENTZ, L. (1934): La pêche et le commerce des seiches en Tunisie. *Nature, Paris* No. 2925: 270-271
LEE, HENRY (1875): *The octopus.* London: Chapman & Hall
LO BIANCO, SALVATORE (1909): Notizie biologiche riguardanti specialmente il periodo di maturità sessuale degli animali del Golfo di Napoli. *Mitt. zool. Sta. Neapel.* 19: 513-761
LORD, JOHN KEAST (1866): *The naturalist in Vancouver Island and British Columbia.* London: Richard Bentley
MENARD, WILMON (1947): Hunting the giant octopus. *Wide World Mag.* 99: 203-207
OLLIS, DON (1955): Monster of the Humboldt. *Outdoor Life*, New York. 116 5: 56-61, 84
PALOMBI, ARTURO & SANTARELLI, MARIO (1953): *Gli animali commestibili dei Mari d'Italia.* Milan: Ulrico Hoepli
PETERSEN, E. ALLEN (1954): *In a junk across the Pacific.* London: Elek Books
PRICE, WILLARD (1953): Cruising Japan's inland sea. *Nat. geogr. Mag.* 104: 619-650
RADCLIFFE, WILLIAM (1921): *Fishing from the earliest times.* London: John Murray
RAO, K. VIRABHADRA (1954): Biology and fishery of the Palk-Bay squid, *Sepioteuthis arctipinnis* Gould. *Indian J. Fish.* 1: 37-66
RUSSO, ACHILLE (1926): Le nasse, con particolare riguardo alla pesca delle Seppie. *Boll. Pesca Piscic. Idrobiol.* 2: 3-47
SCOFIELD, W. L. (1951): Purse seines and other roundhaul nets in California. *Fish Bull., Sacramento* No. 81
SIMMONDS, PETER LUND (1879): *Commercial products of the sea.* London: Griffith & Farran
SINEL, JOSEPH (1906): *An outline of the natural history of our shores.* London: Sonnenschein
SPRATT, THOMAS ABEL BREMAGE & FORBES, EDWARD (1847): *Travels in Lycia, Milyas and the Cibyratis.* London: Van Voorst
STEP, EDWARD (1945): *Shell life.* Ed. revised by A. Laurence Wells. London: Warne
TAUTI, MORISABURO & MATSUMOTO, IWAO (1954): On the protection of spawner of octopus (*Polypus vulgaris* Lamarck) in Hyogo Prefecture. *Bull. Jap. Soc. sci. Fish.* 20: 479-482 [in Japanese with English summary]
THOMPSON, D'ARCY WENTWORTH (1928): How to catch cuttlefish. *Classical Rev.* 42: 14-18
VERRILL, A. E. (1879-1882): The cephalopods of the north-eastern coast of America. *Trans. Conn. Acad. Arts Sci.* 5: 177-446
WENDT, HERBERT (1952): Das Haupt der Medusa. *Kosmos* 48: 15-21
WILLEY, ARTHUR (1897): The pre-ocular and post-ocular tentacles and osphradia of *Nautilus. Quart. J. micr. Sci.* 40: 197-201
—— (1902): *Zoological results.* Cambridge: University Press

CHAPTER X

ECONOMIC

ALLAN, JOYCE (1950): *Australian shells.* Melbourne: Georgian House
ANDRÉ, EMILE & CANAL, HENRI (1926): Contribution à l'étude des huiles d'ani-

maux marins. Recherches sur l'huile de calmar (*Todarus sagittatus* Lk.). *C. R. Acad. Sci., Paris* **183**: 152–154

ANON (1899): Article in *Western Evening Herald*, Plymouth December 18

—— (1900): Article in *Fish. Gaz., Lond.* October 27

—— (1950): Article in *The Times*, London December 27

ARISTOTLE (c. 330 B.C.): *Historia animalium.* Translation by D'Arcy Wentworth Thompson (1910). Oxford: Clarendon Press

BARTSCH, PAUL (1917): Pirates of the deep—stories of the squid and octopus. *Rep. Smithson. Instn.* 1916: 347–375

—— (1931): The octopuses, squids and their kin. *Smithson. Sci. Ser.* **10**: 321–356. New York: published privately by the Smithsonian Institution Series, Inc.

BERRILL, N. J. (1951): *The living tide.* New York: Dodd, Mead

[CHANG HSI, CH'I CHUNG-YEN & LI CHIEH-MIN] (1955): [*Maritime economic Mollusca of North China.*] Peking [in Chinese]

[CHANG HSI & HSIANG-LI CHÜ] (n.d.): [*Maritime edible Mollusca of the Kiaochow Bay and adjacent seas.*] Peking [in Chinese]

CHOPRA, R. N., GHOSH, S. & DUTT, A. T. (1938): Some inorganic preparations of the Indian indigenous medicine. 6. Samudra phena. [*Sepia officinalis?* shell] *Indian J. Med. Res.* **26** 2: 485–486

CLARKE, ROBERT (1954): A great haul of ambergris. *Nature, Lond.* **174**: 155–156

CRILE, JANE & CRILE, BARNEY (1954): *Treasure diving holidays.* New York: Viking Press

CUVIER, GEORGES (1817): *Mémoires pour servir à l'histoire et à l'anatomie des mollusques.* Paris: Deterville

DAVID, ELIZABETH (1956): *A book of Mediterranean food.* London: Penguin Books

DAVIS, J. CHARLES, 2ND (1949): *California salt water fishing.* New York: Barnes

DOERNER, MAX (1935): *The materials of the artist.* London: Harrap

DOUKAN, GILBERT (1954): *Underwater hunting.* New York: John de Graff

FERNIE, W. T. (1899): *Animal simples.* Bristol: Wright

FIELDS, W. GORDON (1950): A preliminary report on the fishery and on the biology of the squid, *Loligo opalescens. Calif. Fish Game* **36**: 366–377

FISHER, L. R., KON, S. K. & THOMPSON, S. Y. (1956): Vitamin A and carotenoids in certain invertebrates. 5. Mollusca; Cephalopoda. *J. Mar. biol. Ass. U.K.* **35**: 63–80

GARSTANG, WALTER (1900): The plague of octopus on the South Coast, and its effect on the crab and lobster fisheries. *J. Mar. biol. Ass. U.K.* **6**: 260–273

GILPATRIC, GUY (1938): *The compleat goggler.* New York: Dodd, Mead

GRAY, J. E. (1828): *Spicilegia zoologica.* London: Treuttel & Würtz

GREY, EGERTON CHARLES (1928): *The food of Japan.* Geneva: League of Nations

GUTMAN, WILLIAM (1943): *Sepia* (a modern explanation of the effects of a homeopathic drug). *J. Amer. Inst. Homeopathy* **36**: 437–441

HATAKOSHI, YASU (1941): [Studies on the nutritional chemistry of the cuttlefish. 3. The mineral composition of meat and liver of cuttlefish and liver amylase.] *J. agric. chem. Soc. Japan* **17**: 101–106 [in Japanese]

HEATH, HAROLD (1917): Devilfish and squid. *Calif. Fish Game* **3** 3: 1–6

HEMPEL, CHARLES J. (1861): *A new and comprehensive system of materia medica and therapeutics.* London: Leath & Ross

HEYERDAHL, THOR (1950): *The Kon-Tiki expedition.* Chicago: Rand McNally

HODGKIN, A. L. & HUXLEY, A. F. (1952): A quantitative description of membrane current and its application to conduction and excitation in nerve. *J. Physiol.* **117**: 500–544

HUGHES, RICHARD (1880): *Manual of pharmacodynamics.* London: Leath & Ross

JONES, DOROTHEA & JONES, STUART E. (1954): Ischia, island of the unexpected. *Nat. geogr. Mag.* **105**: 531–550

KUENTZ, L. (1934): La pêche et le commerce des seiches en Tunisie. *Nature, Paris* No. 2925: 270–271

278 BIBLIOGRAPHY

LANGDON-DAVIES, JOHN (1953): *Gatherings from Catalonia*. London: Cassell

LEE, HENRY (1875): *The octopus*. London: Chapman & Hall

LEUNG, WOOT-TSUEN WU, PECOT, R. K. & WATT, B. K. (1952): Composition of foods used in Far Eastern countries. *Handbook U.S. Dept. Agric*. No. 34

LIVIERATO, S. VAGLIANO, M. & CONSTANTAKATO, G. (1932): Utilisation d'un nouvel antigène pour le diagnostic de la malaria par la méthode de floculation. *C. R. Soc. Biol., Paris* 110: 26–27

MACGINITIE, G. E. & MACGINITIE, NETTIE (1949): *Natural history of marine animals*. New York: McGraw-Hill

MERCIER, L. (1927): Les seiches de la baie de Seine en juillet et août 1927. *Bull. Soc. Linn. Normandie* (7) 10: 105–107

MIGITA, MASAO, TSUJINO, ISAMI *et al.* (1953–1955): Series of papers on the utilization of cephalopods, chiefly as food. *Bull. Jap. Soc. sci. Fish.*

MITCHELL, C. AINSWORTH & HEPWORTH, T. C. (1924): *Inks: their composition and manufacture*. London: Charles Griffin

MORRIS, J. MALCOLM (1953): *Wise bamboo*. Philadelphia: Lippincott

NAGAO, KIYOSHI, TANIKAWA, EIICHI *et al.* (1951–1954): Series of papers on cephalopods as food. *Bull. Fac. Fish. Hokkaido*

ORBIGNY, ALCIDES D' (1953): Los moluscos de Cuba. in La historia fisica, politica y natural de la Isla de Cuba. Parts 1–6. *Circ. Mus. biblio. malacol. Habana* 1953: 717–728 & 741–762

OTTERLIND, GUNNAR (1954): Bläckfisk oche fiske i Skandinavien. *Faunistik Revy* 3: 75–91

PALOMBI, ARTURO & SANTARELLI, MARIO (1953): *Gli animali commestibili dei Mari d'Italia*. Milan: Ulrico Hoepli

PHARMACEUTICAL SOCIETY OF GREAT BRITAIN (1934): *British pharmaceutical codex*. London: Pharmaceutical Press

PRICE, WILLARD (1953): Cruising Japan's inland sea. *Nat. geogr. Mag.* 104: 619–650

RADCLIFFE, WILLIAM (1921): *Fishing from the earliest times*. London: John Murray

REES, W. J. (1952): Octopuses in the Channel. *New Biology* No. 12: 58–67

REES, W. J. & LUMBY, J. R. (1954): The abundance of *Octopus* in the English Channel. *J. Mar. biol. Ass. U.K.* 33: 515–536

RULLIER, F. (1953): Répartition et réproduction d'*Octopus vulgaris* Lamarck dans les eaux françaises. *Bull. Lab. marit. Dinard* No. 39: 22–33

SAAVEDRA, S. J. (1949): Analisis quimico-bromatologico de la carne del *Octopus vulgaris*. *Rev. Fac. Farm., Lima* 10: 142–145

SASAKI, MADOKA (1921): On the life history of an economic cuttlefish of Japan, *Ommastrephes sloani pacificus*. *Trans. Wagner Free Inst.* 9 2: 1–25

—— (1929): Supplementary notes on the life history of an economic cuttlefish *Ommastrephes sloani pacificus* Steenstrup. *Jap. J. Zool.* 2: 199–211

SAUTIER, PHILIP M. (1946): Thiamine assays of fishery products. *Comm. Fish. Rev.* 8: 17–19

—— (1946): Riboflavin assays of fishery products. *Comm. Fish. Rev.* 8: 19–21

SCHMITT, F. O. (1957): The structure and properties of nerve membranes. *Second Int. Neurochem. Symp.*, Aarhus, Denmark, July 1956: 35–47

SCHMITT, F. O. & GESCHWIND, N. (1957): The axon surface. *Progress in Biophysics* 8: 165–215

SHIPLEY, ARTHUR EVERETT (1924): *Islands: West Indian-Aegean*. London: Hopkinson

SIMMONDS, PETER LUND (1879): *Commercial products of the sea*. London: Griffith & Farran

SOEDA, J. (1956): Studies on the ecology and the breeding habits of the squid, *Ommastrephes sloani pacificus*. *Bull. Hokkaido Reg. Fish. Res. Lab.* No. 14: 1–24

STEDMAN, THOMAS LATHROP (1950): *Stedman's medical dictionary*, ed. Taylor, Norman Burte. London: Baillière, Tindall & Cox

STEINBACH, H. B. (1951): The squid. *Sci. Amer.* **184** 4: 64–69

STEPHEN, A. C. (1937): Recent invasion of the squid, *Todarodes sagittatus* (Lam.) on the East Coast of Scotland. *Scot. Nat.* 1937 No. 225: 77–80

—— (1944): The Cephalopoda of Scottish and adjacent waters. *Trans. roy. Soc. Edinb.* **61**: 247–270

TANIKAWA, EIICHI et al. (1952): Studies on the complete utilization of the squid (*Ommastrephes sloani pacificus*). *Bull. Fac. Fish. Hokkaido* **3** 1: 73–94

TOMIYASU, YUKIO, TOYOMIZU, MASAMICHI & TAKAHASHI, KIKUO (1953): Studies on the antibiotic action of fish components. Pt. 6. *Bull. Jap. Soc. sci. Fish.* **18**: 530–535 [in Japanese with English summary]

TRESSLER, DONALD K. & LEMON, JAMES McW. (1951): *Marine products of commerce.* New York: Reinhold

TRYON, GEORGE W., JR. (1879): *Manual of conchology.* **1**: Cephalopoda. Philadelphia: Tryon

WILLIAMS, LEONARD WORCESTER (1909): *The anatomy of the common squid, Loligo pealii, Lesueur.* Leiden: Brill

YAMADA, M. & OBATA, Y. (1949): Adhesives for wood. *Bull. Jap. Soc. sci. Fish.* **15**: 144–146

YASUDA, J. (1951): Some ecological notes on the cuttlefish, *Sepia esculenta* Hoyle. *Bull. Jap. Soc. sci. Fish.* **16**: 350–356

YOSHIMURA, KATSUJI (1955): Studies on the tropomyosin of squid. *Mem. Fac. Fish. Hokkaido* **3**: 159–176

YOSHIMURA, KATSUJI & NARA, SAKAN (1954): Studies on the nutritive value and absorption coefficient of "Surume-Ika" (*Ommastrephes sloani pacificus*) protein. *Bull. Fac. Fish. Hokkaido* **5** 1: 94–98 [in Japanese with English summary]

YOUNG, J. Z. (1939): Fused neurons and synaptic contacts in the giant nerve fibres of cephalopods. *Phil. Trans.* B. **229**: 465–503

—— (1944): Giant nerve-fibres. *Endeavour* **3**: 108–113

CHAPTER XI

DANGER

ACKERMAN, BILL (1946): Under-water jet job. *Outdoors*, Boston, Mass. **14** 5: 31–35, 57

ANON (1921): Article in *The New York Times* April 25

—— (1921): Article in *The Times*, London April 26

BACQ, Z. M. & GHIRETTI, F. (1951): La sécrétion externe et interne des glandes salivaires postérieures des céphalopodes octopodes. *Bull. Acad. Belg. Cl. Sci.* (5) **37**: 79–102

BARADA, BILL (1958): Is the giant octopus a sissy? *Skin Diver*, Lynwood, Calif. January: pp. 28 & 29

BARTLETT, NORMAN (1954): *The pearl seekers.* London: Melrose

BERGE, VICTOR (1954): *Danger is my life.* London: Hutchinson

BERGE, VICTOR & LANIER, HENRY WYSHAM (1930): *Pearl diver.* London: Heinemann

BERRY, S. STILLMAN & HALSTEAD, BRUCE W. (1954): Octopus bites—a second report. *Leafl. Malacol.* **1** 11: 59–66

BRELAND, OSMOND P. (1952): Devils of the deep. *Sci. Digest* **32** 4: 31–33

BRUCE, HENRY J. (1939): *Twenty years under the ocean.* London: Stanley Paul

BUCKLAND, FRANK (1891): *Log-book of a fisherman and zoologist.* London: Chapman & Hall

BURFORD, VIRGIL (1954): *North to danger*. New York: John Day
CAMPBELL, ROY (1952): *Light on a dark horse*. Chicago: Regnery
CRAIG, JOHN D. (1936): Diving among sea killers. *Pop. Mechan.* **65**: 508–511, 138a, 140a, 142a
—— (1938): *Danger is my business*. New York: Simon & Schuster
CRILE, JANE & CRILE, BARNEY (1954): *Treasure diving holidays*. New York: Viking Press
DANIEL, R. J. (1925): *Animal life in the sea*. London: Hodder & Stoughton
DANIELS, GENE (1957): Wrestling match with an eight-armed grappler. *Cavalier Mag.*, New York. December: pp. 20–23
DOUKAN, GILBERT (1954): *Underwater hunting*. New York: John de Graff
DUNCAN, DAVID D. (1941): Fighting giants of the Humboldt. *Nat. geogr. Mag.* **79**: 373–400
DUNTON, SAM (1957): *Hold that tiger!* New York: Greenberg
EVANS, BERGEN (1946): *The natural history of nonsense*. New York: Knopf
FLECKER, H. & COTTON, BERNARD C. (1955): Fatal bite from octopus. *Med. J. Austr.* **2** (42nd year): 429–431
GIBSON, JOHN (1887): *Monsters of the sea*. London: Thomas Nelson
GILL, WILLIAM WYATT (1876): *Life in the Southern Isles*. London: Religious Tract Society
GILPATRIC, GUY (1938): *The compleat goggler*. New York: Dodd, Mead
GRIMBLE, ARTHUR (1952): *We chose the islands*. New York: William Morrow
HALSTEAD, BRUCE W. (1949): Octopus bites in human beings. *Leafl. Malacol.* **1** 5: 17–22
HEYERDAHL, THOR (1950): *The Kon-Tiki expedition*. Chicago: Rand McNally
HORNELL, JAMES (1917): The edible molluscs of the Madras Presidency. *Madras Fish. Bull.* **11**: 1–51
HUGO, VICTOR (1886): *Toilers of the sea*. Translated by W. Moy Thomas. London: Sampson Low
KLINGEL, GILBERT C. (1940): *Inagua*. New York: Dodd, Mead
LEE, HENRY (1875): *The octopus*. London: Chapman & Hall
—— (1884): *Sea monsters unmasked*. London: William Clowes
MABBET, HUGH (1954): Death of a skindiver. *Skin Diving & Spear-fishing Digest*, Sydney. December: pp. 13 & 17
MACGINITIE, G. E. & MACGINITIE, NETTIE (1949): *Natural history of marine animals*. New York: McGraw-Hill
MENARD, WILMON (1947): Hunting the giant octopus. *Wide World Mag.* **99**: 203–207
PRICE, WILLARD (1956): *Adventures in paradise*. London: Heinemann
ROMIJN, C. (1935): Die Verdauungsenzyme bei einigen Cephalopoden. *Arch. néerl. Zool.* **1**: 373–431
SIMPSON, DONALD A. (1948): The octopus is an odd oaf. *Aquar. J.* **19** 10: 18–21, 25
SINEL, JOSEPH (1906): *An outline of the natural history of our shores*. London: Sonnenschein
SUNTER, GEORGE HERBERT (1937): *Adventures of a trepang fisher*. London: Hurst & Blackett
TEMPLE, GRENVILLE T. (1835): *Excursions in the Mediterranean. Algiers and Tunis*. London: Saunders & Otley
WALDRON, T. J. & GLEESON, JAMES (1954): *The frogmen*. London: Pan Books

CHAPTER XII

KRAKEN

AKIMUSHKIN, I. I. (1954): [Cephalopod mollusks in the food of sperm whales.] *Dokl. Akad. nauk. S.S.S.R.* **96**: 665–667 [in Russian]

ALBERT, HONORÉ CHARLES [ALBERT I, PRINCE DE MONACO] (1902): *La carrière d'un navigateur.* Paris: Plon & Nourrit

ALLAN, JOYCE (1948): A rare giant squid. *Austr. Mus. Mag.* **9**: 306–308

—— (1955): The Kraken—legendary terror of the seas. *Aust. Mus. Mag.* **11**: 275–278

ASHLEY, CLIFFORD WARREN (1938): *The Yankee whaler.* Boston: Houghton Mifflin

BARTSCH, PAUL (1917): Pirates of the deep—stories of the squid and octopus. *Rep. Smithson. Instn.* **1916**: 347–375

—— (1931): The octopuses, squids and their kin. *Smithson. Sci. Ser.* **10**: 321–356. New York: published privately by the Smithsonian Institution Series, Inc.

BERTHELOT, SABIN (1861): Quoted in *C. R. Acad. Sci.*, Paris **53**: 1263–1267

BLOND, GEORGES (1954): *The great whale game.* New York: Doubleday

BOUYER, FRÉDÉRIC-MARIE (1861): Quoted in *C. R. Acad. Sci.*, Paris **53**: 1263–1267

BRELAND, OSMOND P. (1952): Devils of the deep. *Sci. Digest* **32** 4: 31–33

—— (1953): Which are the biggest? *Nat. Hist.*, N.Y. **62**: 67–71, 96

BUCHANAN, J. Y. (1919): *Accounts rendered.* Cambridge: University Press

BUCKLAND, FRANK (1891): *Log-book of a fisherman and zoologist.* London: Chapman & Hall

BULLEN, FRANK T. (1948): *The cruise of the "Cachalot."* New York: Dodd, Mead

CADENAT, JEAN (1936): Note sur un Céphalopode géant (*Architeuthis harveyi* Verrill) capturé dans le Golfe de Gascogne. *Bull. Mus. Hist. nat.*, Paris (2) **8**: 277–285

CARRINGTON, RICHARD (1957): *Mermaids and mastodons.* New York: Rinehart

CHEESMAN, EVELYN (1949): *Six-legged snakes in New Guinea.* London: Harrap

CLARKE, ROBERT (1955): A giant squid swallowed by a sperm whale. *Norsk Hvalfangsttid.* **1955**: 589–593

—— (1956): Sperm whales of the Azores. *Discovery Rep.* **28**: 237–298

COE, WESLEY R. (1932): Biographical memoir of Addison Emery Verrill. *Biogr. Mem. Nat. Acad. Sci. U.S.* **14**: 17–66

DANIEL, R. J. (1925): *Animal life in the sea.* London: Hodder & Stoughton

DENYS DE MONTFORT, P. (1802–1805): *Histoire naturelle générale et particulière des mollusques.* Paris: Dufart

—— (1808–1810): *Conchyliologie systématique.* Paris: Schoell

FLOYD, JAMES (1874): Article in *The Times*, London July 4

FRIDRIKSSON, ARNI (1943): Remarks on the age and the growth of the squid. *Greinar* **2**: 2

FROST, NANCY (1934): Notes on a giant squid (*Architeuthis* sp.) captured at Dildo, Newfoundland, in December 1933. *Rep. Newfoundld. Fish. Comm.* **1933** 2 2: 100–114

—— (1936): A further species of giant squid (*Architeuthis* sp.) from Newfoundland waters. *Rep. Newfoundld. Fish. Comm.* **1935** 2 5: 89–95

GIBSON, JOHN (1887): *Monsters of the sea.* London: Thomas Nelson

GOULD, RUPERT T. (1930): *The case for the sea-serpent.* London: Philip Allan

GRØNNINGSAETER, ARNE (1946): Sjøormen—blekkspruten. *Naturen* **70**: 379–380

HARTING, PIETER (1860): Description de quelques fragments de deux céphalopodes gigantesques. *Verh. Akad. Wet.*, Amst. **9** 1:2

HARVEY, MOSES (1879): Article in *The Boston Traveller* January 30

—— (1899): How I discovered the great devil-fish. *Wide World Mag.* **2**: 732–740

282 BIBLIOGRAPHY

IWAI, EIJI (1956): Descriptions on unidentified species of dibranchiate cephalopods. 1. An oegopsiden squid belonging to the genus *Architeuthis*. *Sci. Rep. Whales Res. Inst., Tokyo* No. 11: 139–151

JOUBIN, L. (1895): Céphalopodes recueillis dans l'estomac d'un cachalot, capturé aux îles Açores. *C. R. Acad. Sci., Paris* **121**: 1172–1174

—— (1899): Liste des céphalopodes recueillis pendant les dernières campagnes de la "Princess-Alice" (1895–1897). *Bull. Soc. zool. Fr.* **24**: 62–74

KENT, W. SAVILLE (1874): Note on a gigantic cephalopod from Conception Bay, Newfoundland. *Proc. zool. Soc. Lond.* **1874**: 178–182

—— (1874): A further communication upon certain gigantic cephalopods recently encountered off the coast of Newfoundland. *Proc. zool. Soc. Lond.* **1874**: 489–494

KIRK, T. W. (1880): On the occurrence of giant cuttlefish on the New Zealand coast. *Trans. N.Z. Inst.* **12**: 310–313

—— (1888): Brief description of a new species of large decapod (*Architeuthis longimanus*). *Trans. N.Z. Inst.* **20**: 34–39

KNUDSEN, J. (1957): Some observations on a mature male specimen of *Architeuthis* from Danish waters. *Proc. malacol. Soc. Lond.* **32**: 189–198

LANE, FRANK W. (1941): The great sea-serpent. *Field* **178**: 548–550

—— (1949): Is there a great sea serpent? *Britannia & Eve* **38** 6: 28, 66

LEE, HENRY (1875): *The octopus.* London: Chapman & Hall

—— (1884): *Sea monsters unmasked.* London: William Clowes

LEY, WILLY (1948): *The lungfish, the dodo, and the unicorn.* New York: Viking Press

LINNAEUS, CAROLUS (1735): *Systema Naturae.* Leiden: Haak

MACGINITIE, G. E. & MACGINITIE, NETTIE (1949): *Natural history of marine animals.* New York: McGraw-Hill

MAGNUS, OLAUS (1658): *A compendious history of the Goths, Swedes, and Vandals, and other Northern nations.* London: Printed by J. Streater

MELVILLE, HERMAN (1851): *Moby Dick.* New York: Harper

MITSUKURI, K. & IKEDA, S. (1895): [Notes on a gigantic cephalopod.] *Zool. Mag., Tokyo* **7**: 39–50 [in Japanese]

MORE, A. G. (1875a): Gigantic squid on the west coast of Ireland. *Ann. Mag. nat. hist.* (4) **16**: 123–124

—— (1875b): Notice of a gigantic cephalopod (*Dinoteuthis proboscideus*) which was stranded at Dingle, in Kerry, two hundred years ago. *Zoologist* (2) **10**: 4526–4532

—— (1875c): Some account of the gigantic squid (*Architeuthis dux*) lately captured off Boffin Island, Connemara. *Zoologist* (2) **10**: 4569–4571

MURRAY, JOHN & HJORT, JOHAN (1912): *The depths of the ocean.* London: Macmillan

NORMAN, J. R. & FRASER, F. C. (1948): *Field book of giant fishes.* New York: Putnam

O'CONNOR, THOMAS (1875): Capture of an enormous cuttle-fish off Boffin Island, on the coast of Connemara. *Zoologist* (2) **10**: 4502–4503

PACKARD, A. S. (1873): Colossal cuttlefishes. *Amer. Nat.* **7**: 87–94

PFEFFER, GEORG (1912): Die Cephalopoden der Plankton-Expedition. *Ergebn. Planktonexped.* Pt. 2. Kiel & Leipzig: Lipsius & Tischer

[PLINY] PLINIUS, GAIUS SECUNDUS (A.D. 77): *Pliny—natural history.* With an English translation by H. Rackham & W. H. S. Jones. (1947) 3 Libri 8–11: 225. London: Heinemann

PONTOPPIDAN, ERICH [ERIK] (1755): *The natural history of Norway.* Translated from the Danish. London: Linde

RAE, BENNET B. (1950): Description of a giant squid stranded near Aberdeen. *Proc. malacol. Soc. Lond.* **28**: 163–167

REES, W. J. (1949): Giant squid: the quest for the Kraken. *Ill. Lond. News* **215**: 826

—— (1950): On a giant squid *Ommastrephes caroli* Furtado stranded at Looe, Cornwall. *Bull. Brit. Mus. (nat. Hist.)* (Zool.) 1: 31–41

REES, W. J. & MAUL, G. E. (1956): The Cephalopoda of Madeira. *Bull. Brit. Mus. (nat. Hist.)* (Zool.) 3: 259–281

ROBSON, G. C. (1925): Cephalopoda in Hutchinson's *Animals of all countries* 4: 2145–2177. London: Hutchinson

—— (1933): On *Architeuthis clarkei*, a new species of giant squid, with observations on the genus. *Proc. zool. Soc. Lond.* 1933: 681–697

SHALER, N. S. (1873): Notes on the right and sperm whales. *Amer. Nat.* 7: 1–4

SIVERTSEN, ERLING (1955): Blekksprut, *K. norske vidensk. Selsk.* Årbok 1954: 5–15

STEENSTRUP, JOH. JAPETUS (1849): Meddelelse om tvende kiaempestore Blaeksprutter, opdrevne 1639 og 1790 ved Islands Kyst, og om nogle andre nordiske Dyr. *Førh. skand. naturf.* 5: 950–957

—— (1855): Om den i Kong Christian IIIs tid i Øresundet fangne Havmand (Sømunken kaldet). *Dansk Maanedsskrift* 1: 63–96

—— (1857): Oplysninger om Atlanterhavets colossale Blaeksprutter. *Førh. skand. naturf.* 7: 182–185

—— (1898): Kolossale Blaeksprutter fra det nordlige Atlanterhav. *K. danske vidensk. Selsk. Skr.* (5) 4 3: 409–454

SUTER, HENRY (1913): *Manual of the New Zealand Mollusca.* Wellington, N.Z.: John Mackay

TAGO, KATSUYA (1937): Cetacea found in Japanese waters. *Int. Congr. Zool.* 12: 2192–2228

TRYON, GEORGE W., JR. (1879): *Manual of conchology* 1. Cephalopoda. Philadelphia: Tryon

VERNE, JULES (1876): *Twenty thousand leagues under the sea.* Translated by H. Frith. London: Routledge

VERRILL, A. E. (1879–1881): The cephalopods of the north-eastern coast of America. *Trans. Conn. Acad. Arts Sci.* 5: 177–446

VOSS, GILBERT L. (1956): A review of the cephalopods of the Gulf of Mexico. *Bull. Mar. Sci. Gulf Caribbean* 6: 85–178

WHIPPLE, A. B. C. (1954): *Yankee whalers in the South Seas.* New York: Doubleday

YOUNG, J. Z. (1944): Giant nerve-fibres. *Endeavour* 3: 108–113

REFERENCES RECEIVED AFTER PARTING WITH MS.

ADAM, W. (1954): Cephalopoda. *Siboga Exped.* Monogr. 55C

—— (1955): Céphalopodes. *Ann. Inst. océanogr. Monaco* N. S. 30: 185–194

—— (1957): Notes sur les Céphalopodes. 23. Quelques espèces des Antilles. *Bull. Inst. Sci. nat. Belg.* 33 7:1–10

ANON (1959): Frogman v. octopus. *Time,* New York (Canadian edition) February 2, p. 10

ASANO, M. & ITO, M. (1955): Biochemical studies on the octopus. 2. Pigments of the integument and ink sack of the octopus. *Tohoku J. agric. Res.* 6: 147–158

BOULET, P. (1955): Nouvelles expériences sur la perception visuelle du mouvement chez *Sepia officinalis* L. *C. R. Soc. Biol., Paris* 149: 1472–1477

BOYCOTT, B. B. & YOUNG, J. Z. (1957): Effects of interference with the vertical lobe on visual discrimination in *Octopus vulgaris* Lamarck. *Proc. roy. Soc.* 146B: 439–459

COLMAN, P. (1956): An octopus delicacy and other marine tidbits. *Proc. R. zool. Soc. N.S.W.* 1954–55: 78–79

DODWELL, P. C. (1957): Shape discrimination in the octopus and the rat. *Nature, Lond.* 179: 1088

ERDMAN, D. S. (1957): Vagabond cuttlebones. *Nautilus, Philad.* 70: 106–107

GEREBTZOFF, M. A. (1957): Conditions d'existence des céphalopodes et localiza-

284 BIBLIOGRAPHY

tion de l'acétylcholinestérase au niveau de leurs fibres nerveuses. *C. R. Soc. Biol. Paris* **150**: 1815–1817

HANEDA, Y. (1957): Studies on the luminous organisms found in waters adjacent to the Pacific coasts of Japan. *Rec. oceanogr. Wks Jap.* Spec. No.: 97–102

HEUVELMANS, BERNARD (1958): *Dans le sillage des monstres marins. 1—Le kraken et le poulpe colossal.* Paris; Plon

IWAI, E. (1956): Descriptions on unidentified species of dibranchiate cephalopods. *Sci. Rep. Whales Res. Inst. Tokyo:* **11**: 139–162

KAO, C. Y. & GRUNDFEST, H. (1957): Membrane potentials of the squid giant axon recorded with an inserted antimony microelectrode. *Experientia* **13**: 140–141

KAWABATA, T., HALSTEAD, B. W. & JUDEFIND, T. F. (1957): A report of a series of recent outbreaks of unusual cephalopod and fish intoxications in Japan. *Amer. J. trop. Med. Hyg.* **6**: 935–939

KNUDSEN, J. (1957): Some observations on a mature male specimen of *Architeuthis* from Danish waters. *Proc. Malacol. Soc. Lond.* **32**: 189–198

KRAMER, GUSTAV (1937): Einige Beobachtungen an *Tremoctopus violaceus* Delle Chiaje. *Not. Istit. Biolog. Rovigno* No. 25

MACKINTOSH, N. A. (1956): 2,000 feet down: deep-sea photographs teach us more about the little-known squid. *New Scientist,* London No. 1

MCMICHAEL, D. F. (1957): Poisonous bites by octopus. *Proc. R. Zool. Soc. N.S.W.* **1955–56**: 110–111

MUUS, B. J. (1956): Development and distribution of a North Atlantic pelagic squid, family *Cranchiidae. Medd. Danm. Fisk. Havundersog.* N.S. **I**: No. 15: 1–15

SACARRÃO, G. P. (1956): A "linguagem" das cores nos cephalópodos. *Naturalia* **6**: 5–6, 14–20

SACARRÃO, G. da F. (1954): Quelques aspects sur l'origine et le développement du type d'oeil des céphalopodes. *Rev. Fac. Ciênc. Univ. Lisboa* (2C) **4** 1:123–158

—— (1955): Sur la genèse des chromatophores de *Tremoctopus. Rev. Fac. Ciênc. Univ. Lisboa* (2c) **4** 2:295–304

SATYAMURTI, S. T. (1956): The Mollusca of Krusadai Island (in the Gulf of Manaar). 2. Scaphoda, Pelecyphoda and Cephalopoda. *Bull. Madras Govt. Mus.* N.S. Nat. Hist. Sect. **1** (2) 7: 1–202

STENZEL, H. B. (1957): *Nautilus* annotated bibliography in Hedgpeth, J. W. *Mem. geol. Soc. Amer.* **67** 1: 1135–1141

VOSS, GILBERT L. (1956): Checklist of the cephalopods of Florida. *Quart. J. Fla. Acad. Sci.* **19**: 274–282

—— (1957): Observations on *Ornitholenthus antillaram* Adam, 1957 an ommastrephid squid from the West Indies. *Bull. Mar. Sci. Gulf Caribbean* **7**: 370–378

—— (1957): Observations on abnormal growth of the arms and tentacles in the squid genus *Rossia. Quart. J. Fla. Acad. Sci.* **20**: 129–132

—— (1958): The cephalopods collected by the R/V *Atlantis* during the West Indian cruise of 1954. *Bull. Mar. Sci. Gulf Caribbean* **8**: 369–389

WELLS, M. J. & WELLS, J. (1957): The function of the brain of *Octopus* in tactile discrimination. *J. exp. Biol.* **34**: 131–142

—— (1957): Repeated presentation experiments and the function of the vertical lobe in *Octopus. J. exp. Biol.* **34**: 469–477

—— (1957): The effect of lesions to the vertical and optic lobes in tactile discrimination in *Octopus. J. exp. Biol.* **34**: 378–393

WIRZ, K. (1955): Contribution à l'étude des octopodes de profondeur. *Vie de Milieu* **6**: 129–147

YOUNG, J. Z. (1956): Visual responses by octopus to crabs and other figures before and after training. *J. exp. Biol.* **33**: 709–729

INDEX